ANALYTICAL PHOTOGRAMMETRY

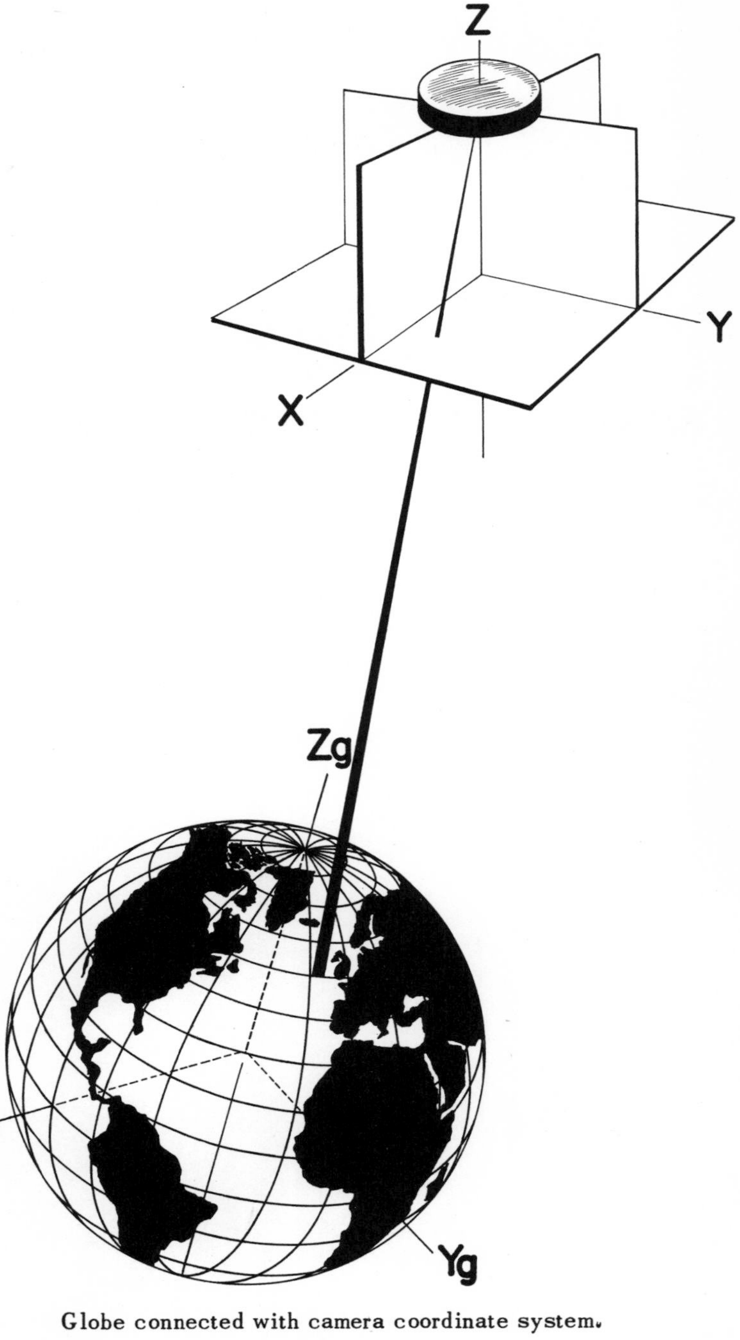

Globe connected with camera coordinate system.

ANALYTICAL PHOTOGRAMMETRY

by EVERETT L. MERRITT

Technical Director
Photogrammetry, Incorporated

PITMAN PUBLISHING CORPORATION

New York Toronto London

First Printing

Library of Congress Catalog Card Number: 58-6204

PRINTED IN THE UNITED STATES OF AMERICA

Dedicated to my wife, Elaine, and my three children,
Blythe, Barry, and Brett

FOREWORD

As a friend, photogrammetric colleague, and business associate of Mr. Everett L. Merritt, I have had the opportunity to observe the development of a practical and comprehensive analytical photogrammetry.

For the past ten years, Mr. Merritt has been in the process of preparing three volumes on analytical photogrammetry. Like a new model aircraft, the desired modifications required to make the ideal aircraft never seem to cease. During the past year, he finally decided to interrupt this apparently ceaseless task and publish one volume. It is hoped that his work will continue on the remaining two volumes very soon. His presentations of the mathematics of photogrammetry will be exploited by science and engineering since the electronic computer can now accommodate the previously tedious calculations in a feasible and expeditious manner.

Will Durant in his preface to "The Story of Philosophy" states: "Every science, and every branch of philosophy, developed a technical terminology intelligible only to its exclusive devotees; as men learned more about the world, they found themselves ever less capable of expressing to their educated fellow-men what it was that they had learned. The gap between life and knowledge grew wider and wider; those who governed could not understand those who thought, and those who wanted to know could not understand those who knew."

This volume is a sincere attempt by Mr. Merritt to impart the knowledge and practice of analytical photogrammetry to those who think and want to know.

Gomer T. McNeil

Silver Spring, Maryland
May 1957

PREFACE

The present volume is a general analytical treatment of photogrammetry. The book commences with the definition of a point in connection with an exposition of the geometric laws of perspective and concludes with the equations for the determination of the position, spatial configuration, and orientation of an irregular object surface without object space control.

There are many excellent works on the subject of photogrammetry. Each of these works describes the procedures, instrumentation, and methods of a time and geographic location. As a consequence of this trend photogrammetrists rise to professional maturity with a viewpoint slanted by the procedures and instrumentation of their particular country. Most books on the subject of photogrammetry contain only those analytical formulae and derivations essential to a functional understanding of the photogrammetric instrument described.

An effort has been made to free the reader from any specific viewpoint other than a general geometric understanding of the basic problems of photogrammetry. To this end general explicit and iterative equations are developed for the single and multiple camera stations. It is shown that any problem, be it the calibration of a camera, the determination of an astronomic position, or the shape of an object, is some simplification of the general analytical equations of photogrammetry. Thus the reader is instilled with the principles of photogrammetry rather than the procedures and instrumentation of a time and place, whereby he is equipped to cope with any problem or to evaluate any system without the mental blocks of an apperception.

All equations described in this volume are original with the writer, or at least arrived at independently. Unavoidably, some will be identical to those found in other works on photogrammetry. This follows from the fact that several investigators working unknowingly on the same problem with the same basic tools of science are very likely to end up with the same formulae, conclusions, or results.

On the other hand, to preserve the continuity and to prevent duplication, photogrammetric formulae characteristic of and described by other writers have been deliberately omitted.

The equations presented are the result of a screening process of solutions derived in connection with problems and researches confronting the writer during the last ten years. Among these problems were (1) the determination of a skid mark length in connection with an auto accident case, (2) the calibration of cameras from star exposures, terrestrial exposures, and goniometric angle measurements, (3) the determination of the space coordinates, direction cosines, velocity and acceleration of a missile in flight from both ground and missile-born camera stations, (4) the space coordinates of ships' array during, before, and after the atom bomb burst at the Bikini Atoll, (5) the space track of the bomb-carrying aircraft, (6) the geodetic coordinates of an isolated nunatak in a field of ice, (7) the astronomic position and orientation of camera stations from star exposures, (8) the static errors of a cine theodolite with star exposure data, (9) the extension of control points with and without ground control, and many others too numerous to list.

All equations presented have yielded reliable results in repeated and varied applications to realistic problems similar to the few listed above.

The decision to write the present volume was inspired by the realization that a great variety of photogrammetric problems are solved with some form of the same general equations. It was following this realization that the writer decided to develop formulae wherever a gap in the complete analytic concept existed, whereby a self-contained, analytical concept could be presented within the boundaries of a medium-sized volume. The date of release is due largely to the fact that the last equations were developed less than a year ago.

The idea of completing the present volume has been abandoned a dozen times during the last ten years. On each of these occasions the idea was rejuvenated because of the insistence and confidence of my friend and associate, Mr. Gomer T. McNeil. Many of the equations are a consequence of Mr. McNeil's suggesting that certain problems (air camera calibration and control extension) are essential to a complete treatment of the subject.

Confidence and encouragement given me by Mr. A.C. Lundahl and Mr. C.G. Mares during the last ten year period contributed in an intangible way to the completion of the text.

All equations contained in the text and many not contained were numerically tested and as a consequence determined to be practical or not practical by Miss Doris L. Rock. Miss Rock also typed the manuscript and proofed the equations of the first, second, and final writings. It is difficult to say how many years the present volume may have been postponed without her devotion and tireless effort given freely in behalf of the present volume.

Charles Williamson meticulously and thoroughly edited the manuscript on three separate occasions, with emphasis at all times on clarity of presentation to the reader. The present volume would have been difficult to read without the clarity of exposition resulting from many hours of editing given freely by Mr. Williamson.

TABLE OF CONTENTS.

LIST OF ILLUSTRATIONS.

Chapter I

FUNDAMENTAL CONCEPTS

A. *DEFINITION*

Photogrammetry is the science of determining the direction angles of objects with respect to an optical photographic reference system from the measurement of images recorded with a camera; that is, the science of measuring angles with a camera. In a more extensive sense photogrammetry is the science of determining the geometry of an area or an object with regard to its configuration from the measurement of conjugate images recorded with a camera at two camera stations. To determine other than direction and configuration involves additional data derived independent of the image-recording camera. The usual problem in photogrammetry entails absolute position, direction, and dimension; consequently, nonphotographic data are generally combined with photographic data in the determination of the desired data.

B. *PERSPECTIVE PROJECTION OF THE IMAGE PLANE.*

Photogrammetry may also be defined as the science of converting the perspective projection of the image plane to an orthographic projection of an object.

In plane geometry the orthographic projection of a point on a line is the foot of the perpendicular from the point to the line. In Figure 1, $p.p.$ is the projection of point L on line x_1x_2.

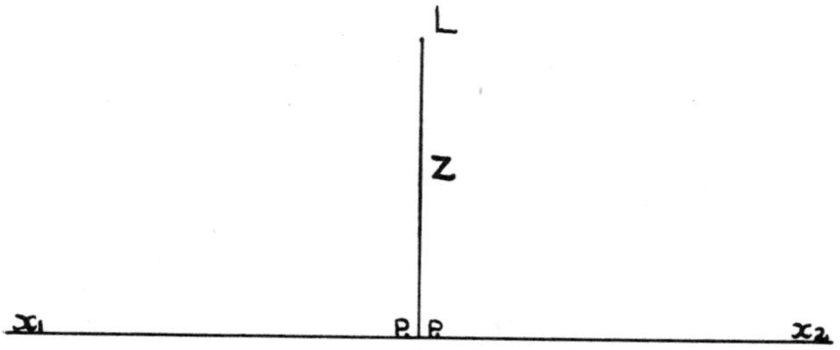

Fig. 1 Projection of a point to a line.

In solid geometry the projection of a point on a plane is the foot of a perpendicular from the point to the plane; that is, the point at which this perpendicular pierces the plane. In Figure 2, *p.p.* is the projection of point L on the xy plane, or camera image plane.

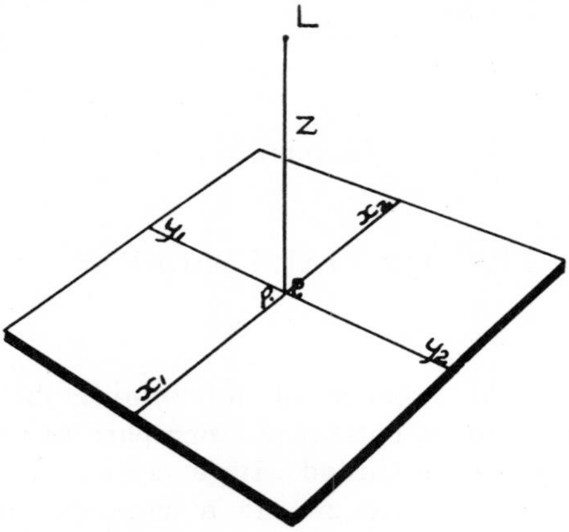

Fig. 2 Projection of a point to a plane.

The orthogonal definition of a point is a conventional way of defining a point. For instance, the streets of many cities are laid out as an orthogonal system of lines and the buildings lining the streets have various elevations according to the number of floors. It is not at all strange to say, for example, that one's place of business is on the 10th floor of the Adamson Building, located at 15th and K Streets. This is the conventional way of giving the orthogonal coordinates of a point. The numbered streets run north and south and the lettered streets run east and west, while the building extends vertically. If we let the numbered street be Y, the lettered street X, and the number of the floor Z, we have defined the orthogonal coordinates of a point in geometric notation.

Now consider three mutually orthogonal planes and a point A within the system shown in Figure 3.

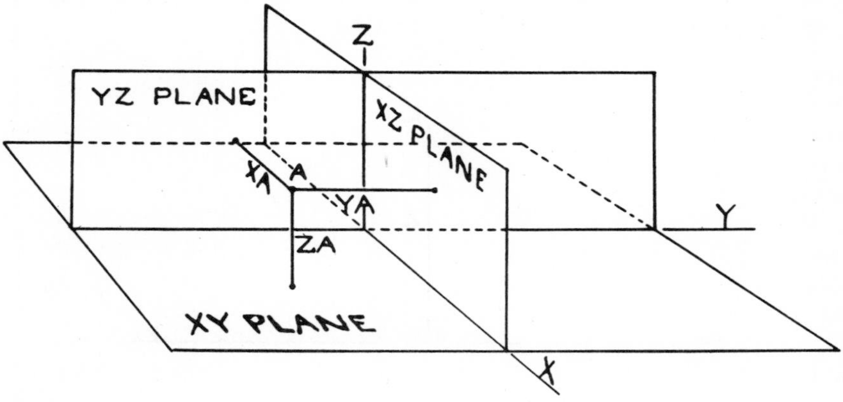

Fig. 3 Orthogonal definition of a point.

The position of A is completely defined when the orthogonal distance of A from each plane is known – that is, XA from the YZ plane, YA from the XZ plane, and ZA from the XY plane. The space coordinates of A are XA, YA, and ZA with respect to a Cartesian coordinate system. Henceforward the space coordinates of a point will have precisely this meaning.

Basically, a projection is the construction of straight lines through every point of an object according to some system and cutting these lines by a plane so as to form a section on that plane which corresponds point for point with the original object. When the projecting rays are parallel and are cut by a plane perpendicular to them, the section on the plane is called an orthographic projection of the object. In Figure 4 lines a^1aA, b^1bB, and c^1cC are parallel to each other.

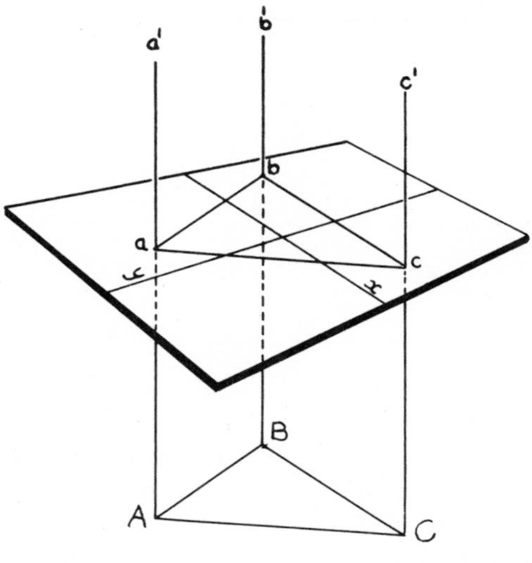

Fig. 4 Orthographic projection of the object.

The xy plane is perpendicular to these lines, and abc in the xy plane forms a section of ABC which by definition is an orthographic projection of ABC, inasmuch as there is a point-for-point correspondence with the original object. Maps are generally orthographic projections of terrestrial points, insofar as these points are placed in the relative position they would occupy if projected vertically to sea-level datum.

When the projecting rays, instead of being parallel, pass through a common point, L, the section cut from these lines by the intersection plane is known as a point projection, or a perspective projection of an object. In Figure 5 LnN is perpendicular to both the xy plane and the XY plane; therefore the xy plane is parallel to the XY plane, and abc is both a perspective projection and an orthographic projection of ABC. abc is a perspective projection because the projection rays forming abc pass through the common point L, and an orthographic projection because abc has the same shape as ABC. The triangle abc differs from the triangle ABC in size only. The quotient of the area of abc divided by the area of ABC is known as the scale of the projection. Since the xy plane is parallel to the XY plane,

$$\frac{ab}{AB} = \frac{bc}{BC} = \frac{ca}{CA} = \frac{abc}{ABC} = \frac{Ln}{LN} = \text{scale}$$

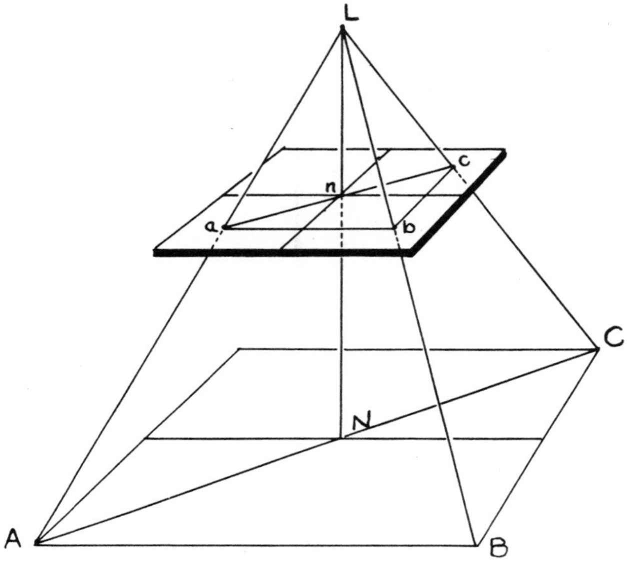

Fig. 5 Perspective projection.

Inasmuch as each ray intersecting the xy plane, which for purposes of this discussion is a transparent screen, forms an image of the corresponding point on the object, the sum of the rays forms an image of the object; hence the designation image plane.

Thus when the image plane is parallel to an object surface, the image formed by the rays passing through a common point is both a perspective projection and an orthographic projection in the sense of true shape. This occurs in aerial exposures when both the image plane and the object surface are parallel to datum. This is not the usual case, because generally the image plane and the object surface are parallel neither to each other nor to the datum. The image plane, however, is readily horizontalized to an orthographic projection of any object surface. Rarely do three randomly selected points in space have equal elevations. If A, B, and C have unequal elevations, those elevations above the lowest elevation are displaced outward from n a distance that is a function of the difference in elevation between the lowest and any other specific elevation. This is illustrated in Figure 6.

The image plane is parallel to $A^1B^1C^1$, which is at sea-level datum. By definition $A^1B^1C^1$ is an orthographic projection of AB^1C, but owing to displacements caused by differences in elevation or relief abc is a perspective projection—not an orthographic projection. The property of true shape characteristic of an orthographic projection has been altered by relief. a^1bc^1, which is not imaged, is the true shape of $A^1B^1C^1$.

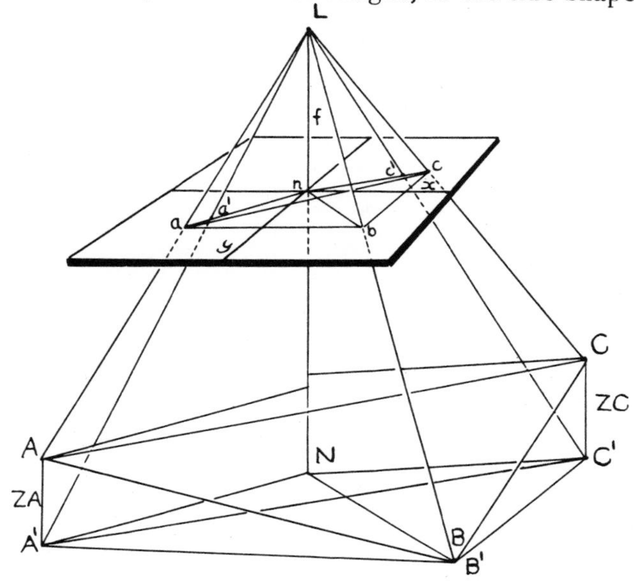

Fig. 6 Image displacement due to relief.

Image displacements aa^1 and cc^1 are called relief displacements and geometrically are direct functions of elevation. From the similar triangles evident in Figure 6,

$$\frac{ZL - ZA}{NA} = \frac{f}{na}$$

$$\frac{ZL}{NA} = \frac{f}{na^1}$$

and

$$ZL - ZA = \frac{NA \cdot f}{na}$$

$$ZL = \frac{NA \cdot f}{na^1}$$

Therefore $$na - na^1 = aa^1 = \frac{na \cdot ZA}{ZL}$$

which is the equation for relief displacement on an image plane that is parallel to the datum plane.

The discussion of perspective and orthographic projections with respect to an image plane parallel to the datum plane is equally applicable to an image plane perpendicular to the datum plane. Suppose, for example, an observer L examines a surface of a three-dimensional, rectilinear object as shown in Figure 7. Let there be passed between L

and the vertical object surface *ABCD* a transparent screen also vertical and parallel to *ABCD*. The intersection of this plane with the rays formed by lines of sight from the eye, *L*, to points *A*,*B*,*C*, and *D* will produce an outline *abcd*, which by previous definition is a perspective projection and an orthographic projection since image and object planes are parallel.

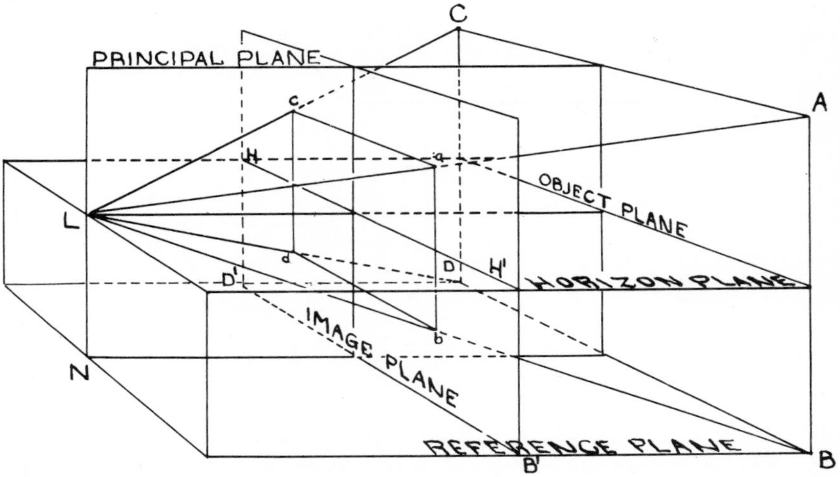

Fig. 7 Vertical perspective and orthographic projection.

Let the image plane be intercepted by three other planes: The one normal to *LN* at *N* and normal to the image plane is called the reference plane and is usually parallel to the datum plane; the second, parallel to the reference plane at an elevation *LN* above *N*, is called the horizon plane; and the third, a vertical plane, perpendicular to the image plane and including *LN*, is called the principal plane. The image trace of the horizon plane HH^1 has significance in photogrammetry as a graphical means of determining the inclination of the image plane with respect to any horizontal plane, usually the datum plane.

Thus far, for the sake of simplicity, the discussion of perspective projections has been confined to the special case of image plane being either parallel or perpendicular to the reference plane. The more general case is where the image plane is inclined to the reference plane at some angle between 0° and 90°. When the image plane has an inclination with the reference plane some angle greater than 0° and less than 90°, horizontal and vertical object surfaces do not form orthographic projections, inasmuch as the boundary lines and perhaps certain systems of parallel lines inherent in the object are not parallel to the image plane. Systems of parallel lines that are not parallel to the image plane exhibit the property of convergence in the image plane. Each system of parallel lines converges in the image plane, or the image plane extended, at a point known as the vanishing point for that system.

The convergence of parallel object lines in the image plane is illustrated in Figure 8.

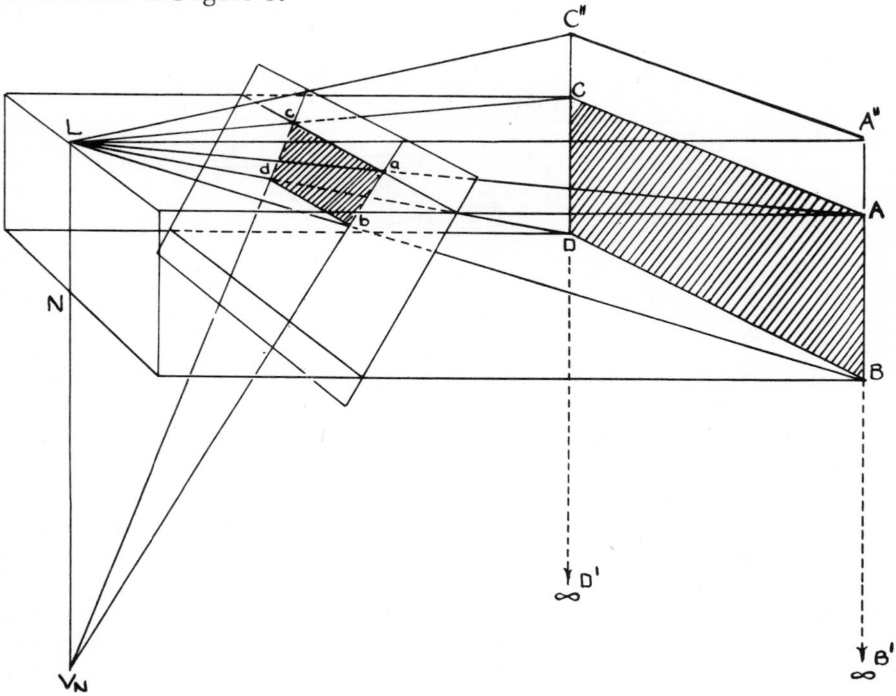

Fig. 8 Convergence of vertical systems of parallel lines in the image plane.

Perspective projection *abcd* is not an orthographic projection inasmuch as *abcd* does not have the same configuration as *ABCD*. *AC* is parallel to *BD* and both are parallel to the reference plane and the image plane. *AB* is parallel to *CD* but neither is parallel to the image plane. Consistent with converging lines and nonconverging lines, *ac* is parallel to *bd* because *ac* is parallel to *AC*, and *bd* is parallel to *BD*, while *ab* and *cd* converge because *AB* and *CD* are not parallel to the image plane. As *AB* and *CD* are produced vertically downward to infinity, the image traces of these lines converge at V_n – that is, when D^1 and B^1 are at infinity, LD^1 and LB^1coincide with LNV_n. Therefore, V_n is the nadir vanishing point for systems of parallel vertical lines on a nonvertical image plane.

This analogy is readily extended to systems of parallel lines lying parallel to the horizon plane that are not parallel to the image plane. In Figure 9 line A_1A_n is parallel to B_1B_n. Let it be assumed that $A\infty$ and $B\infty$ are at infinity. As points A_1, A_2, . . . A_n approach $A\infty$ and points B_1, B_2, . . . B_n approach $B\infty$, the conjugate images a_1, a_2, . . a_n and b_1, b_2, . . . b_n define image lines that intersect and vanish on the horizon line at *V*.

Thus the horizon is the converging point for systems of parallel lines lying parallel to the horizon plane, and the image of the horizon is the vanishing point for all such systems of lines. It may be noted here that the vanishing point is always formed in the direction of

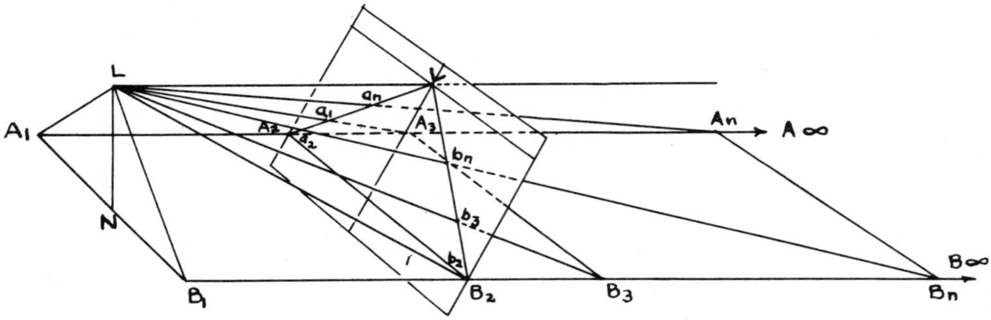

Fig. 9 Convergence of horizontal systems of parallel lines in the image plane.

infinity for any system of parallel lines that are not parallel to the image plane. The direction of infinity is the direction toward the intersection of any system of parallel lines with the image plane or the image plane extended. The direction of infinity is toward the nadir in Figure 8, and the vertical system vanishes where the vertical line *LN* pierces the image plane. The direction of infinity is toward the horizon in Figure 9, and the horizontal system vanishes where a vertical plane having the bearing of the horizontal system cuts the horizon line. A horizontal system vanishes at the intersection of the principal plane and the horizon line only when the system is parallel to the principal plane.

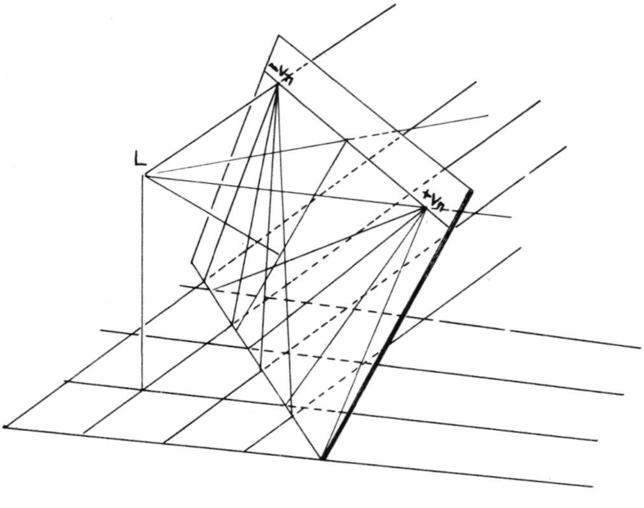

Fig. 10 Convergence of divergent systems of parallel lines in the reference plane.

If one system of horizontal parallel lines makes a positive angle θ with the principal plane in the reference plane and a second system makes a negative angle θ with the principal plane in the reference plane, the positive system will vanish on the image of the horizon line on the positive side and the negative system will vanish on the image of the horizon line on the negative side. This is illustrated in Figure 10.

If the observer occupies a station showing the top and two sides of a rectilinear building, there will be a vertical system of lines and two horizontal systems. Each system will vanish on the image plane in accordance with the definition given above. This point is illustrated in Figure 11.

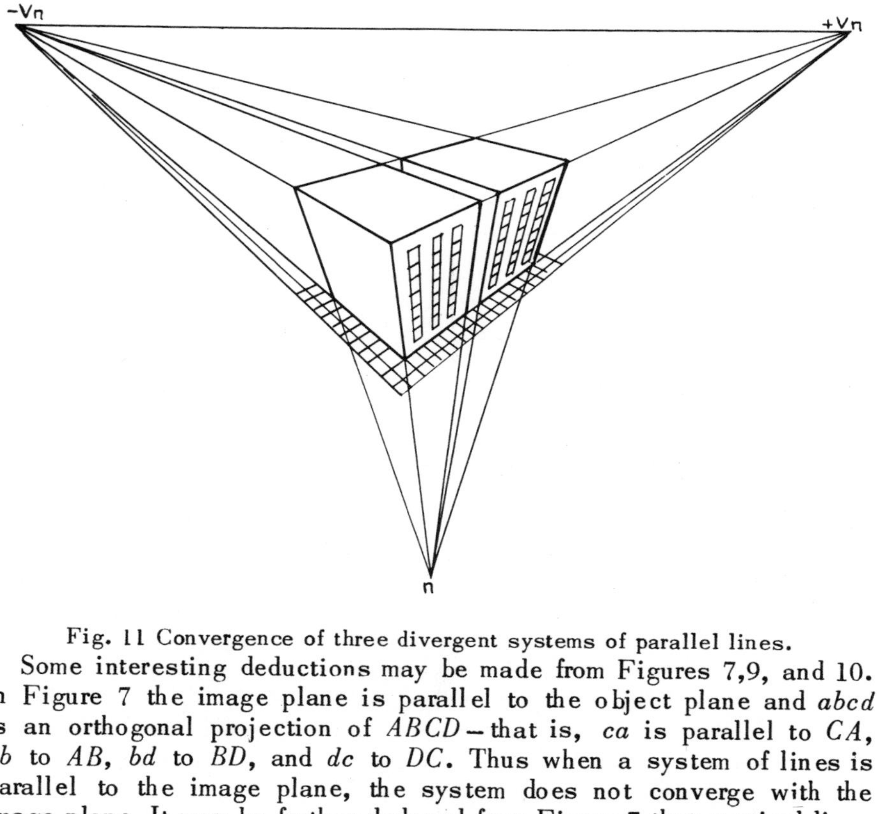

Fig. 11 Convergence of three divergent systems of parallel lines.

Some interesting deductions may be made from Figures 7,9, and 10. In Figure 7 the image plane is parallel to the object plane and *abcd* is an orthogonal projection of *ABCD*—that is, *ca* is parallel to *CA*, *ab* to *AB*, *bd* to *BD*, and *dc* to *DC*. Thus when a system of lines is parallel to the image plane, the system does not converge with the image plane. It may be further deduced from Figure 7 that vertical lines do not converge on a vertical image plane whereas horizontal lines converge sharply. The latter is also evident in Figure 9. Lines A_1B_1, A_2B_2, and A_nB_n are parallel to the image plane and therefore do not converge. Horizontal and vertical systems of parallel lines not parallel to the image plane do converge, however. Now in Figure 6 the image plane is parallel to the reference plane and the lines parallel to the reference plane do not converge. Vertical lines, on the other hand, converge most rapidly as radial relief displacement.

The reader may infer that all systems of parallel object lines converge either at the nadir or on the horizon line, since all converging systems have been referred to either the nadir point or horizon line. This is due to the convention of referring all objects to a horizontal and vertical datum. Any system not parallel to a horizontal or vertical datum does not converge at the nadir or on the horizon line. Consider two parallel lines, one passing each side of the observer and not parallel to either the observer's horizontal or vertical reference and making any angle θ with the observer's principal plane. This is illustrated in Figure 12.

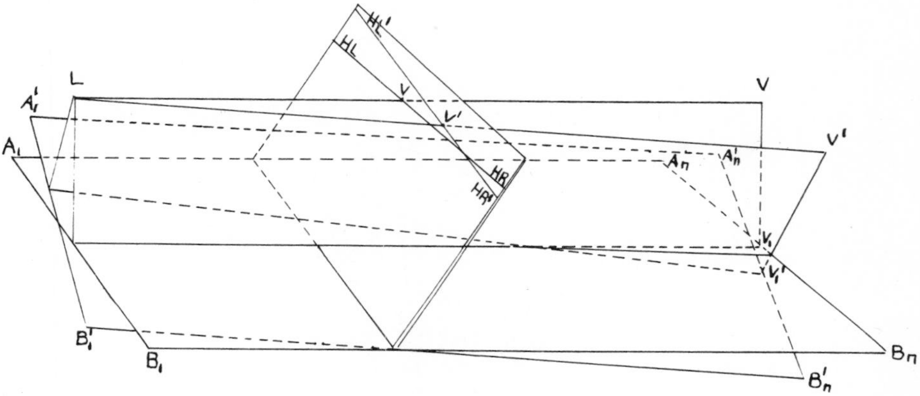

Fig. 12 Convergence of a system of parallel lines that are not parallel to a horizontal or vertical datum or the image plane.

In Figure 12 lines A_1A_n and B_1B_n are parallel to datum and the observer's principal plane $LNVV_1$. These lines converge at V (where the observer's principal plane cuts the horizon line). Lines $A_1{}^1A_n{}^1$ and $B_1{}^1B_n{}^1$ are parallel to each other but are not parallel to the observer's horizontal or vertical datum or principal plane, and therefore do not converge at the nadir or on the conventional horizon line. These lines converge at V^1, which is the image trace of a line passing through L and parallel to lines $A_1{}^1A_n{}^1$ and $B_1{}^1B_n{}^1$. Thus $LN^1V^1V_1{}^1$ is the arbitrary principal plane of the arbitrary reference plane and is perpendicular to the arbitrary reference plane. Similarly, $H_L{}^1H_R{}^1$ is the arbitrary horizon line of the nonstandard horizon plane.

Vanishing points may be summarized as follows: Any line or system of parallel lines not parallel to the image plane vanishes where a line passing through L and parallel to the system pierces the image plane. Parallel lines of any system parallel to the image plane do not converge with the image plane and are orthogonally projected. There is nothing more or less to vanishing points.

C. *ORIENTATION*.

1. Interior Orientation.

A camera, in the most elementary sense, is light-tight box

containing a covered aperture on one side and a light-sensitive material on the opposite inner side. When the aperture is uncovered, light energy from objects outside the camera enters the aperture and records conjugate images on the light-sensitive surface opposite. These basic elements are embodied in the pinhole camera illustrated in Figure 13.

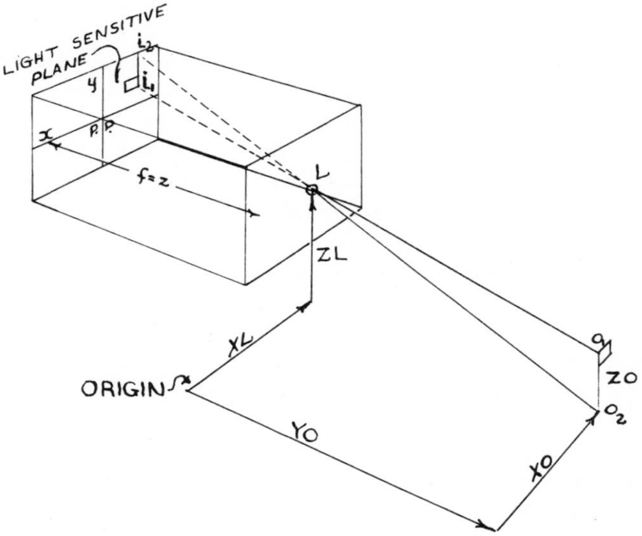

Fig. 13 Pinhole camera.

i_2i_1 is the image of object O_1O_2. The light-sensitive plane on which images are recorded is called the image plane and the space within the box is called image space. The space outside the camera bound by the aperture L and the objects recorded on the image plane is called object space. Line Li_1 is the image distance of image i_1 and line Li_2 is the image distance of image i_2. The line Lpp is perpendicular to the image plane and is defined as the z axis of the camera. The distance Lpp along the z axis is designated the principal distance, or focal length, and is denoted with a lower case f. Lying in the image plane are two mutually perpendicular lines designated the x and y axes, whose intersection defines the plate perpendicular, denoted pp.

The image plane is referred to as the xy plane of the camera. Generally the y axis is approximately parallel to one edge of the image plane and the x axis is approximately parallel to another edge of the image plane, inasmuch as the x axis is perpendicular to the y axis. The x and y axes are usually indicated with reference marks, called fiducial marks, attached to the edge of the image plane frame. The plate perpendicular is recaptured by connecting the images of opposite fiducial marks, the point of intersection being the plate perpendicular. Thus the normal distance f, from L to the xy plane, and the x and y fiducial marks referred to the foot of the normal distance f define the Cartesian coordinate system (xyf) of image space. The length f and the location *pp* are further defined as the interior orientation or interior geometry of the camera. The principles of interior orientation determination form the basis and foundation of analytical photogrammetry. The method of observation and computation is called camera calibration.

2. Exterior Orientation.

a. Space coordinates.

Just as images i_1 and i_2 have x,y, and f values that establish their position in image space, conjugate objects O_1 and O_2 have definite X,Y, and Z values that establish their position in object space. Usually the coordinates of points in object space are based on an orthogonal projection (Fig. 3) referred to an arbitrary origin with the XY plane parallel to a sea-level datum plane. The Y values are usually parallel to a central north-south meridian with the X values simply perpendicular to the Y axis. The Z values are normal to the XY plane and frequently are called the elevations of objects on the ground and the altitude of objects in space or above the ground. The object space coordinates (XL, YL, ZL) of L are considered to be the space coordinates of the camera station. The normal distance ZL of point L from the XY plane is the elevation or altitude of the camera station. The X and Y coordinates (XL, YL) of the foot of ZL designated N are called the plane or datum coordinates of the camera station. The object space coordinates of the camera station may be determined with photogrammetric equations in which the space coordinates of three objects and the image coordinates of three conjugate images are the essential given data. A solution for XL, YL, ZL of the camera station employing image space coordinates as part of the given data is dependent on the camera station. Measurement of the image coordinates of the xy plane referred to the fiducial marks and the subsequent solution for position in space of the exposure camera is known as spatial resection by analytical photogrammetric means. This is a common problem with airborne exposure cameras.

The space coordinates of an exposure camera occupying ground points may be determined independent of the exposure camera by conventional surveying methods. The principal difference between exposures made on the ground and exposures made from the air lies in the fact that a ground station may be deliberately established, occupied, and reoccupied independent of the exposure camera. An air station can be only roughly established, occupied, and reoccupied, and its precise determination depends on postexposure analysis. Determination of the direction angles from ground exposures is terrestrial photogrammetry, while determination of the direction angles from aerial exposures is aerial photogrammetry. The principles of analytical photogrammetry are the same in either case and are presented as such throughout the text.

The Cartesian coordinates of image and object space are now defined. The coordinates of the plate perpendicular and the focal length are the three numbers xp, yp, and f that define the interior geometry of any camera. The coordinates of the plate perpendicular are usually made to be zero, since the plane coordinates of images are generally referred to the fiducial axes defining the plate perpendicular. The space coordinates of *L (XL, YL, ZL)* are the three numbers that define the orthographic position of any camera.

The elements of interior geometry represent a plane and a point not in the plane (Fig. 2) at some fixed location with respect to the plane. The plane is the *xy* image plane at some normal distance *f* from *L*. The elements of exterior geometry also represent a plane and a point not in the plane at some fixed location with respect to the plane. The object space plane is the *XY* datum plane and point *L* is the fixed point at a distance *ZL* from the *XY* plane.

b. Angular orientation.

Consider a spatial camera station, with image plane parallel to object plane, illustrated in Figure 14.

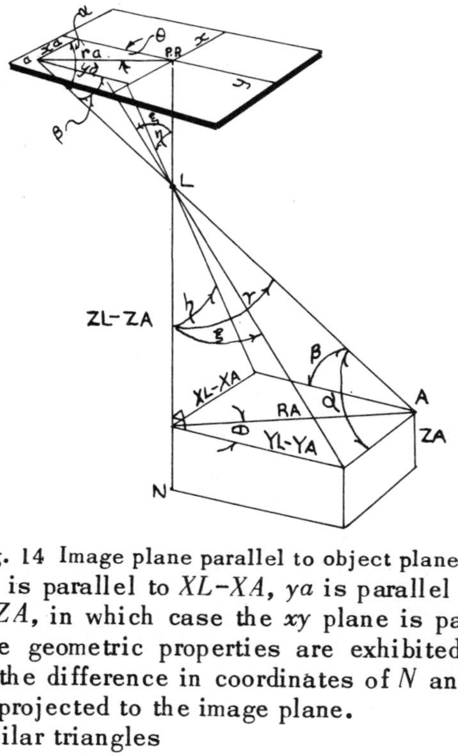

Fig. 14 Image plane parallel to object plane.

In Figure 14 *xa* is parallel to *XL−XA*, *ya* is parallel to *YL−YA*, and *f* is parallel to *ZL−ZA*, in which case the *xy* plane is parallel to the *XY* plane. When these geometric properties are exhibited between image and object space, the difference in coordinates of *N* and *A* may be said to be orthogonally projected to the image plane.

By virtue of similar triangles

$$\frac{XL-XA}{xa} = \frac{YL-YA}{ya} = \frac{ZL-ZA}{f}$$

and

$$XL-XA = \frac{xa}{f}(ZL-ZA)$$

$$YL-YA = \frac{ya}{f}(ZL-ZA)$$

By the Pythagorean theorem

$$ra^2 = xa^2 + ya^2 \dots\dots\dots\dots (1)$$
$$RA^2 = (XL-XA)^2 + (YL-YA)^2 \dots\dots (2)$$

which are quadratic equations of a circle.
Also by the Pythagorean theorem

$$La^2 = ra^2 + f^2$$
$$LA^2 = RA^2 + (ZL-ZA)^2$$

Therefore

$$La^2 = xa^2 + ya^2 + f^2 \dots\dots\dots\dots\dots (3)$$
$$LA^2 = (XL-XA)^2 + (YL-YA)^2 + (ZL-ZA)^2 \dots (4)$$

which are quadratic equations of a line in space.
Dividing equation (1) by *ra* and equation (2) by *RA* we obtain

$$ra = xa \sin\theta + ya \cos\theta$$
$$RA = (XL-XA)\sin\theta + (YL-YA)\cos\theta$$

which are normal forms of the equation of a line in a plane.
Dividing equation (3) by *La* and equation (4) by *LA* we obtain

$$La = xa \cos\alpha + ya \cos\beta + f \cos\gamma$$
$$LA = (XL-XA)\cos\alpha + (YL-YA)\cos\beta + (ZL-ZA)\cos\gamma$$

which are normal forms of a line in space and α, β, γ are the direction angles of lines *La* and *LA*.
Dividing equation (3) by La^2 and (4) by LA^2 we obtain

$$1 = \cos^2\alpha + \cos^2\beta + \cos^2\gamma$$

for both of them. This is the law which states that the sum of the squares of the direction cosines of a line in space is equal to unity and is proof that the radius of a sphere is constant for all direction angles.
Dividing equation (1) by *f* and (2) by *(ZL–ZA)* we obtain.

$$\tan\gamma\, ra = \tan\eta\, xa + \tan\xi\, ya$$
$$\tan\gamma\, RA = \tan\eta (XL-XA) + \tan\xi (YL-YA)$$

where η, ξ, γ are the angles subtended by the *x*, *y*, *r* segments of *a* and the *X*, *Y*, *R* segments of *A*. The angles η and ξ are known as standard coordinates and γ and θ as spherical coordinates.

Dividing equation (1) by f^2 and (2) by $(ZL-ZA)^2$ yields

$$\tan^2\gamma = \tan^2\eta + \tan^2\xi$$

for both lines and this is proof that the sum of the squares of the tangents of the standard coordinates is equal to the tangent of the zenith angle γ squared.

A useful relation between direction angles and spherical angles may be written with Napier's cosine rule: The sine of the middle part is equal to the product of the cosines of the opposite parts.

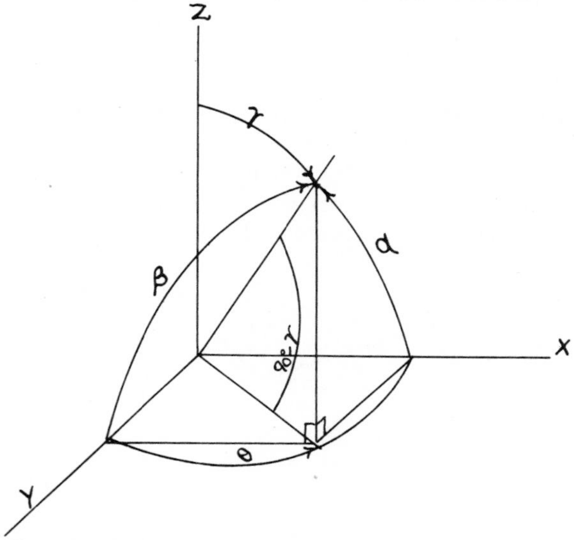

Fig. 15 Direction cosines by Napier's analogies.

From the spherical triangle in Figure 15,

$$\cos\alpha = \sin\gamma\ \sin\theta$$
$$\cos\beta = \sin\gamma\ \cos\theta$$
$$\cos\gamma = \cos\gamma$$

Another useful relation between the standard coordinates and the spherical coordinates may be written with Napier's tangent rule: The sine of the middle part is equal to the product of the tangents of the adjacent parts.

$$\tan\eta = \tan\gamma\sin\theta$$
$$\tan\xi = \tan\gamma\cos\theta$$
$$\tan\theta = \frac{\tan\eta}{\tan\xi}$$

The relations defined with Napier's cosine and tangent rules are combined to establish a relation between direction angles and standard coordinates

$$\frac{\cos \alpha}{\cos \beta} = \frac{\tan \eta}{\tan \xi} = \tan \theta$$

$$\frac{\cos \alpha}{\cos \gamma} = \tan \eta$$

$$\frac{\cos \beta}{\cos \gamma} = \tan \xi$$

The basic relation between the linear and angular coordinate systems of image and object space is now defined when the two systems are collinear.

A fundamental equation in analytical geometry, and one of the most basic in analytical photogrammetry, is interposed here for convenience before proceeding with the development of the elements of angular orientation. This equation is called the cosine of the angle between two lines in space and is illustrated in Figure 16.

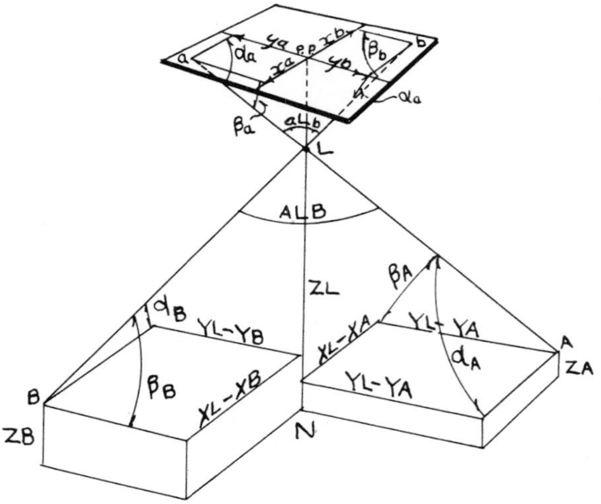

Fig. 16 The angle between two lines in space.

With the cosine formula in plane trigonometry we can write

$$\cos aLb = \frac{La^2 + Lb^2 - ab^2}{2\, La \cdot Lb}$$

and

$$\cos ALB = \frac{LA^2 + LB^2 - AB^2}{2\, LA \cdot LB}$$

Since lines *aLA* and *bLB* intersect at *L*,

$$\text{angle } aLb = \text{angle } ALB$$

From previous considerations

$$
\begin{aligned}
La^2 &= xa^2 + ya^2 + f^2 \\
Lb^2 &= xb^2 + yb^2 + f^2 \\
ab^2 &= (xa-xb)^2 + (ya-yb)^2 \\
LA^2 &= (XL-XA)^2 + (YL-YA)^2 + (ZL-ZA)^2 \\
LB^2 &= (XL-XB)^2 + (YL-YB)^2 + (ZL-ZB)^2 \\
AB^2 &= [(XL-XA)-(XL-XB)]^2 + [(YL-YA)-(YL-YB)]^2 + [(ZL-ZA)-(ZL-ZB)]^2
\end{aligned}
$$

Expanding the right members of these equations and substituting for the left members of the cosine formulas gives

$$\cos aLb = \frac{xa^2 + ya^2 + f^2 + xb^2 + yb^2 + f^2 - xa^2 - xb^2 - ya^2 - yb^2 + 2xa \cdot xb + 2ya \cdot yb}{2\,La \cdot Lb}$$

and

$$\cos ALB = \frac{(XL-XA)^2 + (YL-YA)^2 + (ZL-ZA)^2 + (XL-XB)^2 + (YL-YB)^2 + (ZL-ZB)^2}{2\,LA \cdot LB}$$

$$- \frac{[(XL-XA)^2 + (YL-YA)^2 + (ZL-ZA)^2 + (XL-XB)^2 + (YL-YB)^2 + (ZL-ZB)^2]}{2\,LA \cdot LB}$$

$$+ \frac{2(XL-XA)(XL-XB) + 2(YL-YA)(YL-YB) + 2(ZL-ZA)(ZL-ZB)}{2\,LA \cdot LB}$$

These reduce to

$$\cos aLb = \frac{xa \cdot xb + ya \cdot yb + f^2}{La \cdot Lb}$$

$$\cos ALB = \frac{(XL-XA)(XL-XB) + (YL-YA)(YL-YB) + (ZL-ZA)(ZL-ZB)}{LA \cdot LB}$$

which are analytic equations for the cosine of an angle between two lines in space. From the relation between Cartesian coordinates and direction cosines

$$
\begin{aligned}
&\cos \alpha_a = \frac{xa}{La} \qquad \cos \alpha_b = \frac{xb}{Lb} \qquad \cos \alpha_A = \frac{XL-XA}{LA} \qquad \cos \alpha_B = \frac{XL-XB}{LB} \\
&\cos \beta_a = \frac{ya}{La} \qquad \cos \beta_b = \frac{yb}{Lb} \qquad \cos \beta_A = \frac{YL-YA}{LA} \qquad \cos \beta_B = \frac{YL-YB}{LB} \\
&\cos \gamma_a = \frac{f}{La} \qquad \cos \gamma_b = \frac{f}{Lb} \qquad \cos \gamma_A = \frac{ZL-ZA}{LA} \qquad \cos \gamma_B = \frac{ZL-ZB}{LB}
\end{aligned}
$$

we may write

$$\cos aLb = \cos \alpha_a \cos \alpha_b + \cos \beta_a \cos \beta_b + \cos \gamma_a \cos \gamma_b$$

$$\cos ALB = \cos \alpha_A \cos \alpha_B + \cos \beta_A \cos \beta_B + \cos \gamma_A \cos \gamma_B$$

which is the cosine of the angle between two lines written with the

Therefore,

$$(XL-XA)^1 = \frac{xa(ZL-ZA)\cos Az}{(ya \sin t + f \cos t)} - \frac{(ya \cos t - f \sin t)(ZL-ZA)\sin Az}{(ya \sin t + f \cos t)}$$

$$(YL-YA)^1 = \frac{xa(ZL-ZA)\sin Az}{(ya \sin t + f \cos t)} + \frac{(ya \cos t - f \sin t)(ZL-ZA)\cos Az}{(ya \sin t + f \cos t)}$$

Since the camera *y* axis is never found in the principal plane, let a third rotation *s* be introduced about *Lpp* in the *xy* plane. This is illustrated in Figure 19. The angle *s* is called swing and is defined as the angle measured clockwise at *pp* in the *xy* plane from the *y* axis to the principal line. With a swing rotation *xa* is not parallel to $(XL-XA)^1$ nor *ya* to $(YL-YA)^1$ nor *f* to $(ZL-ZA)$. However, xa^1 is parallel to $(XL-XA)^1$, ya^1 to $(YL-YA)^1$, and za^1 to $(ZL-ZA)$ where

$$\begin{aligned} xa^1 &= xa \cos s - ya \sin s \\ ya^{11} &= (xa \sin s + ya \cos s) \cos t - f \sin t \\ za^1 &= (xa \sin s + ya \cos s) \sin t + f \cos t \end{aligned}$$

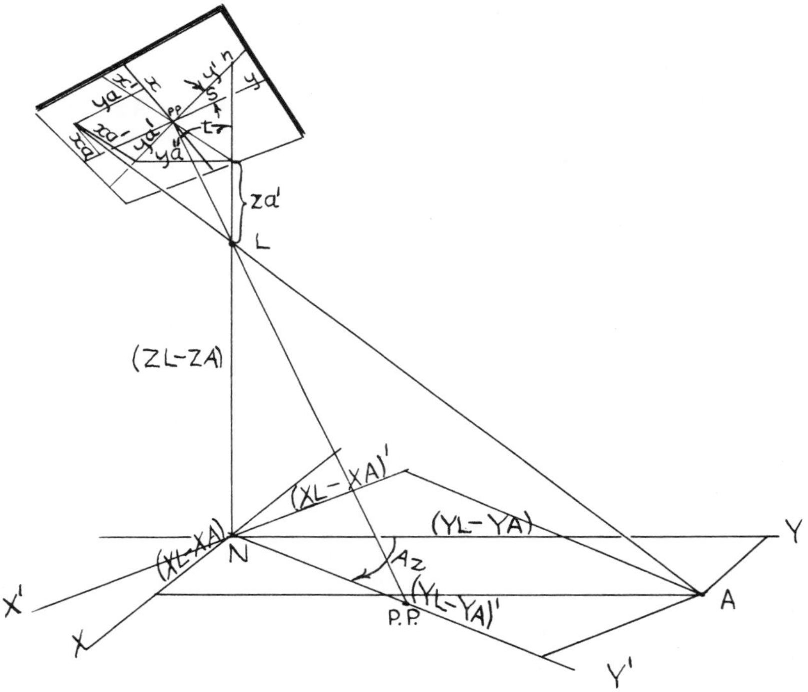

Fig. 19 Tilt, swing, and azimuth rotation.

Therefore,

$$\frac{(XL-XA)^1}{xa^1} = \frac{(YL-YA)^1}{ya^{11}} = \frac{(ZL-ZA)}{za^1} = \frac{LA}{La}$$

$$(XL-XA)^1 = \frac{\{(xa\cos s - ya\sin s)\cos Az - [(xa\sin s + ya\cos s)\cos t - f\sin t]\sin Az\}(ZL-ZA)}{(xa\sin s + ya\cos s)\sin t + f\cos t}$$

$$(YL-YA)^1 = \frac{\{(xa\cos s - ya\sin s)\sin Az + [(xa\sin s + ya\cos s)\cos t - f\sin t]\cos Az\}(ZL-ZA)}{(xa\sin s + ya\cos s)\sin t + f\cos t}$$

Thus three rotation angles – tilt, *t*, swing, *s*, and azimuth, *Az* – completely define the angular orientation of a camera in space. These angles are termed the elements of angular orientation. Angles *s* and *t* are the spherical coordinates of *n* and are referred to the camera coordinate system.

From the quadratic equation of a sphere we have

$$Ln^2 = xn^2 + yn^2 + f^2 \quad . \; . \; . \; . \; . \quad (5)$$

where *xn* and *yn* are the camera coordinates of *n*.
Dividing equation (5) through by *Ln* gives

$$Ln = xn\cos\gamma_x + yn\cos\gamma_y + f\cos\gamma_z$$

and γ_x, γ_y, and γ_z are the direction angles of *ZL* referred to the camera coordinate system. Now *t* and *s* are the spherical coordinates of *n*.
By Napier's cosine rule

$$\cos\gamma_x = \sin s \sin t$$
$$\cos\gamma_y = \cos s \sin t$$
$$\cos\gamma_z = \cos t$$

and by Napier's tangent rule the standard coordinates of *n* are determined

$$\tan\Delta\eta_x = \sin s \tan t$$
$$\tan\Delta\xi_y = \cos s \tan t$$
$$\tan s = \frac{\tan\Delta\eta_x}{\tan\Delta\xi_y}$$

From similar previous considerations the relation between the direction cosines and the standard coordinates are established:

$$\cos\gamma_x\, Ln = xn$$
$$\cos\gamma_y\, Ln = yn$$

$$\cos \gamma_z \, Ln = f$$

and

$$\tan \Delta \eta_x \, f = xn$$
$$\tan \Delta \xi_y \, f = yn$$

Therefore

$$\frac{\cos \gamma_x}{\cos \gamma_z} = \tan \Delta \eta_x$$

$$\frac{\cos \gamma_y}{\cos \gamma_z} = \tan \Delta \xi_y$$

In the same manner angles *Az* and *t* are the spherical coordinates of line *LPP* and from the quadratic equation of a sphere we have

$$(LPP)^2 = (XL-XP)^2 + (YL-YP)^2 + (ZL-ZP)^2 \; . \; . \; . \; . \; . \quad (6)$$

Dividing equation (6) by *LPP* gives

$$LPP = (XL-XP) \cos \alpha_z + (YL-YP) \cos \beta_z + (ZL-ZP) \cos \gamma_z$$

and α_z, β_z, and γ_z are the direction angles of *f* referred to the ground coordinate system.

Again by Napier's cosine rule

$$\cos \alpha_z = \sin Az \, \sin t$$
$$\cos \beta_z = \cos Az \, \sin t$$
$$\cos \gamma_z = \cos t$$

and by Napier's tangent rule

$$\tan \Delta \eta_x = \sin Az \, \tan t$$
$$\tan \Delta \xi_y = \cos Az \, \tan t$$

Combining these relations

$$\frac{\cos \alpha_z}{\cos \gamma_z} = \tan \Delta \eta_x$$

$$\frac{\cos \beta_z}{\cos \gamma_z} = \tan \Delta \xi_y$$

The relation between the tilt, swing, and azimuth is essentially the relation existing between two spherical coordinate systems: the one is of the *Z* axis referred to the camera coordinate system and the latter is the *z*, or *f*, axis produced referred to the ground coordinate system.

These relations are illustrated in Figure 20.

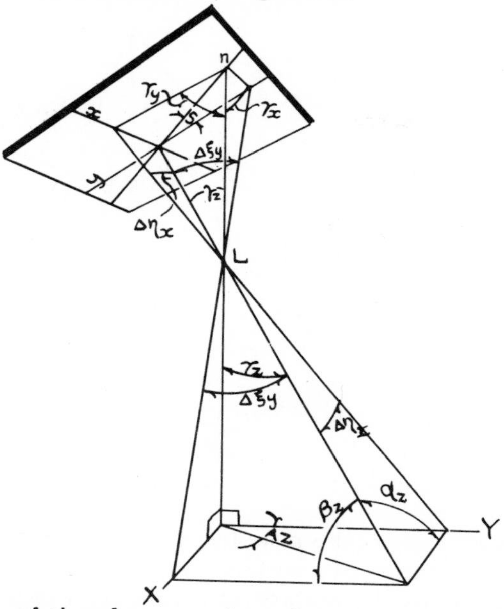

Fig. 20 Relation of the elements of angular orientation to direction cosines, standard coordinates, and spherical coordinates.

When the location of the plate perpendicular and focal length are known, the interior orientation of the camera is known; when the space coordinates *(XL, YL, ZL)* and angular orientation *(t, s, Az)* are known, the exterior orientation of the camera is known; and when the interior and exterior orientation of the camera are known, the angular and linear relation of images and objects are completely established, provided all objects lie in the *XY* plane. This seldom occurs in nature. Any object *A* may have any elevation whatsoever above or below the *XY* plane, and any other object *B* may have any elevation different from *A* above or below the *XY* plane. When objects define an undulating surface with respect to the *XY* plane, the elements of interior and exterior orientation of a single camera in space do not define the angular and linear relation of image and object unless the elevations of the objects with respect to the *XY* plane are also known.

3. Reciprocal Orientation.

Trigonometrically, a point may be located by intersection, which is simply directed rays from two known positions. The photogrammetric analogy is two camera stations, each having regions of image space of the same object space. When the elements of interior orientation of two such camera stations are known, the spatial configuration of the surface in object space having conjugate images may be completely defined. This is known as relative reciprocal orientation of two overlapping image planes. Relative reciprocal orientation, illustrated in Figure 21, is a basic concept of photogrammetry inasmuch as it may be accomplished with none other than photographic measurements.

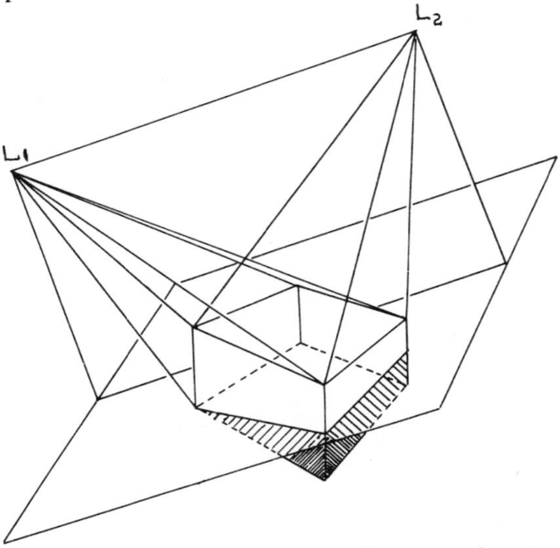

Fig. 21 Relative reciprocal orientation of two overlapping exposures.

The spatial configuration of a surface in object space generally has incomplete meaning unless the surface is established in position, azimuth, and dimension with respect to the earth's geodetic reference system. The latter can be determined only when the elements of both interior and exterior orientation of two overlapping image planes are known. This is known as absolute reciprocal orientation and has the property of completely defining the relation between image and object space without the necessity of the elevations of the objects being known. Absolute reciprocal orientation is illustrated in Figure 22.

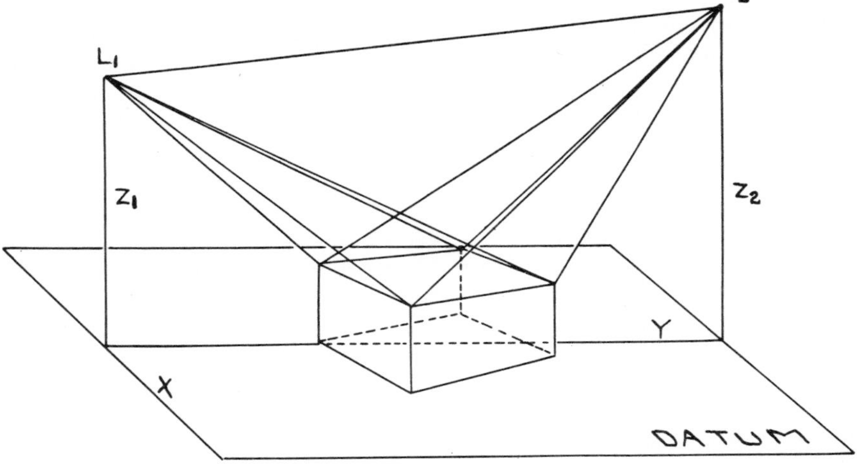

Fig. 22 Absolute reciprocal orientation.

Summarizing, photogrammetry is embraced in three fundamental concepts:

(1) Interior orientation— the camera coordinate system *(x, y, f)* referenced to the focal length *f* and the plate perpendicular *xp* and *yp*.

(2) Exterior orientation— the space coordinates *(XL, YL, ZL)* of the camera referenced to the earth's coordinate system and the angular orientation *(t, s, Az)* of the camera coordinate system with respect to the object-space-coordinate system.

(3) Reciprocal orientation—

(a) Relative reciprocal orientation is the tilt, swing, and azimuth of two photographs with respect to a fictitious *XY* plane that is parallel to the line connecting the two camera stations.

(b) Absolute reciprocal orientation is the tilt, swing, and azimuth of two photographs with respect to an established coordinate system.

The fundamental purpose of this book is to develop equations and to establish computational procedures for translating these concepts into useful numbers. The science of photogrammetry is basically a solution to object mensuration in which the exposure camera is essentially a photographic goniometer or a photographic angle-measuring instument. The camera is the reservoir and source of all image data. The photographic solution to object mensuration may be achieved largely by instrumentation with a minimum of numerical computation and/or graphics, or largely by numerical computations and/or graphics with a minimum of instrumentation. The former is instrumental photogrammetry while the latter is analytical photogrammetry. Presentation of the analytical solution with the minimum required instrumentation to the fundamental problems of photogrammetry is the object of this book. Later it will be seen that there is no instrumental solution that does not involve some numerical computation nor is there any computational solution that does not involve some instrumentation.

D. *SIMPLIFICATION OF THE ANGULAR ORIENTATION EQUATIONS.*

The development of the angular orientation equations, also referred to as transformation equations, began with the image plane parallel to the datum plane. Thereafter one element at a time was introduced in the form of the rotation of a plane about a line— that is, tilt is the rotation of the image plane about point *L*, azimuth is the rotation of the datum plane about line *NLn*, and swing is the rotation of the image plane about line *PPLpp*. The development went from the simple to the complex. The purpose of this section is to show the simplification of the complex or general transformation equations when orthogonal properties are imposed on the angular rotation elements of the equations.

The transformation equations are equally applicable to terrestrial and aerial exposures. The transformations for the existence of tilt and swing are

$$x^1 = x \cos s - y \sin s$$
$$y^1 = x \sin s \cos t + y \cos s \cos t - f \sin t$$
$$z^1 = x \sin s \sin t + y \cos s \sin t + f \cos t$$

Frequently terrestrial cameras are oriented with the *y* axis in the principal plane and the *z* axis in the horizon plane. This is equivalent to making

$$t = 90° \text{ and } s = 180°$$

and then the sine and cosine functions of *t* and *s* are:

t	*s*
$\sin 90° = 1$	$\sin 180° = 0$
$\cos 90° = 0$	$\cos 180° = -1$

Therefore by substituting the numerical value of the functions

$$x^1 = x(-1) - y(0) = -x$$
$$y^1 = x(0)(0) + y(-1)(0) - f(1) = -f$$
$$z^1 = x(0)(1) + y(-1)(1) + f(0) = -y$$

Now assume that

$$t = 0, \text{ in which case, } s = 0$$

and then the sine and cosine functions of *t* and *s* are:

$$\sin 0° = 0$$
$$\cos 0° = 1$$

Therefore

$$x^1 = x(1) - y(0) = x$$
$$y^1 = x(0)(1) + y(1)(1) - f(0) = y$$
$$z^1 = x(0)(0) + y(1)(0) + f(1) = f$$

These are the simplifications consistent with vertical and horizontal orientation of the image plane.

E. *DIRECTION ANGLES OF ONE COORDINATE SYSTEM REFERENCED TO ANOTHER.*

In section C it was shown that a line in space may be expressed as a sum of the products of each direction cosine and the corresponding ordinate:

$$L = X \cos \alpha + Y \cos \beta + Z \cos \gamma$$

These equations may be employed to express the coordinates of one system in terms of the other, which is useful inasmuch as the direction angles between pairs of ordinates are constant for all points. Each ordinate of one system is essentially a line in space that has three direction angles when referred to the other, or nine direction angles completely define the angular relation between two superimposed coordinate systems having different orientation. For convenient notation let the angle symbol refer to the space coordinate and the subscript symbol refer to the camera coordinate. This notation is illustrated in a square array.

	X	Y	Z
x	α_x	β_x	γ_x
y	α_y	β_y	γ_y
f	α_z	β_z	γ_z

Let it be assumed that the image plane has an image *a* that coincides with the conjugate object *A*. This means that there is a one-to-one size ratio between image and object, in which case

$$\begin{aligned} La &= LA \\ xa &= XA^1 \\ ya &= YA^1 \\ f &= ZA^1 \end{aligned}$$

and

$$\begin{aligned} xa^1 &= XA \\ ya^1 &= YA \\ za^1 &= ZA \end{aligned}$$

In practice there is not a one-to-one size ratio between image and object, in which case

$$\begin{aligned} m\cdot La &= LA \\ m\cdot xa &= XA^1 \\ m\cdot ya &= YA^1 \\ m\cdot f &= ZA^1 \end{aligned}$$

and

$$\begin{aligned} m\cdot xa^1 &= XA \\ m\cdot ya^1 &= YA \\ m\cdot za^1 &= ZA \end{aligned}$$

where $m = \frac{LA}{La}$ and differs for each point on an undulating object surface.

The coordinates of one system expressed in terms of the other are called directed line segments. Consider the camera coordinates of image *a* multiplied by some scale factor *m* in terms of the ground coordinates.

$$XA^1 = XA\cos\alpha_x + YA\cos\beta_x + ZA\cos\gamma_x = m\cdot xa$$
$$YA^1 = XA\cos\alpha_y + YA\cos\beta_y + ZA\cos\gamma_y = m\cdot ya$$

$$ZA^1 = XA \cos \alpha_z + YA \cos \beta_z + ZA \cos \gamma_z = m \cdot f$$

These equations are illustrated in Figure 23.

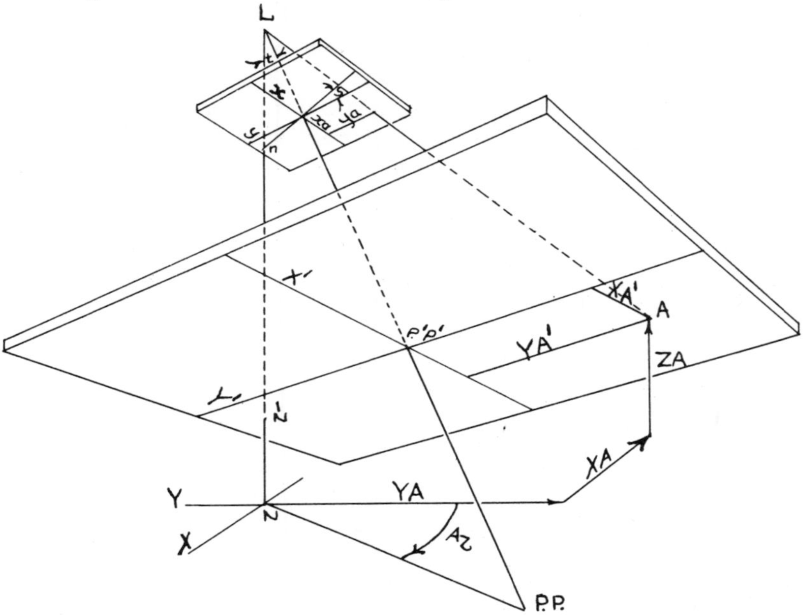

Fig. 23 Camera coordinates in terms of space coordinates.

These equations do not alter the relation between the camera coordinates — only the scale of the camera coordinates by a factor *m*. The factor *m* is the scale the camera coordinates would have if image *a*, without altering the image plane angular orientation, coincided with object *A*. This means that

$$\frac{XA^1}{xa} = \frac{YA^1}{ya} = \frac{ZA^1}{f} = \frac{LA}{La}$$

The direction angles are illustrated in Figure 24 (a), (b), and (c).

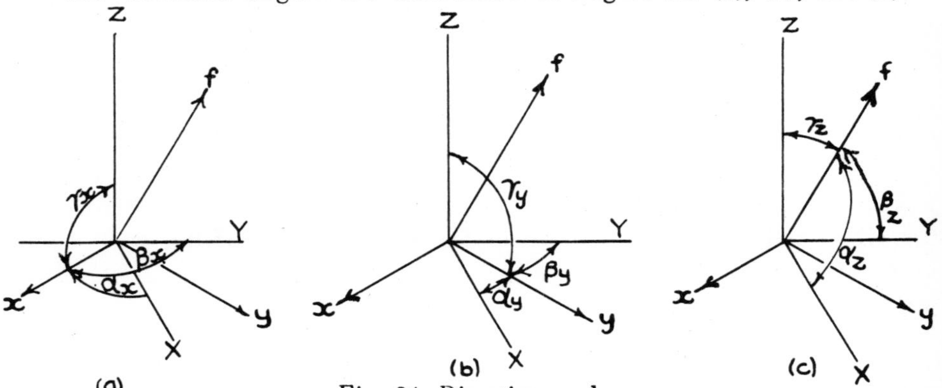

Fig. 24 Direction angles.

Now consider the ground coordinates of object *A* in terms of the camera coordinates multiplied by some factor *m*.

$$\begin{aligned} xa^1 &= xa \cos \alpha_x + ya \cos \alpha_y + f \cos \alpha_z = m \cdot XA \\ ya^1 &= xa \cos \beta_x + ya \cos \beta_y + f \cos \beta_z = m \cdot YA \\ za^1 &= xa \cos \gamma_x + ya \cos \gamma_y + f \cos \gamma_z = m \cdot ZA \end{aligned}$$

These equations are illustrated in Figure 25.

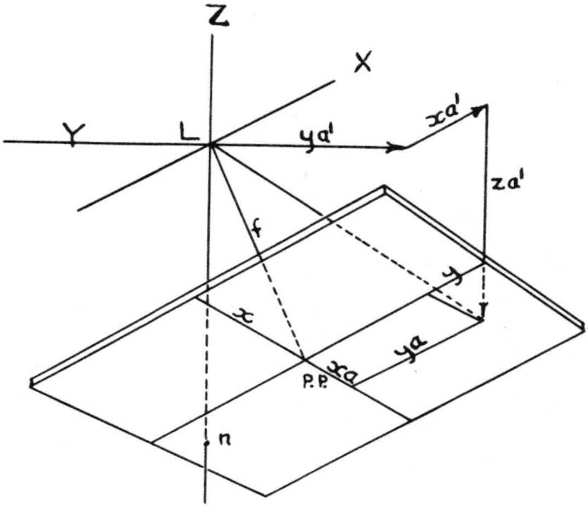

Fig. 25 Space coordinates in terms of camera coordinates.

These equations do not alter the relation between the ground coordinates—only the scale of the ground coordinates by a factor *m*. The factor *m* is the same and is the scale the ground coordinates would have if object *A*, without altering the orientation of the ground coordinates, coincided with image *a*. And this means that

$$\frac{XA}{xa^1} = \frac{YA}{ya^1} = \frac{ZA}{za^1} = \frac{LA}{La}$$

The direction angles are illustrated in Figure 26 (a), (b), and (c).

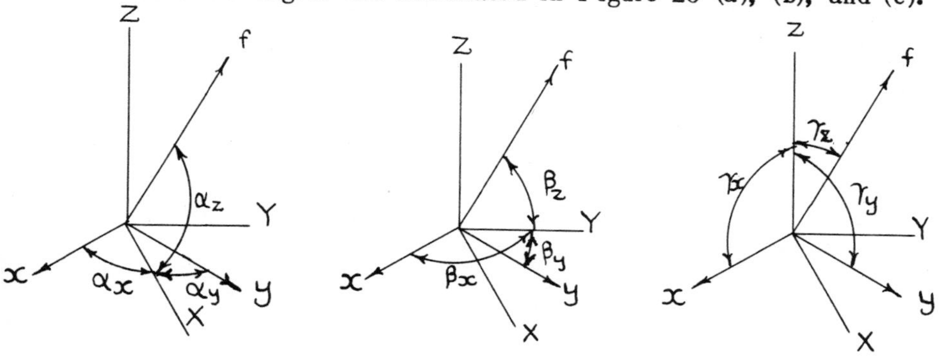

(a) (b) (c)

Fig. 26 Direction angles.

Of interest to the photogrammetrist is the relation between the nine direction cosines and the elements of angular orientation. Recalling that

$$
\begin{aligned}
x^{1} &= (x \cos s - y \sin s) \cos Az \\
&\quad - (x \sin s \cos t + y \cos s \cos t - f \sin t) \sin Az \\
y^{11} &= (x \cos s - y \sin s) \sin Az \\
&\quad + (x \sin s \cos t + y \cos s \cos t - f \sin t) \cos Az \\
z^{1} &= x \sin s \sin t + y \cos s \sin t + f \cos t
\end{aligned}
$$

collecting common coefficients gives

$$
\begin{aligned}
x^{1} &= x(\cos s \cos Az - \sin s \cos t \sin Az) \\
&\quad - y(\sin s \cos Az + \cos s \cos t \sin Az) + f(\sin t \sin Az) \\
y^{11} &= x(\cos s \sin Az + \sin s \cos t \cos Az) \\
&\quad - y \sin s \sin Az - \cos s \cos t \cos Az) - f(\sin t \cos Az) \\
z^{1} &= x(\sin s \sin t) + y(\cos s \sin t) + f(\cos t)
\end{aligned}
$$

By virtue of identical coefficients the relation between the direction angles and the elements of angular orientation is readily established:

$$
\begin{aligned}
\cos \alpha_x &= \cos s \cos Az - \sin s \cos t \sin Az \\
\cos \alpha_y &= -\sin s \cos Az + \cos s \cos t \sin Az \\
\cos \alpha_z &= \sin t \sin Az \\
\cos \beta_x &= \cos s \sin Az - \sin s \cos t \cos Az \\
\cos \beta_y &= -\sin s \sin Az - \cos s \cos t \cos Az \\
\cos \beta_z &= -\sin t \cos Az \\
\cos \gamma_x &= \sin s \sin t \\
\cos \gamma_y &= \cos s \sin t \\
\cos \gamma_z &= \cos t
\end{aligned}
$$

These direction angles make convenient unknowns in determining the angular orientation of a camera in space inasmuch as they have cyclic recurrence in certain linear equations.

Several useful checks are available in unknowns of this nature in that the following sum-of-the-direction-cosines-squared equations are required to be satisfied:

$$
\begin{aligned}
\cos^2 \alpha_x + \cos^2 \alpha_y + \cos^2 \alpha_z &= 1 \qquad \text{X axis} \\
\cos^2 \beta_x + \cos^2 \beta_y + \cos^2 \beta_z &= 1 \qquad \text{Y axis} \\
\cos^2 \gamma_x + \cos^2 \gamma_y + \cos^2 \gamma_z &= 1 \qquad \text{Z axis}
\end{aligned}
$$

and

$$
\begin{aligned}
\cos^2 \alpha_x + \cos^2 \beta_x + \cos^2 \gamma_x &= 1 \qquad \text{x axis} \\
\cos^2 \alpha_y + \cos^2 \beta_y + \cos^2 \gamma_y &= 1 \qquad \text{y axis} \\
\cos^2 \alpha_z + \cos^2 \beta_z + \cos^2 \gamma_z &= 1 \qquad \text{z axis}
\end{aligned}
$$

Also the angle-between-two-lines formula, since the cosine of 90° is zero

$$\cos\alpha_x \cos\alpha_y + \cos\beta_x \cos\beta_y + \cos\gamma_x \cos\gamma_y = 0 \quad xy$$
$$\cos\alpha_y \cos\alpha_z + \cos\beta_y \cos\beta_z + \cos\gamma_y \cos\gamma_z = 0 \quad yz$$
$$\cos\alpha_z \cos\alpha_x + \cos\beta_z \cos\beta_x + \cos\gamma_z \cos\gamma_x = 0 \quad zx$$

and

$$\cos\alpha_x \cos\beta_x + \cos\alpha_y \cos\beta_y + \cos\alpha_z \cos\beta_z = 0 \quad XY$$
$$\cos\beta_x \cos\gamma_x + \cos\beta_y \cos\gamma_y + \cos\beta_z \cos\gamma_z = 0 \quad YZ$$
$$\cos\gamma_x \cos\alpha_x + \cos\gamma_y \cos\alpha_y + \cos\gamma_z \cos\alpha_z = 0 \quad ZX$$

F. *APPLICATION OF PERSPECTIVE TO INTERIOR AND EXTERIOR ORIENTATION OF THE EXPOSURE STATION.*

The focal length [1]*, location of the principal point [2], tilt, swing, and azimuth of an exposure station may be determined from a single photograph of a three-dimensional object, such as a building, without any given linear object-space data. A photograph showing a three-dimensional view of a building is illustrated in Figure 27.

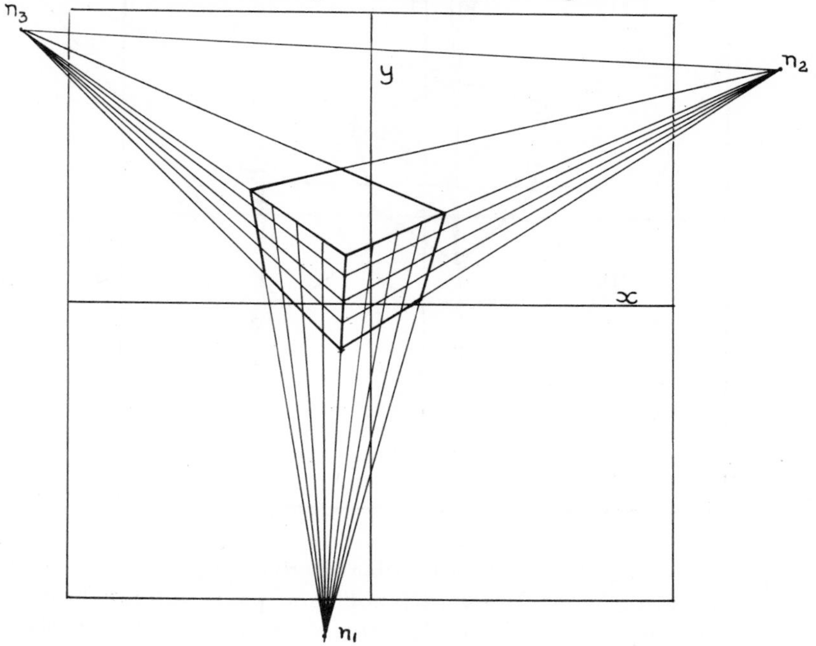

Fig. 27 Three-dimensional view of a building.

Two assumptions are made: (1) The vertical lines of the building are parallel in object space. (2) The horizontal lines of the building are parallel to a plane which is assumed to be perpendicular to the vertical lines.

All vertical lines in object space will intersect at the nadir vanishing point which is vertically below the camera station. To this end, vertical lines defined by building corners and window sides are extended

* Numbers in brackets refer to items listed in Appendix: Literature Cited.

downward until they intersect. The point of intersection is the nadir point of the photograph. The nadir-point image will probably fall outside the photograph unless the cone angle of the camera is very large. For this reason, the lines are extended on a larger transparent overlay. At least two systems of horizontal lines must be selected to define the horizon line. One such system could be the top and bottom edges of the building, the windows, and the doors of one side of the building. Those of another side of the building could comprise a second system. For each system the lines are extended until they intersect. A line connecting the intersections of the systems defines the conventional horizon line. Thus, three vanishing points have been located: two defining the horizon line and one, the nadir point. Let these be denoted n_1, n_2, and n_3. The overlay is illustrated in Figure 28.

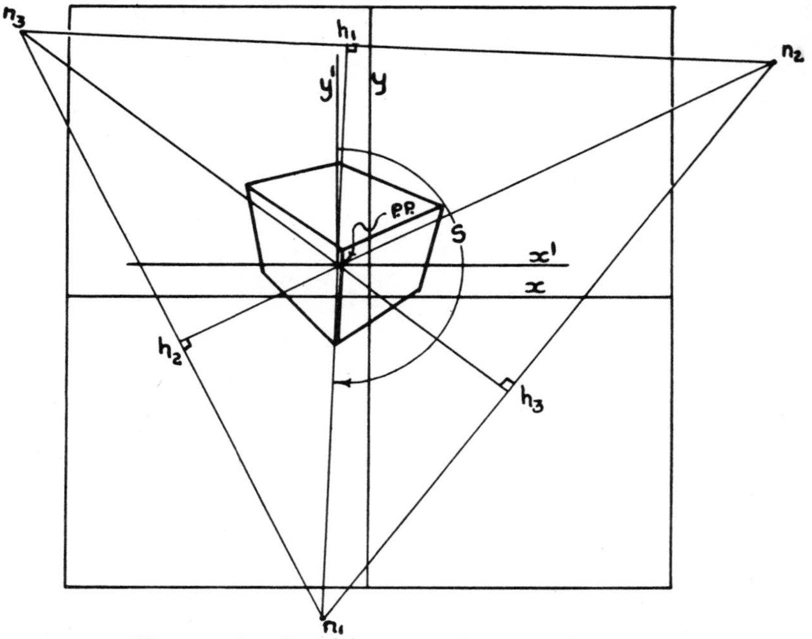

Fig. 28 Graphical location of principal point.

The various systems of lines will not form point intersections owing to the deviations of the line directions caused by differential lens distortion and inaccuracies in the orthogonality of the building.

At this point, three definitions are required:

(1) The principal line is defined by the principal point and nadir point.

(2) The principal line is the image trace of the principal plane which is perpendicular to the horizon plane.

(3) The horizon line is the image trace of the horizontal plane passing through the camera lens.

From these definitions it may be deduced that the principal line is a line passing through the nadir point and perpendicular to the horizon line. A perpendicular is drawn on the overlay from the nadir point to the horizon line.

The principal point, by definition, lies somewhere on this line. As a matter of convention, the two intersections, from the systems of lines believed to be perpendicular to vertical lines, are said to define the horizon line. If the sides of the building are orthogonal to each other, a line connecting each horizon vanishing point with the nadir vanishing point defines two unconventional horizon lines that are rotated in object space, each 90° from the conventional horizon. If the three systems of parallel lines do not intersect perpendicularly in object space, the direction of each vanishing point is not 90° from the corresponding horizon line and therefore will not intersect to define the principal point. In fact, a large triangle of error is a measure of nonorthogonality of object-space planes. The horizon vanishing point opposite each unconventional horizon line is the corresponding unconventional nadir point. Thus a line is drawn from the nadir point to each horizon point.

Since the laws of perspective are independent of absolute orientation, two more principal lines are constructed by drawing a perpendicular to each unconventional horizon line from the corresponding unconventional nadir point. Let these points be designated h_1, h_2, and h_3. The one invariant point lies at the intersection of the three principal lines. This is the principal point, designated *p*.

Tilt is the angle defined by the intersection of the optical axis and a vertical line through the lens, the image of which is n_1.

$$\tan t = \frac{n_1p}{f}$$

Tilt is also the angle defined by the intersection of the film plane and the horizon plane; therefore,

$$\tan t = \frac{f}{h_1p}$$

and

$$\cot t = \frac{h_1p}{f}$$

These relations are seen in the first principal plane (Fig. 29).
Since $\tan t \cdot \cot t = 1$,

$$f^2 = (n_1p)(h_1p)$$

$$f = \sqrt{(n_1p)(h_1p)}$$

Thus the distance from the *p* intersection point and each vanishing point, *n*, along with the distance from *p* to each perpendicular horizon point, *h*, is measured on the overlay. These measured values give the data for three determinations of *f*:

$$f = \sqrt{(n_1p)\,(h_1p)}$$

$$f = \sqrt{(n_2p)\,(h_2p)}$$

$$f = \sqrt{(n_3p)\,(h_3p)}$$

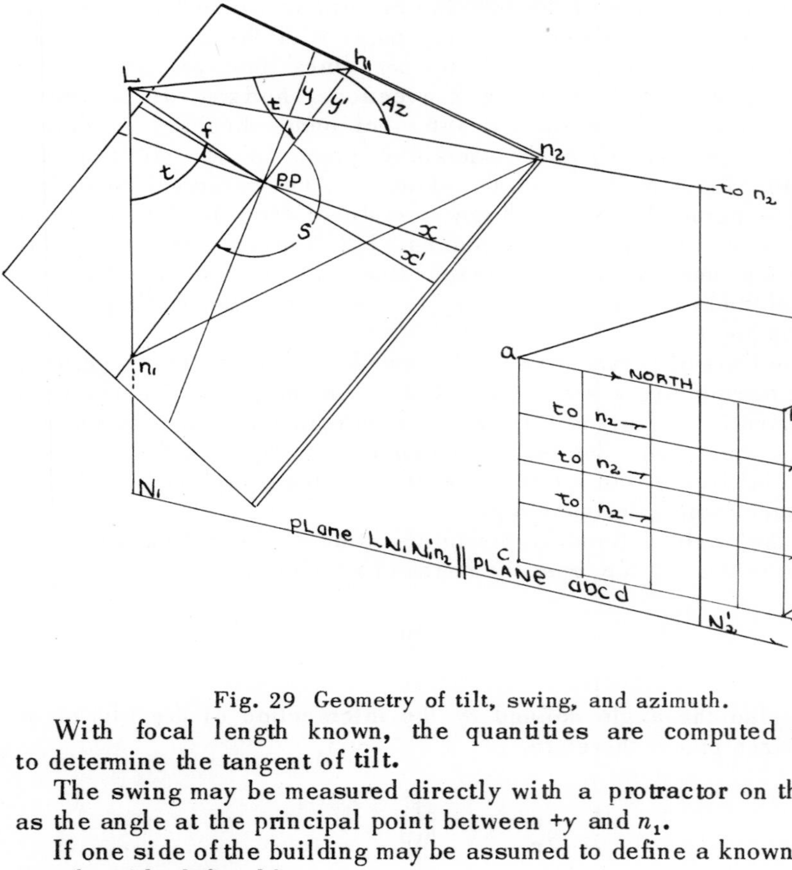

Fig. 29 Geometry of tilt, swing, and azimuth.

With focal length known, the quantities are computed in reverse to determine the tangent of tilt.

The swing may be measured directly with a protractor on the overlay, as the angle at the principal point between $+y$ and n_1.

If one side of the building may be assumed to define a known direction, say the side defined by n_2,

$$\tan Az = \frac{h_1n_2}{(f^2 + ph_1{}^2)^{1/2}}$$

Thus f, xp, yp, t, s, and Az have been determined, without a linear measurement in object space, on a single photograph, as a consequence of the laws of perspective. The arbitrary space coordinates of the camera station could be determined if one dimension on the building were known. This, however, is beyond the intent and purpose of the method. The method is not practical for many reasons. It is described here because it presents a geometric interpretation of the fundamental concepts outlined in this chapter.

G. *USES OF ANALYTICAL PHOTOGRAMMETRY.*

The general trend of development in any science, technique, or procedure is toward automatic execution with, or with the aid of, electronics, mechanics, and optics. In photogrammetry these supporting physical sciences are usually embodied in some type of measuring or plotting instrument. The purpose of automatic instrumentation is economy in personnel, greater production, standardization of results, and the removal of complicated operations requiring a high degree of skill or knowledge. It would appear then that the automatic execution through instrumentation is the ultimate objective of photogrammetric development. An analytical solution to a photogrammetric problem of object mensuration is an extravagant solution if large quantities are involved and if there exists an automatic instrument, or instruments, capable of performing the object mensuration in accordance with the standards set down in a specific problem. With these preliminary remarks the uses of analytical photogrammetry enumerated are briefly evaluated.

1. Education and training of photogrammetrists.

Analytical photogrammetry is the principle of metrical photography (photogrammetry) expressed in the universal language of mathematics. A photogrammetric plotting instrument is a mechanical embodiment of a photogrammetric equation. The student of photogrammetry has a nebulous appreciation of the theory of the more complex photogrammetric equipment until he has first hurdled the barrier of analytical photogrammetry. The photogrammetric engineer cannot solve photogrammetric problems and evaluate photogrammetric procedure unless he has mastered the mathematical equations underlying the fundamental concepts of photogrammetry.

2. Verification of newly developed theory and principles.

Newly developed photogrammetric theory and principles can be verified by fictitious numerical examples. This verification is usually the most inexpensive and therefore comprises the initial evaluation of photogrammetric theory.

3. Analysis of proposed instrumentation.

The expense of constructing a prototype based on unsound principles or faulty photogrammetric design can be prevented by subjecting the design to photogrammetric analyses before it leaves the drafting board.

4. Testing, evaluation, and calibration of instruments.

The calibration of cameras involves linear and angular measurement of images. These data are used in calibration equations for determining the interior geometry of a camera and are a class of analytical photogrammetry.

Many mechanical, electronic, or optical prototypes can be shown to be practical and accurate, or impractical and inaccurate, by analytical computations. Suppose, for example, an airborne camera gyro has been constructed with a maximum permissible deviation written into the specifications. Subjecting exposures from the gyro-oriented camera to angular orientation determinations would reveal at once the gyro deviation at each exposure station evaluated. The tilt of the camera at each exposure station corresponds to the gyro deviation. This would be called a photogrammetric evaluation of the gyro under flight conditions.

Many plotting instruments are mechanical analogies of photogrammetric equations. The most efficient test of such an instrument is to subject the test exposure plates to the analytical equations on which the design of the instrument is based.

5. Solution of problems for which instrumentation is not practical or not available.

(a) Quantity is insufficient to justify instrumentation.

Many problems entail a prolonged detailed study of a single photograph coupled with the precise measurement of minute images. Problems of this class are commonplace in photographic intelligence and various types of commercial photographic interpretation. Determinations based on single photographic studies and the measurement of minute images are not efficiently or economically handled with automatic instrumentation.

Many problems arising in photogrammetry defy instrumentation by virtue of their complexity or because they occur too infrequently to justify the investment of money in the construction of a suitable instrumental solution. The analytical solution is always an expedient for inadequate instrumentation.

Special problems frequently arise in research and tests where the camera is employed to record objects in motion, or where the camera is the photographic witness of action too rapid or hazardous for direct observation.

An example of the former is the angular orientation of guided missiles. Recently a roll of film was recovered from an expended missile. The negatives had no fiducial marks imaged and therefore the location of the plate perpendicular was unknown. The absence of a principal point location, the exaggerated altitude of the missile, and the total range of tilts from 0° to 360° precluded any but an analytical computational solution to the problem of determining the missile orientation.

An example of the latter was the determination of the space coordinates of an atomic bomb burst and the disposition of nearby objects before, during, and after the burst. The violence of the explosion permitted only a photographic record for determining the three-dimensional characteristics of the phenomena. The long focal lengths and accuracy requirements eliminated any but a careful analytical solution to the problem, because conventional plotting instruments are adapted to conventional, shorter focal lengths.

(b) Recency is ahead of instrumental development.

Photogrammetric monocular and binocular plotting instruments are generally designed about a range of standard focal lengths in order to insure maximum utility. Many problems of mensuration require the use of cameras having focal lengths much longer than the standard focal lengths, owing perhaps to excessively large object distances or a requirement for large image size. Exposures from nonstandard-focal-length cameras generally necessitate an analytical solution.

(c) Requirements exceed limits of instrumentation.

In 1949 the Banshee aircraft was put through a high altitude test. It was necessary to obtain an irrefutable determination of the Banshee aircraft's highest altitude. To achieve this, six exposures made during the test flight were subjected to three-point explicit space resection and angular-orientation calculations. The precision requirements combined with the high altitude necessitated an analytical solution.

Another example of the type of situation where photogrammetric measurements are not possible to execute instrumentally is the star exposure method of determining astronomic position. It is neither practical nor sufficiently accurate to determine the camera's astronomic coordinates with any but analytical photogrammetric equations in which the plate and astronomic coordinates are the given data.

Chapter II

TRANSFORMATIONS

Transformations are conversions of image-space coordinates to object space coordinates and vice versa. They form the basis for the equations developed in the next chapter. Transformations may also be employed to test the numerical efficiency of a photogrammetric equation by subjecting the equation to the solution of a fictitious example in which all the solved-for elements are precisely known. The problem may be approached in any one of three ways. Transformations are based on three types of data: (1) The object-space Cartesian coordinate system for defining the position of point-objects including the camera station (X,Y,Z); (2) The image-space coordinate system for defining the position of conjugate point-images (x,y,f); and (3) The relation existing between the coordinate systems of object and image space in terms of angular orientation (t,s,Az).

If values are preassigned to the elements of angular orientation, to the z ordinates of both coordinate systems, and to the plane coordinates of either coordinate system, then the plane coordinates of the other system are readily determined. For example, let values of t, s, Az, f, and the object space coordinates (X,Y,Z) of a suitable number of objects, including the camera station, be assumed. Then the camera coordinates (x,y) corresponding to the object space coordinates are simply calculated. Similarly, let values of t, s, Az, and the image-space coordinates (x,y,f) of a suitable number of images, including the z ordinates of the corresponding objects, be assumed. Then the object space coordinates (X,Y) corresponding to the image-space coordinates are simply calculated.

The solution in either case is based on expressing one system in terms of the other by use of functions of t, s, and Az, which become coefficients for the variables x and y or X and Y, depending upon which are assumed and which are to be determined. There are three rotations in each system. These were outlined in Chapter I. For the camera system,

$$\left.\begin{aligned} x^1 &= x \cos s - y \sin s \\ y^1 &= x \sin s + y \cos s \end{aligned}\right\} \quad \text{swing rotation}$$

$$\left.\begin{aligned} y_z &= y^1 \cos t - f \sin t \\ z &= y^1 \sin t + f \cos t \end{aligned}\right\} \quad \text{tilt rotation}$$

$$\left.\begin{aligned} x^{11} &= x^{1} \cos Az - y_z \sin Az \\ y^{11} &= x^{1} \sin Az + y_z \cos Az \end{aligned}\right\} \text{azimuth rotation}$$

For the object-space system,

$$\left.\begin{aligned} X^{1} &= X \cos Az - Y \sin Az \\ Y^{1} &= X \sin Az + Y \cos Az \end{aligned}\right\} \text{azimuth rotation}$$

$$\left.\begin{aligned} Y_z &= Y^{1} \cos t - Z \sin t \\ Z^{1} &= Y^{1} \sin t + Z \cos t \end{aligned}\right\} \text{tilt rotation}$$

$$\left.\begin{aligned} X^{11} &= X^{1} \cos s - Y_z \sin s \\ Y^{11} &= X^{1} \sin s + Y_z \cos s \end{aligned}\right\} \text{swing rotation}$$

Successive rotations of the camera system through swing, tilt, and azimuth result in the coordinates of image space being parallel to the coordinates of object space in such manner that similar triangles. referred to the object-space coordinate system, exist and the following relations may be written:

$$\frac{X}{Z} = \frac{x^{11}}{z} \qquad \frac{Y}{Z} = \frac{y^{11}}{z}$$

$$X = \frac{x^{11}}{z} Z \quad . . (1) \qquad Y = \frac{y^{11}}{z} Z \quad . . (2)$$

Successive rotations of the object-space system through azimuth, tilt, and swing result in the object space coordinates being parallel to the coordinates of image space, so that similar triangles, referred to the image-space coordinate system, exist and the following relations may be written:

$$\frac{x}{f} = \frac{X^{11}}{Z^{1}} \qquad \frac{y}{f} = \frac{Y^{11}}{Z^{1}}$$

$$x = \frac{X^{11}}{Z^{1}} f \quad . . (3) \qquad y = \frac{Y^{11}}{Z^{1}} f \quad . . (4)$$

Substituting in the right members of equations (1) and (2) yields:

$$X = \frac{Z[(x \cos s - y \sin s) \cos Az - (x \sin s \cos t + y \cos s \cos t - f \sin t) \sin Az]}{x \sin s \sin t + y \cos s \sin t + f \cos t}$$

$$Y = \frac{Z[(x \cos s - y \sin s) \sin Az + (x \sin s \cos t + y \cos s \cos t - f \sin t) \cos Az]}{x \sin s \sin t + y \cos s \sin t + f \cos t}$$

These are the equations for computing the plane coordinates of object space when all other elements have been assumed.

Substituting in the right members of equations (3) and (4) yields:

$$x = \frac{f[(X\cos Az - Y\sin Az)\cos s - (X\sin Az\cos t + Y\cos Az\cos t - Z\sin t)\sin s]}{X\sin Az\ \sin t + Y\cos Az\sin t + Z\cos t}$$

$$y = \frac{f[(X\cos Az - Y\sin Az)\sin s + (X\sin Az\cos t + Y\cos Az\cos t - Z\sin t)\cos s]}{X\sin Az\ \sin t + Y\cos Az\sin t + Z\cos t}$$

These are the equations for computing the plane coordinates of image space when all other elements have been assumed. The expanded forms of both equations (1) and (2), and (3) and (4) are rather awkward. Some simplification is obtained by collecting coefficients of x, y, and f in equations (1) and (2), and coefficients of X, Y, and Z in equations (3) and (4):

$$X = \frac{Z[x(\cos s\cos Az - \sin s\cos t\sin Az) - y(\sin s\cos Az + \cos s\cos t\sin Az) + f(\sin t\sin Az)]}{x\sin s\ \sin t + y\cos s\sin t + f\cos t}$$

$$Y = \frac{Z[x(\cos s\sin Az + \sin s\cos t\cos Az) - y(\sin s\sin Az - \cos s\cos t\cos Az) - f(\sin t\cos Az)]}{x\sin s\ \sin t + y\cos s\ \sin t + f\cos t}$$

$$x = \frac{f[X(\cos s\cos Az - \sin s\cos t\sin Az) - Y(\cos s\sin Az + \sin s\cos t\cos Az) + Z(\sin t\sin s)]}{X\sin t\ \sin Az + Y\sin t\ \cos Az + Z\cos t}$$

$$y = \frac{f[X(\sin s\cos Az + \cos s\cos t\sin Az) - Y(\sin s\sin Az - \cos s\cos t\cos Az) - Z(\sin t\cos s)]}{X\sin t\ \sin Az + Y\sin t\ \cos Az + Z\cos t}$$

These coefficients are identical to the direction cosines expressing the relation between two coordinate systems. Therefore, if the plane space coordinates are to be determined,

$$X = Z\,\frac{(x\cos\alpha_x + y\cos\alpha_y + f\cos\alpha_z)}{x\cos\gamma_x + y\cos\gamma_y + f\cos\gamma_z}$$

$$Y = Z\,\frac{(x\cos\beta_x + y\cos\beta_y + f\cos\beta_z)}{x\cos\gamma_x + y\cos\gamma_y + f\cos\gamma_z}$$

where

$$\begin{aligned}
\cos\alpha_x &= +(\cos s\ \cos Az - \sin s\ \cos t\ \sin Az)\\
\cos\alpha_y &= -(\sin s\ \cos Az + \cos s\ \cos t\ \sin Az)\\
\cos\alpha_z &= +(\sin t\ \sin Az)\\
\cos\beta_x &= +(\cos s\ \sin Az + \sin s\ \cos t\ \cos Az)\\
\cos\beta_y &= -(\sin s\ \sin Az - \cos s\ \cos t\ \cos Az)\\
\cos\beta_z &= -(\sin t\ \cos Az)\\
\cos\gamma_x &= +(\sin s\ \sin t)
\end{aligned}$$

$$\cos \gamma_y = +(\cos s \sin t)$$
$$\cos \gamma_z = +(\cos t)$$

or, if the plane image coordinates are to be determined,

$$x = f\frac{(X \cos \alpha_x + Y \cos \beta_x + Z \cos \gamma_x)}{X \cos \alpha_z + Y \cos \beta_z + Z \cos \gamma_z}$$

$$y = f\frac{(X \cos \alpha_y + Y \cos \beta_y + Z \cos \gamma_y)}{X \cos \alpha_z + Y \cos \beta_z + Z \cos \gamma_z}$$

In this instance, the numerical values of the direction cosines are the same. Only a sign change occurs:

$$\cos \alpha_x = +(\cos s \cos Az - \sin s \cos t \sin Az)$$
$$\cos \beta_x = -(\cos s \sin Az + \sin s \cos t \cos Az)$$
$$\cos \gamma_x = +(\sin s \sin t)$$
$$\cos \alpha_y = +(\sin s \cos Az + \cos s \cos t \sin Az)$$
$$\cos \beta_y = -(\sin s \sin Az - \cos s \cos t \cos Az)$$
$$\cos \gamma_y = -(\cos s \sin t)$$
$$\cos \alpha_z = +(\sin t \sin Az)$$
$$\cos \beta_z = +(\sin t \cos Az)$$
$$\cos \gamma_z = +(\cos t)$$

If (1) in the case of converting the plane image coordinates to ground coordinates, the supplement to the azimuth is employed *(180°-Az)*, and (2) in the case of converting the ground coordinates to plane image coordinates, the supplement of swing is employed *(180°-s)*, then the transformation equations remain:

$$X = Z\frac{(x \cos \alpha_x + y \cos \alpha_y + f \cos \alpha_z)}{x \cos \gamma_x + y \cos \gamma_y + f \cos \gamma_z}$$

$$Y = Z\frac{(x \cos \beta_x + y \cos \beta_y + f \cos \beta_z)}{x \cos \gamma_x + y \cos \gamma_y + f \cos \gamma_z}$$

$$x = f\frac{(X \cos \alpha_x + Y \cos \beta_x + Z \cos \gamma_x)}{X \cos \alpha_z + Y \cos \beta_z + Z \cos \gamma_z}$$

$$y = f\frac{(X \cos \alpha_y + Y \cos \beta_y + Z \cos \gamma_y)}{X \cos \alpha_z + Y \cos \beta_z + Z \cos \gamma_z}$$

where, in each of the four equations,

$$\cos \alpha_x = -\cos Az \cos s - \sin Az \cos t \sin s$$
$$\cos \beta_x = +\sin Az \cos s - \cos Az \cos t \sin s$$
$$\cos \gamma_x = +\sin t \sin s$$
$$\cos \alpha_y = +\cos Az \sin s - \sin Az \cos t \cos s$$

$$\cos \beta_y = -\sin Az \sin s - \cos Az \cos t \cos s$$
$$\cos \gamma_y = +\sin t \cos s$$
$$\cos \alpha_z = +\sin Az \sin t$$
$$\cos \beta_z = +\cos Az \sin t$$
$$\cos \gamma_z = +\cos t$$

While these equations are introduced as a means of constructing fictitious exposure stations for the testing of photogrammetric formulae, they are also the basis of general equations to be introduced in the following chapter. It may be noted that the solved-for ordinate is always treated as a line in space referred to the alternate coordinate system. Thus, the direction angles express all possible angles defined by the intersection of *x*, *y*, and *z* lines with *X*, *Y*, and *Z* lines. This may be conveniently expressed as the square array introduced in Chapter I.

	X	Y	Z
x	α_x	β_x	γ_x
y	α_y	β_y	γ_y
f	α_z	β_z	γ_z

For example, the angle defined by the *Z* axis and the *x* axis is found by moving along the *x* line to the *Z* column. The direction angles of the *x* line in the *X,Y,Z* system are α_x, β_x, γ_x or of the *X* line in the *x, y, z* system are α_x, α_y, α_z.

Chapter III

GENERAL EXPLICIT EQUATIONS FOR A SINGLE PHOTOGRAPH

A. *DERIVATION OF EQUATIONS.*

1. Total Orientation (Geodetic Object Space).

It is possible to develop a single equation in *x*, *y*, and *f* expressed in terms of *X*, *Y*, and *Z*, and the appropriate direction cosines, or conversely. Such an equation contains sixteen complicated unknowns and therefore requires sixteen sets of coordinate data to provide a basic solution. It is also possible to combine an *x* and *y* equation, expressed in terms of *X*, *Y*, *Z*, and the appropriate direction cosines, that contains nine complicated unknowns, the elements of which cannot be resolved. Analysis demonstrates that a solution in *x* and in *y* in terms of *X*, *Y*, and *Z*, or in *X* and in *Y* in terms of *x*, *y*, and *f* is essential to a practical computational procedure.

Consider two equations expressing the standard coordinates of object space in terms of the camera coordinates and appropriate direction cosines.

$$\frac{X-XL}{Z-ZL} = \frac{(x-\Delta x)\cos\alpha_x + (y-\Delta y)\cos\alpha_y + f\cos\alpha_z}{(x-\Delta x)\cos\gamma_x + (y-\Delta y)\cos\gamma_y + f\cos\gamma_z}$$

$$\frac{Y-YL}{Z-ZL} = \frac{(x-\Delta x)\cos\beta_x + (y-\Delta y)\cos\beta_y + f\cos\beta_z}{(x-\Delta x)\cos\gamma_x + (y-\Delta y)\cos\gamma_y + f\cos\gamma_z}$$

The unknowns are the space coordinates of the lens *(XL, YL, ZL)*; the focal length *(f)*; the coordinates of the principal point $(\Delta x, \Delta y)$; and the nine direction cosines defining the angular orientation. Expansion of these equations by cross-multiplication and collection of coefficients with common unknowns results, after equating for a constant term, in two equations containing eight complicated unknowns and, therefore, eight sets of data.

Now consider two equations expressing the standard coordinates of image space in terms of object space and the appropriate direction cosines:

$$\frac{x-\Delta x}{f} = \frac{(X-XL)\cos\alpha_x + (Y-YL)\cos\beta_x + (Z-ZL)\cos\gamma_x}{(X-XL)\cos\alpha_z + (Y-YL)\cos\beta_z + (Z-ZL)\cos\gamma_z} \quad \ldots(1)$$

$$\frac{y - \Delta y}{f} = \frac{(X-XL)\cos\alpha_y + (Y-YL)\cos\beta_y + (Z-ZL)\cos\gamma_y}{(X-XL)\cos\alpha_z + (Y-YL)\cos\beta_z + (Z-ZL)\cos\gamma_z} \quad \ldots(2)$$

The unknowns are the same as those in the previous two expressions. Reducing these equations to a form adapted to simultaneous solution results in seven complicated unknowns and therefore seven sets of data. Thus, equations (1) and (2), designated *x* and *y* equations [3], are the fundamental form of the general equations for total orientation. Cross-multiplying, collecting unknowns having common coefficients, and rearranging, we have

$$\begin{aligned}
&x\,X(\cos\alpha_z) + x\,Y(\cos\beta_z) + x\,Z(\cos\gamma_z)\\
&- X(f\cos\alpha_x + \Delta x\cos\alpha_z) - Y(f\cos\beta_x + \Delta x\cos\beta_z)\\
&- Z(f\cos\gamma_x + \Delta x\cos\gamma_z)\\
&- x(XL\cos\alpha_z + YL\cos\beta_z + ZL\cos\gamma_z)\\
&+ \Delta x(XL\cos\alpha_z + YL\cos\beta_z + ZL\cos\gamma_z)\\
&+ f(XL\cos\alpha_x + YL\cos\beta_x + ZL\cos\gamma_x) = 0 \quad \ldots(1)
\end{aligned}$$

$$\begin{aligned}
&y\,X(\cos\alpha_z) + y\,Y(\cos\beta_z) + y\,Z(\cos\gamma_z)\\
&- X(f\cos\alpha_y + \Delta y\cos\alpha_z) - Y(f\cos\beta_y + \Delta y\cos\beta_z)\\
&- Z(f\cos\gamma_y + \Delta y\cos\gamma_z)\\
&- y(XL\cos\alpha_z + YL\cos\beta_z + ZL\cos\gamma_z)\\
&+ \Delta y(XL\cos\alpha_z + YL\cos\beta_z + ZL\cos\gamma_z)\\
&+ f(XL\cos\alpha_y + YL\cos\beta_y + ZL\cos\gamma_y) = 0 \quad \ldots(2)
\end{aligned}$$

Subtracting six *x*-equations and six *y*-equations from the seventh, we obtain six equations of the form:

$$\begin{aligned}
&(x_1 X_1 - xX)(\cos\alpha_z) + (x_1 Y_1 - xY)(\cos\beta_z) + (x_1 Z_1 - xZ)(\cos\gamma_z)\\
&+(X-X_1)(f\cos\alpha_x + \Delta x\cos\alpha_z) + (Y-Y_1)(f\cos\beta_x + \Delta x\cos\beta_z)\\
&+(Z-Z_1)(f\cos\gamma_x + \Delta x\cos\gamma_z) = (x_1-x)(XL\cos\alpha_z + YL\cos\beta_z + ZL\cos\gamma_z)
\end{aligned}$$

for the *x* equations, and of the form

$$\begin{aligned}
&(y_1 X_1 - yX)(\cos\alpha_z) + (y_1 Y_1 - yY)(\cos\beta_z) + (y_1 Z_1 - yZ)(\cos\gamma_z)\\
&+(X-X_1)(f\cos\alpha_y + \Delta y\cos\alpha_z) + (Y-Y_1)(f\cos\beta_y + \Delta y\cos\beta_z)\\
&+(Z-Z_1)(f\cos\gamma_y + \Delta y\cos\gamma_z) = (y_1-y)(XL\cos\alpha_z + YL\cos\beta_z + ZL\cos\gamma_z)
\end{aligned}$$

for the *y* equations. Equating for a constant term, let

$$(XL\cos\alpha_z + YL\cos\beta_z + ZL\cos\gamma_z) = Q\cdot m$$

where *Q* is any approximate value of the lens altitude and *m* is the exact quotient of the true value of ($XL \cos \alpha_z + YL \cos \beta_z + ZL \cos \gamma_z$) divided by Q. Dividing the equation through by m, we obtain

$$(x_1X_1-xX)\upsilon+(x_1Y_1-xY)\nu+(x_1Z_1-xZ)\mu+(X-X_1)\omega_x+(Y-Y_1)\lambda_x+(Z-Z_1)\rho_x=(x_1-x)\,Q$$

for the x equation, and

$$(y_1X_1-yX)\upsilon+(y_1Y_1-yY)\nu+(y_1Z_1-yZ)\mu+(X-X_1)\omega_y+(Y-Y_1)\lambda_y+(Z-Z_1)\rho_y=(y_1-y)Q$$

for the y equation, where

$$\upsilon = \frac{\cos \alpha_z}{m}$$

$$\nu = \frac{\cos \beta_z}{m}$$

$$\mu = \frac{\cos \gamma_z}{m}$$

$$\omega_x = (f \cos \alpha_x + \Delta x \cos \alpha_z)/m$$

$$\lambda_x = (f \cos \beta_x + \Delta x \cos \beta_z)/m$$

$$\rho_x = (f \cos \gamma_x + \Delta x \cos \gamma_z)/m$$

$$\omega_y = (f \cos \alpha_y + \Delta y \cos \alpha_z)/m$$

$$\lambda_y = (f \cos \beta_y + \Delta y \cos \beta_z)/m$$

$$\rho_y = (f \cos \gamma_y + \Delta y \cos \gamma_z)/m$$

Solving six x-equations or six y-equations for the unknowns listed above, we proceed to equate for the desired unknowns. For the moment, let it be assumed that we have solved six x-equations simultaneously Recalling that the sum of the squares of the direction cosines of a line in space is equal to unity,

$$\cos^2 \alpha_z + \cos^2 \beta_z + \cos^2 \gamma_z = 1$$

Therefore,

$$\upsilon^2 + \nu^2 + \mu^2 = \frac{1}{m^2}$$

or

$$m = \frac{1}{(\upsilon^2 + \nu^2 + \mu^2)^{1/2}}$$

and $$\cos \alpha_z = \upsilon m = (XL-XP)/ZL \cdot \sec \gamma_z$$

$$\cos \beta_z = \nu m = (YL-YP)/ZL \cdot \sec \gamma_z$$

$$\cos \gamma_z = \mu m = (ZL-ZP)/ZL \cdot \sec \gamma_z$$

and since $$\tan Az = \frac{XL-XP}{YL-YP},$$

$$\tan Az = \frac{\cos \alpha_z}{\cos \beta_z} = \frac{\upsilon}{\nu}$$

The equating to this point is equally applicable to the simultaneous solution of six y-equations. Recalling also that the sum of the products of the direction cosines of two lines enclosing a right angle is equal to zero,

$$\cos \alpha_x \cos \alpha_z + \cos \beta_x \cos \beta_z + \cos \gamma_x \cos \gamma_z = 0$$

$$\cos \alpha_y \cos \alpha_z + \cos \beta_y \cos \beta_z + \cos \gamma_y \cos \gamma_z = 0$$

or, in terms of the solved-for values directly,

$$\frac{\upsilon\omega_x + \nu\lambda_x + \mu\rho_x}{\upsilon^2 + \nu^2 + \mu^2} = f \cos \alpha_x \cos \alpha_z + \Delta x \cos^2\alpha_z + f \cos \beta_x \cos \beta_z$$

$$+ \Delta x \cos^2 \beta_z + f \cos \gamma_x \cos \gamma_z + \Delta x \cos^2\gamma_z$$

$$= f(0) + \Delta x (1) = \Delta x$$

and, for a similar solution of the y equations,

$$\frac{\upsilon\omega_y + \nu\lambda_y + \mu\rho_y}{\upsilon^2 + \nu^2 + \mu^2} = \Delta y$$

Now, since

$$f^2 \cos^2\alpha_x + f^2 \cos^2\beta_x + f^2 \cos^2\gamma_x = f^2$$

and $$f^2 \cos^2\alpha_y + f^2 \cos^2 \beta_y + f^2 \cos^2\gamma_y = f^2$$

$$f = [(\omega_x m - \Delta x \cos \alpha_z)^2 + (\lambda_x m - \Delta x \cos \beta_z)^2 + (\rho_x m - \Delta x \cos \gamma_z)^2]^{1/2}$$

$$= [(\omega_y m - \Delta y \cos \alpha_z)^2 + (\lambda_y m - \Delta y \cos \beta_z)^2 + (\rho_y m - \Delta y \cos \gamma_z)^2]^{1/2}$$

Then

$$\cos \alpha_x = (\omega_x m - \Delta x \cos \alpha_z)/f$$

$$\cos \beta_x = (\lambda_x m - \Delta x \cos \beta_z) / f$$

$$\cos \gamma_x = (\rho_x m - \Delta x \cos \gamma_z) / f$$

$$\cos \alpha_y = (\omega_y m - \Delta y \cos \alpha_z) / f$$

$$\cos \beta_y = (\lambda_y m - \Delta y \cos \beta_z) / f$$

$$\cos \gamma_y = (\rho_y m - \Delta y \cos \gamma_z) / f$$

and then

$$\tan s = \frac{\cos \gamma_x}{\cos \gamma_y}$$

$$x_n = \frac{f \cos \gamma_x}{\cos \gamma_z}$$

$$y_n = \frac{f \cos \gamma_y}{\cos \gamma_z}$$

The values v, ν, μ, m, and f should be the same for the solution of both x and y equations. Solving either the x or the y equations initially, the remaining can be depressed to three unknowns by utilization of the solved-for values common to each. In practical applications, however, a unique solution of six x-equations and six y-equations, independently, yields the more reliable values for the solved-for unknowns.

In any case, the space coordinates of the lens remain to be determined. The space coordinates of the lens are obtained from the simultaneous solution of three linear equations of the form

$$(XL) \tan \eta_1 + (YL) \tan \xi_1 - (ZL) \tan^2 \gamma_1 = Q_1$$

where

$$\tan \eta_1 = \frac{(x_1 - \Delta x) \cos \alpha_x + (y_1 - \Delta y) \cos \alpha_y + f \cos \alpha_z}{(x_1 - \Delta x) \cos \gamma_x + (y_1 - \Delta y) \cos \gamma_y + f \cos \gamma_z}$$

$$\tan \xi_1 = \frac{(x_1 - \Delta x) \cos \beta_x + (y_1 - \Delta y) \cos \beta_y + f \cos \beta_z}{(x_1 - \Delta x) \cos \gamma_x + (y_1 - \Delta y) \cos \gamma_y + f \cos \gamma_z}$$

$$\tan^2 \gamma_1 = \tan^2 \eta_1 + \tan^2 \xi_1$$

$$Q_1 = X_1 \tan \eta_1 + Y_1 \tan \xi_1 - Z_1 \tan^2 \gamma_1$$

The data from any three points of the seven may be employed to form linear equations for a unique solution of XL, YL, and ZL; or the data from the seven points may be employed to form seven linear equations which are converted to three normal equations, the simultaneous solution of which yields average values of XL, YL, and ZL. This completes the explicit determination of the nine elements of total orientation (Δx, Δy, f, XL, YL, ZL, t, Az, and s), and the nine direction cosines (of α_x, α_y, α_z, β_x, β_y, β_z, γ_x, γ_y, and γ_z) defining the orientation relation between the coordinate systems of image and object space. A rigorous check is available on the independent solution of the six x-equations and six y-equations in the direct comparison of common unknowns, and from the fact that

$$\cos\alpha_x \cos\alpha_y + \cos\beta_x \cos\beta_y + \cos\gamma_x \cos\gamma_y = 0$$

$$\cos\alpha_y \cos\alpha_z + \cos\beta_y \cos\beta_z + \cos\gamma_y \cos\gamma_z = 0$$

$$\cos\alpha_z \cos\alpha_x + \cos\beta_z \cos\beta_x + \cos\gamma_z \cos\gamma_x = 0$$

$$\cos\alpha_x \cos\beta_x + \cos\alpha_y \cos\beta_y + \cos\alpha_z \cos\beta_z = 0$$

$$\cos\beta_x \cos\gamma_x + \cos\beta_y \cos\gamma_y + \cos\beta_z \cos\gamma_z = 0$$

$$\cos\gamma_x \cos\alpha_x + \cos\gamma_y \cos\alpha_y + \cos\gamma_z \cos\alpha_z = 0$$

$$\cos^2\alpha_x + \cos^2\alpha_y + \cos^2\alpha_z = 1$$

$$\cos^2\beta_x + \cos^2\beta_y + \cos^2\beta_z = 1$$

$$\cos^2\gamma_x + \cos^2\gamma_y + \cos^2\gamma_z = 1$$

$$\cos^2\alpha_x + \cos^2\beta_x + \cos^2\gamma_x = 1$$

$$\cos^2\alpha_y + \cos^2\beta_y + \cos^2\gamma_y = 1$$

$$\cos^2\alpha_z + \cos^2\beta_z + \cos^2\gamma_z = 1$$

2. Total Orientation (Celestial Object Space).

Some simplification occurs when a celestial object space is employed owing to the concentricity of the celestial sphere with the exposure station. Expressing the camera coordinates in terms of the standard coordinates of imaged stars provides the most practical data reduction.

$$\frac{x - \Delta x}{f} = \frac{\tan\eta_s \cos\alpha_x + \tan\xi_s \cos\beta_x + \cos\gamma_x}{\tan\eta_s \cos\alpha_z + \tan\xi_s \cos\beta_z + \cos\gamma_z}$$

$$\frac{y - \Delta y}{f} = \frac{\tan \eta_s \cos \alpha_y + \tan \xi_s \cos \beta_y + \cos \gamma_y}{\tan \eta_s \cos \alpha_z + \tan \xi_s \cos \beta_z + \cos \gamma_z}$$

where $$\tan \eta_s = \frac{\sin GHA}{\tan \delta}$$

$$\tan \xi_s = \frac{\cos GHA}{\tan \delta}$$

and $$GHA = RA - GST$$

GST = GCT + GST 0^h + solar to sidereal correction.
δ = star declination.
RA = star right ascension.
GHA = Greenwich hour angle.
GST = Greenwich sidereal time.
GST 0^h = Greenwich sidereal time for zero hours.

The preliminary values are obtained from well-known tables and astronomic formulae. After some reduction, two equations are obtained, of the form:

$$x \tan \eta_s (v) + x \tan \xi_s (\nu) + \tan \eta_s (\omega_x) + \tan \xi_s (\lambda_x) + \rho_x = -x$$

$$y \tan \eta_s (v) + y \tan \xi_s (\nu) + \tan \eta_s (\omega_y) + \tan \xi_s (\lambda_y) + \rho_y = -y$$

where

$$v = \frac{\cos \alpha_z}{\cos \gamma_z}$$

$$\nu = \frac{\cos \beta_z}{\cos \gamma_z}$$

$$\omega_x = \frac{-(f \cos \alpha_x + \Delta x \cos \alpha_z)}{\cos \gamma_z}$$

$$\lambda_x = \frac{-(f \cos \beta_x + \Delta x \cos \beta_z)}{\cos \gamma_z}$$

$$\rho_x = \frac{-(f \cos \gamma_x + \Delta x \cos \gamma_z)}{\cos \gamma_z}$$

$$\omega_y = \frac{-(f \cos \alpha_y + \Delta y \cos \alpha_z)}{\cos \gamma_z}$$

$$\lambda_y = \frac{-(f \cos \beta_y + \Delta y \cos \beta_z)}{\cos \gamma_z}$$

$$\rho_y = \frac{-(f \cos \gamma_y + \Delta y \cos \gamma_z)}{\cos \gamma_z}$$

Solving five x-equations and five y-equations simultaneously yields the above unknowns, of which v and ν should be identical for both solutions.

Then

$$\cos \gamma_z = \frac{1}{(1 + v^2 + \nu^2)^{1/2}}$$

$$\cos \gamma_z = \sin \varphi$$

$$\cos \alpha_z = v \cos \gamma_z$$

$$\cos \beta_z = \nu \cos \gamma_z$$

$$\tan \lambda = \frac{\cos \alpha_z}{\cos \beta_z} = \frac{v}{\nu}$$

where φ = latitude of principal point
λ = longitude of principal point

and

$$\Delta x = \frac{v\omega_x + \nu\lambda_x + \rho_x}{1 + v^2 + \nu^2}$$

$$\Delta y = \frac{v\omega_y + \nu\lambda_y + \rho_y}{1 + v^2 + \nu^2}$$

$$f = [(\omega_x \cos \gamma_z - \Delta x \cos \alpha_z)^2 + (\lambda_x \cos \gamma_z - \Delta x \cos \beta_z)^2 + (\rho_x \cos \gamma_z - \Delta x \cos \gamma_z)^2]^{1/2}$$

$$= [(\omega_y \cos \gamma_z - \Delta y \cos \alpha_z)^2 + (\lambda_y \cos \gamma_z - \Delta y \cos \beta_z)^2 + (\rho_y \cos \gamma_z - \Delta_y \cos \gamma_z)^2]^{1/2}$$

$$\cos \alpha_x = (\omega_x \cos \gamma_z - \Delta x \cos \alpha_z)/f$$

$$\cos \beta_x = (\lambda_x \cos \gamma_z - \Delta x \cos \beta_z)/f$$

$$\cos \gamma_x = (\rho_x \cos \gamma_z - \Delta x \cos \gamma_z)/f$$

$$\cos \alpha_y = (\omega_y \cos \gamma_z - \Delta y \cos \alpha_z)/f$$

$$\cos \beta_y = (\lambda_y \cos \gamma_z - \Delta y \cos \beta_z)/f$$

$$\cos \gamma_y = (\rho_y \cos \gamma_z - \Delta y \cos \gamma_z)/f$$

and then

$$\tan Az = \frac{\cos \gamma_x}{\cos \gamma_y}$$

which is the angle measured clockwise from the positive y axis to the plane of the film.

Thus, with five sets of data, the total orientation of the camera in a spherical object space may be determined. Here total orientation is calibration data consisting of Δx, Δy, and f, the spherical coordinates of the lens consisting of φ, λ, Az, and the nine direction angles. These direction cosines may also be expressed as sine and cosine functions of φ, λ, and Az:

$$\cos \alpha_x = - \cos \lambda \cos Az - \sin \lambda \sin \varphi \sin Az$$

$$\cos \beta_x = + \sin \lambda \cos Az - \cos \lambda \sin \varphi \sin Az$$

$$\cos \gamma_x = + \cos \varphi \sin Az$$

$$\cos \alpha_y = + \cos \lambda \sin Az - \sin \lambda \sin \varphi \cos Az$$

$$\cos \beta_y = - \sin \lambda \sin Az - \cos \lambda \sin \varphi \cos Az$$

$$\cos \gamma_y = + \cos \varphi \cos Az$$

$$\cos \alpha_z = + \sin \lambda \cos \varphi$$

$$\cos \beta_z = + \cos \lambda \cos \varphi$$

$$\cos \gamma_z = + \sin \varphi$$

The checks provided by the sums of the squares of the cosines and the cosine of the angle defined by any perpendicular pair of coordinates are equally applicable to this solution.

3. Interior Orientation.

Let it be assumed that an exposure is made of a geodetic or celestial object space.

The general equations described in the previous sections must be employed if an exposure is made of a geodetic or celestial object space without autocollimation of the camera focal plane to a reference line in the former case, or to the direction of gravity in the latter case. The camera orientation cannot be considered known without autocollimation. Therefore, determination of the direction angles would necessarily be a part of the solution. Assume an exposure has been made of an array of known points from a known station, or from a point where the horizontal and vertical angles have been measured with a theodolite. These angles may be measured on images, through the lens, or the corresponding objects.

If the survey coordinates are known,

$$\tan \eta = \frac{X-XL}{Z-ZL} \qquad \tan \xi = \frac{Y-YL}{Z-ZL}$$

If the horizontal and vertical angles are known,

$$\tan \eta = \frac{\sin H}{\sin V} \qquad \tan \xi = \frac{\cos H}{\tan V}$$

These tangent functions are combined with the camera coordinates to form the previously described equations, having a spherical object space,

$$x \tan \eta\,(v) + x \tan \xi\,(\nu) + \tan \eta(\omega_x) + \tan \xi\,(\lambda_x) + \rho_x = -x$$

$$y \tan \eta\,(v) + x \tan \xi\,(\nu) + \tan \eta(\omega_y) + \tan \xi\,(\lambda_y) + \rho_y = -y$$

Unique solutions of five x- and five y-equations yield v, ν, ω_x, λ_x, ρ_x, ω_y, λ_y, and ρ_y, from which are deduced f, Δx, Δy, and the nine direction cosines.

If an exposure of the zenith is made without autocollimation, the astronomic coordinates of the observer cannot be considered to be the astronomic coordinates of the principal point. Therefore, even though the exposure is made from a known camera station, the orientation of the camera is unknown. Thus, again, the general equation for a spherical object space is required. Let it be assumed that there are n sets of data, whereby normal equations may be formed. Camera focal length and principal point coordinates may be determined from Least Squares values of the direction angles. Then the standard coordinates referred to the camera are computed for each point with the observed data and the Least Squares values of the direction cosines.

$$\tan \eta_a = \frac{\tan \eta_A \cos \alpha_x + \tan \xi_A \cos \beta_x + \cos \gamma_x}{\tan \eta_A \cos \alpha_z + \tan \xi_A \cos \beta_z + \cos \gamma_z}$$

$$\tan \xi_a = \frac{\tan \eta_A \cos \alpha_y + \tan \xi_A \cos \beta_y + \cos \gamma_y}{\tan \eta_A \cos \alpha_z + \tan \xi_A \cos \beta_z + \cos \gamma_z}$$

Then

$$f \tan \eta_a - (xa - \Delta x) = dx_a$$

$$f \tan \xi_a - (ya - \Delta y) = dy_a$$

which are the Cartesian coordinates of lens distortion [4, 5]. These may be converted to radial and tangential values:

(Radial distortion) $\quad dr = dx \sin \theta + dy \cos \theta$
(Tangential distortion) $\quad dt = dx \cos \theta - dy \sin \theta$

where

$$\sin \theta = \frac{(x - \Delta x)}{[(x - \Delta x)^2 + (y - \Delta y)^2]^{1/2}}$$

$$\cos \theta = \frac{(y - \Delta y)}{[(x - \Delta x)^2 + (y - \Delta y)^2]^{1/2}}$$

It is obvious that it is more practical to autocollimate the camera in either case if obtaining calibration data is the sole purpose of the exposures. If a terrestrial exposure is made autocollimated to a line of known direction angles and the camera y axis is made to lie in a vertical plane, the standard coordinates of camera images may be computed independent of the camera data:

$$\tan \eta_A = \frac{\cos H}{\tan V} \qquad \tan \xi_A = \frac{\sin H}{\tan V}$$

$$\cos \alpha_x = \sin H_o$$

$$\cos \beta_x = \cos H_o$$

$$\cos \gamma_x = 0$$

$$\cos \alpha_y = \sin H_o \sin V_o$$

$$\cos \beta_y = \cos H_o \sin V_o$$

$$\cos \gamma_y = \cos V_o$$

$$\cos \alpha_z = \sin H_o \cos V_o$$

$$\cos \beta_z = \cos H_o \cos V_o$$

$$\cos \gamma_z = \sin V_o$$

where the subscript $_o$ denotes the autocollimated line. Then, as before,

$$\tan \eta_a = \frac{\tan \eta_A \cos \alpha_x + \tan \xi_A \cos \beta_x + \cos \gamma_x}{\tan \eta_A \cos \alpha_z + \tan \xi_A \cos \beta_z + \cos \gamma_z}$$

$$\tan \xi_a = \frac{\tan \eta_A \cos \alpha_y + \tan \xi_A \cos \beta_y + \cos \gamma_y}{\tan \eta_A \cos \alpha_z + \tan \xi_A \cos \beta_z + \cos \gamma_z}$$

The equations now reduce to an x and a y equation with two unknowns.

$$\Delta x + f \tan \eta = x$$
$$\Delta y + f \tan \xi = y$$

With n points, Least Squares values of Δx, Δy, and f would be determined. A determination giving three simultaneous equations may be more desirable:

$$\tan \eta = \frac{x - \Delta x}{f}$$

$$\tan \xi = \frac{y - \Delta y}{f}$$

$$\tan^2 \eta + \tan^2 \xi = \tan^2 \gamma$$

Therefore,

$$\tan \eta \, (x - \Delta x) + \tan \xi \, (y - \Delta y) = f \tan^2 \gamma$$

Rearranging,

$$\tan \eta \, \Delta x + \tan \xi \, \Delta y + \tan^2 \gamma \, f = Q$$

where $$Q = x \tan \eta + y \tan \xi$$

Simultaneous solution of three equations provides Δx, Δy, and f.

The calibration data are determined in the same manner with the exposure autocollimated to the zenith, except that

$$\tan \eta_A = \frac{\sin GHA_A}{\tan \delta_A} \qquad \tan \xi_A = \frac{\cos GHA_A}{\tan \delta_A}$$

The direction cosines employing λ, φ, and Az as arguments have been previously defined in the preceding section.

Computation of the coefficients is simplified appreciably if orthogonal geometry is imposed on the camera; that is, for terrestrial exposures the camera is autocollimated to a horizontal line, the x axis placed in a horizontal plane, and the y axis, in a vertical plane.

Then

$$\tan \eta_a = \tan H$$

$$\tan \xi_a = \frac{\sin V}{\cos H}$$

Here H is the horizontal angle between the line of autocollimation and the point. For zenithal exposures, the camera is autocollimated to the vertical and the y axis placed in the observer's meridian.
Then

$$\cos \gamma = \sin \varphi \sin \delta + \cos \varphi \cos \delta \cos(\lambda - GHA)$$

$$\sin \theta = \frac{\sin(\lambda - GHA) \cos \delta}{\sin \gamma}$$

$$\tan \eta = \cos \theta \tan \gamma$$
$$\tan \xi = \sin \theta \tan \gamma$$

This completes the equations for explicit analytical determination of calibration data.

4. Exterior Orientation.

a. Six-point solution [6].

No reduction in the number of unknowns or simplification takes place in the general equation for a geodetic object space when the interior orientation is known. Transformation of the camera coordinates to an origin of known object space coordinates reduces the required number of linear equations to five. These five equations are formed from six, in place of seven, sets of data essential to total orientation.

Assume some point O, whose coordinates are known, is imaged on the photograph near the principal point. Let the camera coordinates be x_o, y_o, and the geodetic coordinates be X_o, Y_o, Z_o. The remaining five camera coordinates are transformed to lie in a plane normal to L_o at a distance f from the rear nodal point.

$$x^1 = \frac{(x \cos s_o - y \sin s_o)f}{(x \sin s_o + y \cos s_o) \sin t_o + f \cos t_o}$$

$$y^1 = \frac{[(x \sin s_o + y \cos s_o) \cos t_o - f \sin t_o]f}{(x \sin s_o + y \cos s_o) \sin t_o + f \cos t_o}$$

where

$$\sin s_o = \frac{x_o}{(x_o^2 + y_o^2)^{1/2}}$$

$$\cos s_o = \frac{y_o}{(x_o^2 + y_o^2)^{1/2}}$$

$$\sin t_o = \frac{(x_o^2 + y_o^2)^{1/2}}{(x_o^2 + y_o^2 + f^2)^{1/2}}$$

$$\cos t_o = \frac{f}{(x_o^2 + y_o^2 + f^2)^{1/2}}$$

Now

$$\tan \theta = \frac{x^1}{y^1}$$

where θ is an angle in the transformed plane at o defined by an image and the rotated y axis, or

$$\tan \theta = \frac{x \cos s_o - y \sin s_o}{(x \sin s_o + y \sin s_o) \cos t_o - f \sin t_o}$$

Furthermore,

$$\tan \theta = \frac{(X-X_o) \cos \alpha_x^1 + (Y-Y_o) \cos \beta_x^1 + (Z-Z_o) \cos \gamma_x^1}{(X-X_o) \cos \alpha_y^1 + (Y-Y_o) \cos \beta_y^1 + (Z-Z_o) \cos \gamma_y^1}$$

Cross-multiplying,

$$\tan \theta(X-X_o) \cos \alpha_y^1 + \tan \theta(Y-Y_o) \cos \beta_y^1 + \tan \theta(Z-Z_o) \cos \gamma_y^1$$

$$= (X-X_o) \cos \alpha_x^1 + (Y-Y_o) \cos \beta_x^1 + (Z-Z_o) \cos \gamma_x^1$$

Rearranging and equating for a constant term,

$$(X-X_o)v + (Y-Y_o)\nu + (Z-Z_o)\mu - \tan \theta (Y-Y_o)\omega - \tan\theta(Z-Z_o)\lambda = \tan \theta(X-X_o)$$

where

$$v = \frac{\cos \alpha_x^1}{\cos \alpha_y^1}$$

$$\nu = \frac{\cos \beta_x^1}{\cos \alpha_y^1}$$

$$\mu = \frac{\cos \gamma_x^1}{\cos \alpha_y^1}$$

$$\omega = \frac{\cos \beta_y^1}{\cos \alpha_y^1}$$

$$\lambda = \frac{\cos \gamma_y^1}{\cos \alpha_y^1}$$

Solving five equations simultaneously yields the desired unknowns. Then

$$\cos \alpha_y^1 = \frac{1}{(\upsilon^2 + \nu^2 + \mu^2)^{1/2}}$$

$$\cos \alpha_x^1 = \upsilon \cos \alpha_y^1$$

$$\cos \beta_x^1 = \nu \cos \alpha_y^1$$

$$\cos \gamma_x^1 = \mu \cos \alpha_y^1$$

$$\cos \beta_y^1 = \omega \cos \alpha_y^1$$

$$\cos \gamma_y^1 = \lambda \cos \alpha_y^1$$

$$\cos \alpha_z^1 = [1 - \cos^2 \alpha_x^1 - \cos^2 \alpha_y^1]^{1/2}$$

$$\cos \beta_z^1 = [1 - \cos^2 \beta_x^1 - \cos^2 \beta_y^1]^{1/2}$$

$$\cos \gamma_z^1 = [1 - \cos^2 \gamma_x^1 - \cos^2 \gamma_y^1]^{1/2}$$

These direction angles define the orientation of the transformed camera coordinate system with respect to the geodetic coordinate system. A preliminary determination of *LO* is required.

$$\tan \eta = \frac{(X-X_o)\cos \alpha_x^1 + (Y-Y_o)\cos \beta_x^1 + (Z-Z_o)\cos \gamma_x^1}{LO - [(X-X_o)\cos \alpha_z^1 + (Y-Y_o)\cos \beta_z^1 + (Z-Z_o)\cos \gamma_z^1]} = \frac{x^1}{f}$$

$$\tan \xi = \frac{(X-X_o)\cos \alpha_y^1 + (Y-Y_o)\cos \beta_y^1 + (Z-Z_o)\cos \gamma_y^1}{LO - [(X-X_o)\cos \alpha_z^1 + (Y-Y_o)\cos \beta_z^1 + (Z-Z_o)\cos \gamma_z^1]} = \frac{y^1}{f}$$

Therefore,

$$LO = \frac{X^1 - Z^1 \tan \eta}{\tan \eta} = \frac{Y^1 - Z^1 \tan \xi}{\tan \xi}$$

where

$$X^1 = (X-X_o)\cos \alpha_x^1 + (Y-Y_o)\cos \beta_x^1 + (Z-Z_o)\cos \gamma_x^1$$

$$Y^1 = (X-X_o)\cos \alpha_y^1 + (Y-Y_o)\cos \beta_y^1 + (Z-Z_o)\cos \gamma_y^1$$

$$Z^1 = (X-X_o)\cos\alpha_z{}^1 + (Y-Y_o)\cos\beta_z{}^1 + (Z-Z_o)\cos\gamma_z{}^1$$

Then

$$X_o + LO\cos\alpha_z{}^1 = XL$$

$$Y_o + LO\cos\beta_z{}^1 = YL$$

$$Z_o + LO\cos\gamma_z{}^1 = ZL$$

The angular orientation may be determined with the coordinate data of any two points when the space coordinates of the lens have been determined. However, a simultaneous solution of three equations provides a more elegant solution. It may be done in any one of several ways:

$$\left.\begin{array}{l} \cos\alpha_a\cos\alpha_x + \cos\beta_a\cos\alpha_y + \cos\gamma_a\cos\alpha_z = \cos\alpha_A \\ \cos\alpha_b\cos\alpha_x + \cos\beta_b\cos\alpha_y + \cos\gamma_b\cos\alpha_z = \cos\alpha_B \\ \cos\alpha_c\cos\alpha_x + \cos\beta_c\cos\alpha_y + \cos\gamma_c\cos\alpha_z = \cos\alpha_C \end{array}\right\} 1$$

$$\left.\begin{array}{l} \cos\alpha_a\cos\beta_x + \cos\beta_a\cos\beta_y + \cos\gamma_a\cos\beta_z = \cos\beta_A \\ \cos\alpha_b\cos\beta_x + \cos\beta_b\cos\beta_y + \cos\gamma_b\cos\beta_z = \cos\beta_B \\ \cos\alpha_c\cos\beta_x + \cos\beta_c\cos\beta_y + \cos\gamma_c\cos\beta_z = \cos\beta_C \end{array}\right\} 2$$

$$\left.\begin{array}{l} \cos\alpha_a\cos\gamma_x + \cos\beta_a\cos\gamma_y + \cos\gamma_a\cos\gamma_z = \cos\gamma_A \\ \cos\alpha_b\cos\gamma_x + \cos\beta_b\cos\gamma_y + \cos\gamma_b\cos\gamma_z = \cos\gamma_B \\ \cos\alpha_c\cos\gamma_x + \cos\beta_c\cos\gamma_y + \cos\gamma_c\cos\gamma_z = \cos\gamma_C \end{array}\right\} 3$$

$$\left.\begin{array}{l} \cos\alpha_A\cos\alpha_x + \cos\beta_A\cos\beta_x + \cos\gamma_A\cos\gamma_x = \cos\alpha_a \\ \cos\alpha_B\cos\alpha_x + \cos\beta_B\cos\beta_x + \cos\gamma_B\cos\gamma_x = \cos\alpha_b \\ \cos\alpha_C\cos\alpha_x + \cos\beta_C\cos\beta_x + \cos\gamma_C\cos\gamma_x = \cos\alpha_c \end{array}\right\} 4$$

$$
\left.\begin{aligned}
\cos\alpha_A \cos\alpha_y + \cos\beta_A \cos\beta_y + \cos\gamma_A \cos\gamma_y &= \cos\beta_a \\
\cos\alpha_B \cos\alpha_y + \cos\beta_B \cos\beta_y + \cos\gamma_B \cos\gamma_y &= \cos\beta_b \\
\cos\alpha_C \cos\alpha_y + \cos\beta_C \cos\beta_y + \cos\gamma_C \cos\gamma_y &= \cos\beta_c
\end{aligned}\right\} \quad 5
$$

$$
\left.\begin{aligned}
\cos\alpha_A \cos\alpha_z + \cos\beta_A \cos\beta_z + \cos\gamma_A \cos\gamma_z &= \cos\gamma_a \\
\cos\alpha_B \cos\alpha_z + \cos\beta_B \cos\beta_z + \cos\gamma_B \cos\gamma_z &= \cos\gamma_b \\
\cos\alpha_C \cos\alpha_z + \cos\beta_C \cos\beta_z + \cos\gamma_C \cos\gamma_z &= \cos\gamma_c
\end{aligned}\right\} \quad 6
$$

where

$$\cos\alpha_a = \frac{xa}{La} \qquad \cos\beta_a = \frac{ya}{La} \qquad \cos\gamma_a = \frac{f}{La}$$

$$\cos\alpha_b = \frac{xb}{Lb} \qquad \cos\beta_b = \frac{yb}{Lb} \qquad \cos\gamma_b = \frac{f}{Lb}$$

$$\cos\alpha_c = \frac{xc}{Lc} \qquad \cos\beta_c = \frac{yc}{Lc} \qquad \cos\gamma_c = \frac{f}{Lc}$$

$$La = (xa^2 + ya^2 + f^2)^{1/2}$$

$$Lb = (xb^2 + yb^2 + f^2)^{1/2}$$

$$Lc = (xc^2 + yc^2 + f^2)^{1/2}$$

$$\cos\alpha_A = \frac{XA-XL}{LA} \qquad \cos\beta_A = \frac{YA-YL}{LA} \qquad \cos\gamma_A = \frac{ZA-ZL}{LA}$$

$$\cos\alpha_B = \frac{XB-XL}{LB} \qquad \cos\beta_B = \frac{YB-YL}{LB} \qquad \cos\gamma_B = \frac{ZB-ZL}{LB}$$

$$\cos\alpha_C = \frac{XC-XL}{LC} \qquad \cos\beta_C = \frac{YC-YL}{LC} \qquad \cos\gamma_C = \frac{ZC-ZL}{LC}$$

$$LA = [(XA-XL)^2 + (YA-YL)^2 + (ZA-ZL)^2]^{1/2}$$

$$LB = [(XB-XL)^2 + (YB-YL)^2 + (ZB-ZL)^2]^{1/2}$$

$$LC = [(XC-XL)^2 + (YC-YL)^2 + (ZC-ZL)^2]^{1/2}$$

Simultaneous solution of any three of group 1, 2, or 3 provides an unknown that may be substituted in group 4, 5, or 6. Suppose group 3 is solved simultaneously for cos γ_x, cos γ_y, and cos γ_z,

$$\cos \gamma_z = \cos t$$

$$\tan s = \frac{\cos \gamma_x}{\cos \gamma_y}$$

cos γ_z substituted in group 6 reduces group 6 to two unknowns, cos α_z and cos β_z.

$$\tan Az = \frac{\cos \alpha_z}{\cos \beta_z}$$

Expanding the determinant of cos α_z, cos β_z, cos γ_z, cos γ_x, and cos γ_y is practical, since the coefficients of the first three arrays are identical.

Let

$$\cos \beta_b \cos \alpha_c - \cos \beta_c \cos \alpha_b = m_1$$

$$\cos \beta_a \cos \alpha_c - \cos \beta_c \cos \alpha_a = m_2$$

$$\cos \beta_a \cos \alpha_b - \cos \beta_b \cos \alpha_a = m_3$$

$$\cos \beta_B \cos \alpha_C - \cos \beta_C \cos \alpha_B = n_1$$

$$\cos \beta_A \cos \alpha_C - \cos \beta_C \cos \alpha_A = n_2$$

$$\cos \beta_A \cos \alpha_B - \cos \beta_B \cos \alpha_A = n_3$$

and

$$\cos \gamma_a m_1 + \cos \gamma_b m_2 + \cos \gamma_c m_3 = q$$

$$\cos \gamma_A n_1 + \cos \gamma_B n_2 + \cos \gamma_C n_3 = Q$$

Then

$$\cos \alpha_z = (\cos \alpha_A m_1 + \cos \alpha_B m_2 + \cos \alpha_C m_3)/q$$

$$\cos \beta_z = (\cos \beta_A m_1 + \cos \beta_B m_2 + \cos \beta_C m_3)/q$$

$$\cos \gamma_z = (\cos \gamma_A m_1 + \cos \gamma_B m_2 + \cos \gamma_C m_3)/q$$

$$\cos \gamma_x = (\cos \alpha_a n_1 + \cos \alpha_b n_2 + \cos \alpha_c n_3)/Q$$

$$\cos \gamma_y = (\cos \beta_a \, n_1 + \cos \beta_b \, n_2 + \cos \beta_c \, n_3)/Q$$

$$\cos \gamma_z = (\cos \gamma_a \, n_1 + \cos \gamma_b \, n_2 + \cos \gamma_c \, n_3)/Q$$

Then

$$\cos t = \cos \gamma_z$$

$$\tan s = \frac{\cos \gamma_x}{\cos \gamma_y}$$

$$\tan Az = \frac{\cos \alpha_z}{\cos \beta_z}$$

An exact solution to exterior orientation requiring the image and object coordinates of six points has been described. The solution reduces to four [7] sets of data when the z ordinates are equal or the object space is a plane, since then, $Z - Z_0 = 0$.

b. Explicit solution to three-point resection [8, 9].

Iterative solutions are more practical when the camera and object-space data are restriced to three points. However, a treatment of analytical photogrammetry would not be complete without a brief description of the explicit three-point resection in space.

The method consists of first solving a fourth-degree equation for m by Ferrari's solution of the biquadratic. When m is known, the perspective ray lengths are computed directly, after which the six elements of exterior orientation are computed with the perspective ray lengths as the additional required data beyond the ground and camera coordinates. m is simply the ratio of one perspective ray to another. The quartic in m reduces to a simple quadratic when four points are used.

1. Derivation of the quartic in m.

The elements of the derivation are illustrated in Figure 30.

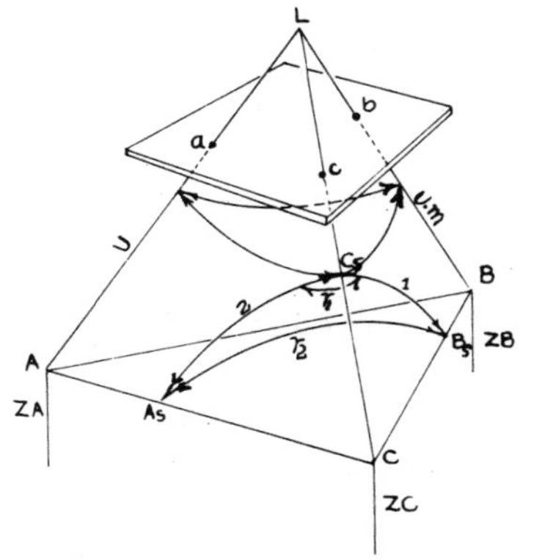

Fig. 30 Three-point space pyramid.

Let point C be the vertex of spherical triangle $A_sB_sC_s$ whose sides are 1, 2, and γ_2 and whose angle at C_s is γ_1. By the law of cosines in spherical trigonometry,

$$\cos \gamma_2 = \cos 1 \cos 2 + \sin 1 \sin 2 \cos \gamma_1$$

Let $\quad LA = U \quad \text{and} \quad LB = U \cdot m$

or

$$m = \frac{LB}{LA}$$

By the law of sines,

$$\frac{\sin 1}{U \cdot m} = \frac{\sin bLc}{BC}$$

and

$$\frac{\sin 2}{U} = \frac{\sin aLc}{AC}$$

The chord of any circle divided by the sine of the inscribed angle is equal to the diameter of the circle. That is,

$$D_{AC} = \frac{AC}{\sin aLc} \qquad D_{BC} = \frac{BC}{\sin bLc}$$

Therefore,

$$\sin 1 = \frac{U.m}{D_1}$$

$$\sin 2 = \frac{U}{D_2}$$

where

$$D_2 = D_{AC} \quad \text{and} \quad D_1 = D_{BC}$$

Having an expression for the sines, we may write an expression for the cosines:

$$\cos 1 = \frac{(D_1^2 - U^2m^2)^{1/2}}{D_1}$$

$$\cos 2 = \frac{(D_2^2 - U^2)^{1/2}}{D_2}$$

γ_1 is a dihedral angle at the intersection of planes ALC and CLB. Since γ_1 is a dihedral angle, it may be computed with the camera data:

$$\cos \gamma_1 = \frac{\cos aLb - \cos aLc \cdot \cos bLc}{\sin aLc \cdot \sin bLc}$$

where

$$\cos aLb = \frac{xa \cdot xb + ya \cdot yb + f^2}{La \cdot Lb}$$

$$\cos bLc = \frac{xb \cdot xc + yb \cdot yc + f^2}{Lb \cdot Lc}$$

$$\cos cLa = \frac{xc \cdot xa + yc \cdot ya + f^2}{Lc \cdot La}$$

γ_2 is the angle at *C* in the hillside plane between slope lengths *CA* and *CB*:

$$\cos \gamma_2 = \frac{(XA-XC)(XB-XC) + (YA-YC)(YB-YC) + (ZA-AC)(ZB-ZC)}{AC \cdot BC}$$

where

$$AB^2 = (XA-XB)^2 + (YA-YB)^2 + (ZA-ZB)^2$$

$$BC^2 = (XB-XC)^2 + (YB-YC)^2 + (ZB-ZC)^2$$

$$CA^2 = (XC-XA)^2 + (YC-YA)^2 + (ZC-ZA)^2$$

Recapitulating, we have an expression for *sin 1*, *cos 1*, *sin 2*, and *cos 2*, and the values of γ_1 and γ_2 are known. Substituting in the original cosine formula we have

$$\cos \gamma_2 = \frac{(D_1^2 - U^2m^2)^{1/2}(D_2^2 - U^2)^{1/2} + U^2m \cos \gamma_1}{D_1D_2}$$

Transposing,

$$\cos \gamma_2 D_1D_2 - U^2m \cos \gamma_1 = (D_1^2 - U^2m^2)^{1/2}(D_2^2 - U^2)^{1/2}$$

Squaring,

$$\cos^2\gamma_2 D_1^2D_2^2 - U^2m\, 2 \cos \gamma_1 \cos \gamma_2 D_1D_2 + U^4m^2 \cos^2\gamma_1$$

$$= D_1^2D_2^2 - D_1^2U^2 - D_2^2U^2m^2 + U^4m^2$$

Two trigonometric identities are substituted:

$$D_1^2D_2^2 - D_1^2D_2^2 \cos^2\gamma_2 = D_1^2D_2^2 \sin^2\gamma_2$$

$$U^4m^2 - U^4m^2 \cos^2\gamma_1 = U^4m^2 \sin^2\gamma_1$$

Substituting these identities and factoring out the U^2 terms,

$$U^2(D_1^2 + D_2^2m^2 - 2 \cos \gamma_1 \cos \gamma_2 D_1D_2m) - U^4m^2 \sin^2\gamma_1 = D_1^2D_2^2 \sin^2\gamma_2$$

Now,

$$AB^2 = LA^2 + LB^2 - 2\, LA \cdot LB \cos aLb$$

Since $\qquad LA = U \qquad$ and $\qquad LB = Um$

$$AB^2 = U^2 + U^2m^2 - 2\, U^2m \cos aLb = U^2(1 + m^2 - 2\, m \cos aLb)$$

$$U^2 = \frac{AB^2}{1 + m^2 - 2\, m \cos aLb}$$

Substituting the right-hand expression for U^2,

$$\frac{AB^2(D_1^2+D_2^2m^2-2 \cos \gamma_1 \cos \gamma_2 D_1D_2m)}{(1 + m^2 - 2\, m \cos aLb)} - \frac{AB^4 \sin^2\gamma_1 m^2}{(1+m^2-2\, m \cos aLb)^2} = D_1^2D_2^2 \sin^2\gamma_2$$

Multiplying both sides of the equation by

$$\frac{(1 + m^2 - 2\, m \cos aLb)^2}{AB^2}$$

we obtain

$$\begin{aligned}
&+ m^4 (D_2^2) \\
&- m^3 (2\, D_2^2 \cos aLb + 2 \cos \gamma_1 \cos \gamma_2 D_1D_2) \\
&+ m^2 (D_1^2 + D_2^2 + 4 \cos \gamma_1 \cos \gamma_2 \cos aLb\, D_1D_2 - AB^2\sin^2\gamma_1) \\
&- m\ (2\, D_1^2 \cos aLb + 2 \cos \gamma_1 \cos \gamma_2 D_1D_2) \\
&+ D_1^2 \\
= &+ m^4 \left[\frac{D_1^2D_2^2}{AB^2} \sin^2\gamma_2\right] \\
&- m^3 \left[4 \cos aLb \frac{D_1^2\, D_2^2}{AB^2} \sin^2\gamma_2\right]
\end{aligned}$$

$$+ \quad m^2 \left[(2 + 4\cos^2 aLb) \frac{D_1^2 D_2^2}{AB^2} \sin^2\gamma_2 \right]$$

$$- \quad m \left[4 \cos aLb \frac{D_1^2 D_2^2}{AB^2} \sin^2\gamma_2 \right]$$

$$+ \quad \frac{D_1^2 D_2^2}{AB^2} \sin^2\gamma_2$$

Collecting the coefficients of like powers and the constant terms,

$$m^4 \left[D_2^2 - \frac{D_1^2 D_2^2}{AB^2} \sin^2\gamma_2 \right]$$

$$- 2m^3 \left[D_2^2 \cos aLb + \cos\gamma_1 \cos\gamma_2 D_1 D_2 - 2\cos aLb \frac{D_1^2 D_2^2}{AB^2} \sin^2\gamma_2 \right]$$

$$+ \quad m^2 \left[D_1^2 + D_2^2 + 4\cos\gamma_1 \cos\gamma_2 \cos aLb\, D_1 D_2 - AB^2 \sin^2\gamma_1 - (2 + 4\cos^2 aLb) \frac{D_1^2 D_2^2}{AB^2} \sin^2\gamma_2 \right]$$

$$- 2m \left[D_1^2 \cos aLb + \cos\gamma_1 \cos\gamma_2 D_1 D_2 - 2\cos aLb \frac{D_1^2 D_2^2}{AB^2} \sin^2\gamma_2 \right]$$

$$+ \quad D_1^2 - \frac{D_1^2 D_2^2}{AB^2} \sin^2\gamma_2$$

$$= 0$$

Simplifying further and dividing through by $D_1 D_2$, we have a fourth-degree equation in m.

$$A_1 m^4 + B_1 m^3 + C_1 m^2 + E_1 m + F_1 = 0$$

where

$$A_1 = \frac{D_2}{D_1} \left[1 - \frac{D_1^2}{AB^2} \sin^2\gamma_2 \right]$$

$$B_1 = -2 \left[\cos\gamma_1 \cos\gamma_2 + \cos aLb \frac{D_2}{D_1} \left(1 - 2\frac{D_1^2}{AB^2} \sin^2\gamma_2 \right) \right]$$

$$C_1 = \left[\frac{D_1}{D_2} + \frac{D_2}{D_1} + 4 \cos \gamma_1 \cos \gamma_2 \cos aLb - \frac{AB^2}{D_1 D_2} \sin^2\gamma_1 - (2 + 4 \cos^2 aLb)\frac{D_1 D_2}{AB^2} \sin^2\gamma_2\right]$$

$$E_1 = -2\left[\cos \gamma_1 \cos \gamma_2 + \cos aLb \frac{D_1}{D_2}\left(1 - 2\frac{D_2^2}{AB^2} \sin^2\gamma_2\right)\right]$$

$$F_1 = \frac{D_1}{D_2}\left[1 - \frac{D_2^2}{AB^2} \sin^2\gamma_2\right]$$

The equation may now be solved by Ferrari's solution of a quartic which reduces to a biquadratic. According to Descartes' rule of signs, $f(m)$ shows four variations and therefore has four, two, or no real roots. However, we are interested in only one of the four roots. The desired root is real and positive because $m = \frac{LB}{LA}$ and both LB and LA are real and positive. It becomes necessary to determine which of the four roots is the desired one, since repeated solutions of the quartic demonstrates that all four roots are real. Since all values of m satisfy the equation

$$AB^2 = LA^2 + LA^2m^2 - 2\, LA^2m^2 \cos aLb,$$

another relation must be selected. For this relation, LC is expressed in terms of LA and LB:

$$LA \cos aLc + (D_2^2 - LA^2)^{1/2} \sin aLc = LB \cos bLc + (D_1^2 - LB^2)^{1/2} \sin bLc = LC$$

The root m that gives values of LA and LB which satisfy the above equality is the correct root, and in determining this value of m we automatically obtain LC. Thus the three perspective ray lengths, LA, LB, and LC, have been determined explicitly without recourse to iteration.

2. Derivation of equations for space coordinates and angular orientation.

At this point, the elements of exterior orientation could be readily determined by iteration. For the sake of continuity, an explicit method is described. The method consists of rotating the ground coordinates through an azimuth and tilt defined by the hillside plane (the plane defined by three points with at least one elevation different from the other two), solving for the space coordinates of the lens in the geodetic system transformed to the hillside plane, and then rotating the space coordinates of the lens back to the geodetic system. The azimuth of the dihedral angle defined by the hillside plane is determined:

$$\tan Az^1 = \frac{(YA-YB)(ZA-ZC) - (YA-YC)(ZA-ZB)}{(XA-XB)(ZA-ZC) - (XA-XC)(ZA-ZB)}$$

Then

$$XA^1 = XA \cos Az^1 - YA \sin Az^1$$

$$XB^1 = XB \cos Az^1 - YB \sin Az^1$$

$$XC^1 = XC \cos Az^1 - YC \sin Az^1$$

$$YA^1 = XA \sin Az^1 + YA \cos Az^1$$

$$YB^1 = XB \sin Az^1 + YB \cos Az^1$$

$$YC^1 = XC \sin Az^1 + YC \cos Az^1$$

and then

$$\tan \gamma_z^1 = \frac{YA^1 - YB^1}{ZA - ZB} = \frac{YB^1 - YC^1}{ZB - ZC} = \frac{YC^1 - YA^1}{ZC - ZA}$$

Finally,

$$YA^{11} = YA^1 \sin \gamma_z^1 + ZA \cos \gamma_z^1$$

$$YB^{11} = YB^1 \sin \gamma_z^1 + ZB \cos \gamma_z^1$$

$$YC^{11} = YC^1 \sin \gamma_z^1 + ZC \cos \gamma_z^1$$

$$\left.\begin{aligned} ZA^1 &= YA^1 \cos \gamma_z^1 - ZA \sin \gamma_z^1 \\ ZB^1 &= YB^1 \cos \gamma_z^1 - ZB \sin \gamma_z^1 \\ ZC^1 &= YC^1 \cos \gamma_z^1 - ZC \sin \gamma_z^1 \end{aligned}\right\} = Z^1$$

The Z values should be identical. In any case,

$$ZL^1 = \frac{LA \cdot LB \cdot LC}{D_1 D_2} \cdot \frac{\sin \gamma_1}{\sin \gamma_2} + Z^1$$

From the sum of the squares of the coordinates of a line in space we may write

$$U - XL^1 \cdot XA^1 - YL^{11} \cdot YA^{11} = Q_1$$

$$U - XL^1 \cdot XB^1 - YL^{11} \cdot YB^{11} = Q_2$$

$$U - XL^{1} \cdot XC^{1} - YL^{11} \cdot YC^{11} = Q_3$$

where

$$U = \frac{XL^{1^2} + YL^{11^2}}{2}$$

$$Q_1 = \frac{LA^2 - XA^{1^2} - YA^{11^2} - (Z^1 - ZL^1)^2}{2}$$

$$Q_2 = \frac{LB^2 - XB^{1^2} - YB^{11^2} - (Z^1 - ZL^1)^2}{2}$$

$$Q_3 = \frac{LC^2 - XC^{1^2} - YC^{11^2} - (Z^1 - ZL^1)^2}{2}$$

Having solved for XL^1 and YL^{11},

$$YL^1 = YL^{11} \sin \gamma_z{}^1 - ZL^1 \cos \gamma_z{}^1$$

$$ZL = YL^{11} \cos \gamma_z{}^1 + ZL^1 \sin \gamma_z{}^1$$

$$XL = XL^1 \cos Az^1 + YL^1 \sin Az^1$$

$$YL = XL^1 \sin Az^1 - YL^1 \cos Az^1$$

These are the space coordinates which, combined with the perspective ray lengths and camera coordinates, may be employed to determine angular orientation.

$$xa \cos \gamma_x + ya \cos \gamma_y + f \cos \gamma_z = \frac{(ZA-ZL)La}{LA}$$

$$xb \cos \gamma_x + yb \cos \gamma_y + f \cos \gamma_z = \frac{(ZB-ZL)Lb}{LB}$$

$$xc \cos \gamma_x + yc \cos \gamma_y + f \cos \gamma_z = \frac{(ZC-ZL)Lc}{LC}$$

Solving for $\cos \gamma_x$, $\cos \gamma_y$, and $\cos \gamma_z$,

$$\tan s = \frac{\cos \gamma_x}{\cos \gamma_y}$$

Then

$$(XA-XL) \cos \alpha_z + (YA-YL) \cos \beta_z = \frac{f}{La} - \frac{(ZA-ZL)}{LA} \cos \gamma_z$$

$$(XB-XL)\cos\alpha_z + (YB-YL)\cos\beta_z = \frac{f}{Lb} - \frac{(ZB-ZL)}{LB}\cos\gamma_z$$

$$(XC-XL)\cos\alpha_z + (YC-YL)\cos\beta_z = \frac{f}{Lc} - \frac{(ZC-ZL)}{LC}\cos\gamma_z$$

Any two of the above equations may be solved for $\cos\alpha_z$ and $\cos\beta_z$, giving

$$\tan Az = \frac{\cos\alpha_z}{\cos\beta_z}$$

It was pointed out earlier, in the development of the fourth-degree equation, that the equation reduced to a quadratic in *m* when a fourth point was available. Reference is made to Figure 31.

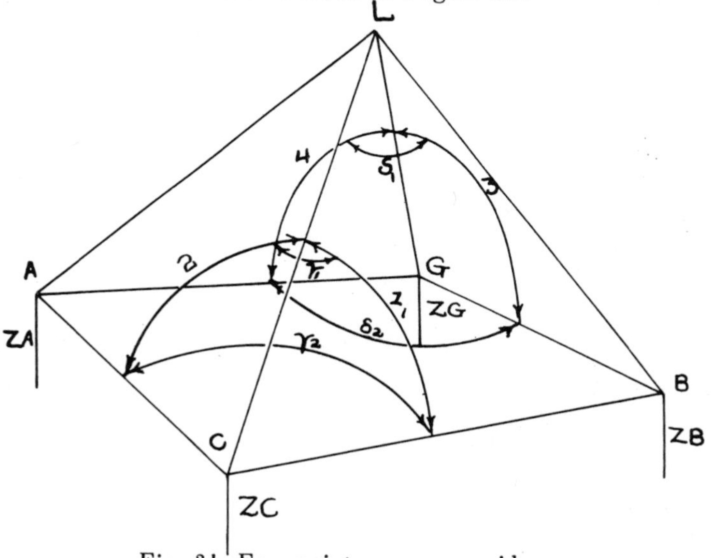

Fig. 31 Four-point space pyramid.

Let there be a fourth point, *G*, on the opposite side of plane *ALB* from *C*. Let the angles at *G* corresponding to γ_1 and γ_2 be δ_1 and δ_2, and the diameters corresponding to D_1 and D_2 be D_3 and D_4. Prior to the substitution of

$$U^2 = \frac{AB^2}{1 + m^2 - 2m\cos aLb}$$

in the previous derivation, the following pair of equations can be written:

$$U^2(D_1^2 + D_2^2m^2 - 2\cos\gamma_1\cos\gamma_2 D_1D_2m) - U^4m^2\sin^2\gamma_1 = D_1^2D_2^2\sin^2\gamma_2$$

$$U^2(D_3^2 + D_4^2m^2 - 2\cos\delta_1\cos\delta_2 D_3D_4m) - U^4m^2\sin^2\delta_1 = D_3^2D_4^2\sin^2\delta_2$$

Eliminating the U^4m^2 term, we obtain

$$U^2[(D_1^2 + D_2^2m^2 - 2\cos\gamma_1 \cos\gamma_2 D_1D_2m)\sin^2\delta_1 - (D_3^2 + D_4^2m^2 - 2\cos\delta_1 \cos\delta_2 D_3D_4m)\sin^2\gamma_1]$$

$$= D_1^2D_2^2 \sin^2\gamma_2 \sin^2\delta_1 - D_3^2D_4^2 \sin^2\delta_2 \sin^2\gamma_1$$

Now substituting

$$U^2 = \frac{AB^2}{1 + m^2 - 2m \cos aLb}$$

we have a quadratic in m

$$\eta m^2 + \xi m + \omega = 0$$

where

$$\eta = A_2 - K$$

$$\xi = B_2 + 2 \cos aLb\, K$$

$$\omega = C_2 - K$$

and

$$A_2 = (D_2^2 \sin^2\delta_1 - D_4^2 \sin^2\gamma_1)$$

$$B_2 = 2(\cos\delta_1 \cos\delta_2 \sin^2\gamma_1 D_3D_4 - \cos\gamma_1 \cos\gamma_2 \sin^2\delta_1 D_1D_2)$$

$$C_2 = (D_1^2 \sin^2\delta_1 - D_3^2 \sin^2\gamma_1)$$

$$K = \frac{D_1^2D_2^2}{AB^2}\sin^2\gamma_2 \sin^2\delta_1 - \frac{D_3^2D_4^2}{AB^2} \sin^2\gamma_1 \sin^2\delta_2$$

Frequently the data of four points are available, in which case the solution of the quartic may be replaced with a solution of a quadratic.

Reference is again made to Figure 30 in deriving equal lengths of the omitted ray with respect to selecting the correct root of the quartic.

$$\sin 1 = \frac{LB}{D_1} \quad \text{and} \quad \sin 2 = \frac{LA}{D_2}$$

By the sum-and-difference-of-sines of two angles,

$$\sin LBC = \sin (1 + bLc)$$

$$\sin LAC = \sin (2 + aLc)$$

$$\sin LBC = \frac{LB}{D_1} \cos bLc + \frac{(D_1^2 - LB^2)^{1/2}}{D_1} \sin bLc$$

$$\sin LAC = \frac{LA}{D_2} \cos aLc + \frac{(D_2^2 - LA^2)^{1/2}}{D_2} \sin aLc$$

and

$$LC = D_2 \sin LAC = D_1 \sin LBC$$

or

$$LC = LB \cos bLc + (D_1^2 - LB^2)^{1/2} \sin bLc$$

$$= LA \cos aLc + (D_2^2 - LA^2)^{1/2} \sin aLc$$

c. Two-point solution for angular orientation [10].

It is clear from the previous equations that the angular orientation may be determined with the data of two, or preferably three, points if the space coordinates and interior orientation of the camera are known. The two-point solution for angular orientation is illustrated in Figure 32.

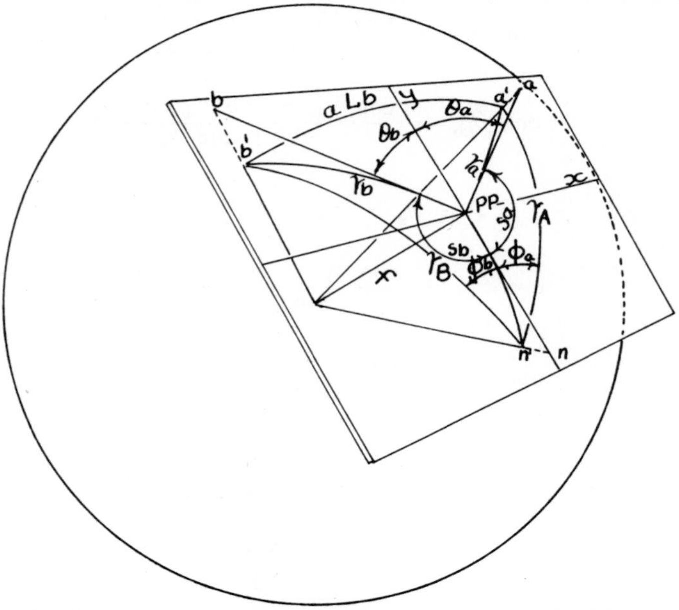

Fig. 32 Two-point spherical solution for angular orientation.

$$\cos aLb = \frac{xa \cdot xb + ya \cdot yb + f^2}{La \cdot Lb}$$

$$\cos \gamma_A = \frac{ZA-ZL}{LA} \qquad \cos \gamma_B = \frac{ZB-ZL}{LB}$$

$$\cos a_f = \frac{\cos \gamma_b - \cos aLb \cos \gamma_a}{\sin aLb \sin \gamma_a}$$

$$\cos a_n = \frac{\cos \gamma_B - \cos aLb \cos \gamma_A}{\sin aLb \sin \gamma_A}$$

$$\cos b_f = \frac{\cos \gamma_a - \cos aLb \cos \gamma_b}{\sin aLb \sin \gamma_b}$$

$$\cos b_n = \frac{\cos \gamma_A - \cos aLb \cos \gamma_B}{\sin aLb \sin \gamma_B}$$

$$\cos \gamma_z = \cos \gamma_a \cos \gamma_A + \sin \gamma_a \sin \gamma_A \cos (a_f + a_n)$$

$$\cos \gamma_z = \cos \gamma_b \cos \gamma_B + \sin \gamma_b \sin \gamma_B \cos (b_f + b_n)$$

$$\tan \theta_a = \frac{xa}{ya} \qquad \tan \theta_b = \frac{xb}{yb}$$

$$\cos \theta_{sa} = \frac{\cos \gamma_A - \cos \gamma_a \cos \gamma_z}{\sin \gamma_a \sin \gamma_z}$$

$$\cos \theta_{sb} = \frac{\cos \gamma_B - \cos \gamma_b \cos \gamma_z}{\sin \gamma_b \sin \gamma_z}$$

$$s = \theta_a - \theta_{sa} = \theta_b - \theta_{sb}$$

$$\cos \theta_{NA} = \frac{\cos \gamma_a - \cos \gamma_A \cos \gamma_z}{\sin \gamma_A \sin \gamma_z}$$

$$\cos \theta_{NB} = \frac{\cos \gamma_b - \cos \gamma_B \cos \gamma_z}{\sin \gamma_B \sin \gamma_z}$$

$$\tan \theta_A = \frac{XA-XL}{YA-YL}$$

$$\tan \theta_B = \frac{XB-XL}{YB-YL}$$

$$Az = \theta_A - \theta_{NA} = \theta_B - \theta_{NB}$$

If the angular orientation is known by direct observation or by automatic recording, the space coordinates of the lens are easily determined with two known points. With functions of tilt, swing, and azimuth, the direction cosines may be computed. Then

$$\tan \eta = \frac{x \cos \alpha_x + y \cos \alpha_y + f \cos \alpha_z}{x \cos \gamma_x + y \cos \gamma_y + f \cos \gamma_z} = \frac{X-XL}{Z-ZL}$$

$$\tan \xi = \frac{x \cos \beta_x + y \cos \beta_y + f \cos \beta_z}{x \cos \gamma_x + y \cos \gamma_y + f \cos \gamma_z} = \frac{Y-YL}{Z-ZL}$$

With two points, two equations are written and solved for *XL* and *ZL*.

$$XL - \tan \eta_1 \, ZL = X_1 - \tan \eta_1 \, Z_1$$

$$XL - \tan \eta_2 \, ZL = X_2 - \tan \eta_2 \, Z_2$$

Two more are written and solved for *YL* and *ZL*:

$$YL - \tan \xi_1 \, ZL = Y_1 - \tan \xi_1 \, Z_1$$

$$YL - \tan \xi_2 \, ZL = Y_2 - \tan \xi_2 \, Z_2$$

or, for *XL* and *YL*:

$$XL - \tan \theta_1 \, YL = X_1 - \tan \theta_1 \, Y_1$$

$$XL - \tan \theta_2 \, YL = X_2 - \tan \theta_2 \, Y_2$$

or if data from three points are available,

$$\tan \eta_1 \, XL + \tan \xi_1 \, YL - \tan^2 \gamma_1 \, ZL = X_1 \tan \eta_1 + Y_1 \tan \xi_1 - \tan^2 \gamma_1 \, Z_1$$

$$\tan \eta_2 \, XL + \tan \xi_2 \, YL - \tan^2 \gamma_2 \, ZL = X_2 \tan \eta_2 + Y_2 \tan \xi_2 - \tan^2 \gamma_2 \, Z_2$$

$$\tan \eta_3 \, XL + \tan \xi_3 \, YL - \tan^2 \gamma_3 \, ZL = X_3 \tan \eta_3 + Y_3 \tan \xi_3 - \tan^2 \gamma_3 \, Z_3$$

Determining the spherical coordinates of a camera station when the interior orientation is known is extremely simple. It may be accomplished with two or three points. The same equations are employed. The direction cosines of the star images referred to the camera are identical, while the direction cosines referred to the celestial coordinate system are:

$$\cos \alpha_s = \sin GHA \cos \delta$$

$$\cos \beta_s = \cos GHA \cos \delta$$

$$\cos \gamma_s = \sin \delta$$

The solved-for direction cosines defining the relation between the camera and celestial coordinate systems are functions of the latitude and longitude of the principal point and the azimuth of the camera y axis.

B. *NUMERICAL EXAMPLE OF GENERAL EXPLICIT EQUATIONS (TOTAL ORIENTATION).*

1. Given Data.

Plate coordinates

Point	x (mm.)	y (mm.)
(1)	− 18.660	− 1.340
(2)	+ 5.981	+ 35.981
(3)	+ 56.962	+ 7.680
(4)	− 57.321	+ 45.622
(5)	+ 33.660	− 51.962
(6)	− 41.962	− 60.981
(7)	− 70.622	− 31.340

Ground coordinates

Point	X (ft.)	Y (ft.)	Z (ft.)
(1)	+ 1,045.25	+ 2,236.47	200.0
(2)	+ 3,618.75	+ 2,075.57	300.0
(3)	+ 3,581.91	− 1,201.93	500.0
(4)	+ 2,249.54	+ 5,427.91	600.0
(5)	+ 64.46	− 1,730.82	400.0
(6)	− 2,519.68	+ 1,662.34	350.0
(7)	− 1,993.81	+ 4,003.95	100.0

2. Computations.

a. Formation and solution of six x-equations for υ, ν, μ, ω_x, λ_x, and ρ_x.

$$(x_1X_1-xX)\upsilon+(x_1Y_1-xY)\nu+(x_1Z_1-xZ)\mu+(X-X_1)\omega_x+(Y-Y_1)\lambda_x+(Z-Z_1)\rho_x=(x_1-x)Q$$

($Q = 9{,}000$). See Example 1.

b. Solving for m, $\cos\alpha_z$, $\cos\beta_z$, $\cos\gamma_z$, and $\tan Az$.

$$m = \frac{1}{(\upsilon^2+\nu^2+\mu^2)^{1/2}} = \frac{1}{0.90773511} = 1.10164297$$

$$\cos\alpha_z = \upsilon m = +\,0.0261680$$

$$\cos\beta_z = \nu m = +0.0453241$$

$$\cos\gamma_z = \mu m = -0.9986295 = \cos t$$

$$\tan Az = \frac{v}{\nu} = +0.57735273$$

c. Solving for Δx, f, $\cos a_x$, $\cos\beta_x$, $\cos\gamma_x$, and x_n.

$$\Delta x = \frac{v\omega_x + \nu\lambda_x + \mu\rho_x}{v^2 + \nu^2 + \mu^2} = -5.000$$

$$f = [(\omega_x m - \Delta x \cos a_z)^2 + (\lambda_x m - \Delta x \cos\beta_z)^2 + (\rho_x m - \Delta x \cos\gamma_z)^2]^{1/2} = 170.0$$

$$\cos a_x = (\omega_x m - \Delta x \cos a_z)/f = +0.50034263$$

$$\cos\beta_x = (\lambda_x m - \Delta x \cos\beta_z)/f = -0.86543197$$

$$\cos\gamma_x = (\rho_x m - \Delta x \cos\gamma_z)/f = -0.02616784$$

$(xX - x_1X_1)v$	+ $(xY - x_1Y_1)\nu$	+ $(xZ - x_1Z_1)\mu$	+ $(X_1 - X)\omega_x$	+ $(Y_1 - Y)\lambda_x$	+ $(Z_1 - Z)\rho_x$	= $(x_1 - x)Q$
+ 41,147.47924	+ 54,146.56111	+ 5,526.2794	− 2,573.495896	+ 160.897336	− 100	− 221,769.144
+ 223,535.7623	− 26,730.94187	+ 32,212.8128	− 2,536.661888	+ 3,438.402507	− 300	− 680,596.002
− 109,440.0834	− 269,397.6936	− 30,660.2540	− 1,204.289176	− 3,191.445255	− 400	+ 347,942.286
+ 21,674.53056	− 16,526.66031	+ 17,196.1524	+ 980.784664	+ 3,967.284827	− 200	− 470,884.572
+ 125,234.2362	− 28,021.32661	− 10,954.4826	+ 3,564.929625	+ 574.126521	− 150	+ 209,711.430
+ 160,310.7665	− 241,033.1147	− 3,330.1270	+ 3,039.055886	− 1,767.483345	+ 100	+ 467,653.716
+ 1	+ 1.315914416	+ .1343042029	− .0625432212	+ .0039102598	− .0024302825	− 5.38961677
+ 1	− .119582395	+ .1441058579	− .0113479018	+ .0153818900	− .0013420671	− 3.04468509
+ 1	− 2.461599857	− .2801556162	− .0110040959	− .0291615755	− .0036549680	+ 3.17929478
+ 1	− .762492192	+ .7933806157	+ .0452505608	+ .1830390197	− .0092274201	− 21.72524894
+ 1	− .223751328	− .0874719480	+ .0284660947	+ .0045844215	− .0011977555	+ 1.67455351
+ 1	− 1.503536662	− .0207729467	+ .0189572787	− .0110253565	+ .0006237884	+ 2.91716973
	− 1.145685441	− .1458514133	− .0735473171	− .0252513157	− .0060852505	− 2.21032199
	− 2.581182252	− .1360497583	− .0223519977	− .0137796855	− .0049970351	+ .13460969
	− 3.224092049	+ .5132249995	+ .0342464649	+ .1538774442	− .0128823881	− 18.54595416
	− 2.685351185	− .3676275642	+ .0174619988	− .0245771540	− .0048527235	+ 4.85384829
	− 3.965136519	− .3009285629	+ .0079531828	− .0401869320	− .0030311796	+ 6.09646451
	− 1	− .1273049374	− .0641950351	− .0220403566	− .0053114496	− 1.929257291
	− 1	− .0527083115	− .0086595969	− .0053385171	− .0019359482	+ .052130401
	− 1	+ .1591843507	+ .0106220494	+ .0477273731	− .0039956639	− 5.752302936
	− 1	− .1369011123	+ .0065026872	− .0091523053	− .0018071094	+ 1.807528310
	− 1	− .0758936197	+ .0020057778	− .0101350689	− .0007644578	+ 1.537516926
		+ .2864892881	+ .0748170845	+ .0697677297	+ .0013157857	− 3.823045645
		+ .2118926622	+ .0192816463	+ .0530658902	− .0020597157	− 5.804453337
		+ .2960854630	+ .0041193622	+ .0568796784	− .0021885545	− 7.559831246
		+ .2350779704	+ .0086162716	+ .0578624420	− .0032312061	− 7.289819862
		+1	+ .2611514203	+ .2435264863	+ .0045927920	+ 13.34446279
		+1	+ .0909972346	+ .2504376020	− .0097205617	− 27.39336642
		+1	+ .0139127472	+ .1921056097	− .0073916310	− 25.53259849
		+1	+ .0366528245	+ .2461414904	− .0137452527	− 31.01022120
			− .1701541857	+ .0069111157	− .0143133537	− 14.04890363
			+ .0770844874	+ .0583319923	− .0023289307	− 1.86076793
			+ .0543444101	+ .0042961116	+ .0040246910	+ 3.61685478
			− 1	+ .0406167834	− .0841199036	− 82.56572456
			+ 1	+ .7567280301	− .0302127027	− 24.13933066
			+ 1	+ .0790534223	+ .0740589693	+ 66.55431117
				+ .7973448135	− .1143326063	− 106.70505522
				+ .1196702057	− .0100609343	− 16.01141339
				+ 1	− .1433916724	− 133.8254835
				+ 1	− .0840721735	− 133.7961550

Values of x-unknowns determined by consecutive substitutions:

$\rho_x = + 0.4944158421$

$\lambda_x = - 133.7545884$

$\omega_x = + 77.09145319$

$\mu = - 0.9064910954$

$\nu = + 0.0411422996$

$v = + 0.0237536188$

Example 1

$$x_n = \frac{f \cos \gamma_x}{\cos \gamma_z} = +\ 4.455$$

d. Formation and solution of six y-equations for v, ν, μ, ω_y, λ_y, and ρ_y.

$$(y_1X_1-yX)v+(y_1Y_1-yY)\nu+(y_1Z_1-yZ)\mu+(X-X_1)\omega_y+(Y-Y_1)\lambda_y+(Z-Z_1)\rho_y=(y_1-y)Q$$

(Q = 9,000). See Example 2.

e. Solving for $\cos \alpha_z$, $\cos \beta_z$, $\cos \gamma_z$, and $\tan Az$, using values from y equations.

$$m = 1.10163773$$

$$\cos \alpha_z = +\ 0.02616778$$

$$\cos \beta_z = +\ 0.04532383$$

$$\cos \gamma_z = -0.99862956$$

$$\tan Az = +0.57735141$$

f. Solving for Δy, f, $\cos \alpha_y$, $\cos \beta_y$, $\cos \gamma_y$, y_n, $\tan s$.

$$\Delta y = \frac{v\omega_y + \nu\lambda_y + \mu\rho_y}{v^2 + \nu^2 + \mu^2} = -\ 5.000$$

$$f = [(\omega_y m-\Delta y \cos \alpha_z)^2+(\lambda_y m-\Delta y \cos \beta_z)^2+(\rho_y m-\Delta y \cos \gamma_z)^2]^{1/2} = 170.0$$

$$\cos \alpha_y = (\omega_y m - \Delta y \cos \alpha_z)/f = +\ 0.86543204$$

$$\cos \beta_y = (\lambda_y m - \Delta y \cos \beta_z)/f = +\ 0.49897208$$

$$\cos \gamma_y = (\rho_y m - \Delta y \cos \gamma_z)/f = +\ 0.04532387$$

$$y_n = \frac{f \cos \gamma_y}{\cos \gamma_z} = -\ 7.716$$

$$\tan s = \frac{-\ 0.02616784}{+\ 0.04532387} = -\ 0.57735229$$

$$s = 30^\circ$$

g. Space coordinates of lens.

$$\tan \eta = \frac{x \cos \alpha_x + y \cos \alpha_y + f \cos \alpha_z}{x \cos \gamma_x + y \cos \gamma_y + f \cos \gamma_z}$$

$$\tan \xi = \frac{x \cos \beta_x + y \cos \beta_y + f \cos \beta_z}{x \cos \gamma_x + y \cos \gamma_y + f \cos \gamma_z}$$

$(yX - y_1X_1)v$	+ $(yY - y_1Y_1)\nu$	+ $(yZ - y_1Z_1)\mu$	+ $(X_1 - X)\omega_y$	+ $(Y_1 - Y)\lambda_y$	+ $(Z_1 - Z)\rho_y$	= $(y_1 - y)Q$
+ 131,605.5904	+ 77,676.92224	+ 11,062.1778	- 2,573.495896	+ 160.897336	- 100	- 335,881.572
+ 28,907.62983	- 6,233.945173	+ 4,107.6952	- 2,536.661888	+ 3,438.402507	- 300	- 81,173.142
+ 104,028.3289	+ 250,627.36400	+ 27,641.0160	- 1,204.289176	- 3,191.445255	- 400	- 422,653.716
- 1,949.328715	+ 92,932.16680	- 20,516.6604	+ 980.784664	+ 3,967.284827	- 200	+ 455,596.002
+ 155,052.3753	- 98,374.56559	- 21,075.3175	+ 3,564.929625	+ 574.126521	- 150	+ 536,769.144
+ 63,885.75074	- 122,486.52640	- 2,866.0254	+ 3,039.055886	- 1,767.483345	+ 100	+ 270,000.000
+ 1	+ .59022510	+ .08405553	- .0195546093	+ .001222572	- .0007598461	- 2.5522060
+ 1	- .21565051	+ .14209727	- .0877506009	+ .118944463	- .0103778830	- 2.8080179
+ 1	+ 2.40922224	+ .26570662	+ .0115765502	- .030678617	- .0038451065	- 4.0628713
- 1	+ 47.67393313	- 10.52498752	+ .5031396996	+ 2.035205656	- .1025994223	+ 233.7194330
+ 1	- .63446023	- .13592386	+ .0229917769	+ .003702791	- .0009674150	+ 3.4618570
+ 1	- 1.91727459	- .04486173	+ .0475701679	- .027666316	+ .0015652943	+ 4.2262945
	+ 48.26415823	- 10.44093199	+ .4835850903	+ 2.036428228	- .1033592684	+ 231.1672270
	+ 47.45828262	- 10.38289025	+ .4153890987	+ 2.154150119	- .1129773053	+ 230.9114151
	+ 50.08315537	- 10.25928090	+ .4915631494	+ 2.004527039	- .1064445288	+ 229.6565617
	+ 47.03947290	- 10.66091138	+ .5261314765	+ 2.038908447	- .1055668373	+ 237.1812900
	+ 45.75665854	- 10.56984925	+ .5507098675	+ 2.007539340	- .1010341280	+ 237.9457275
	+ 1	- .2163288944	+ .0100195488	+ .0421933854	- .0021415326	+ 4.789625169
	+ 1	- .2187793084	+ .0087527208	+ .0453903934	- .0023805603	+ 4.865566185
	+ 1	- .2048449389	+ .0098149397	+ .0400239766	- .0021253559	+ 4.585505047
	+ 1	- .2266375604	+ .0111848931	+ .0433446278	- .0022017006	+ 5.042175760
	+ 1	- .2310013359	+ .0120356225	+ .0438742558	- .0022080749	+ 5.200242655
		- .0146724415	+ .0020160737	+ .0016808704	- .0000665423	+ .410617486
		- .0122220275	+ .0032829017	- .0015161376	+ .0001724854	+ .334676470
		- .0261563970	+ .0022206828	+ .0038502792	- .0000827190	+ .614737608
		- .0043637755	+ .0008507294	+ .0005296280	- .0000063743	+ .158066895
		- 1	+ .1374054686	+ .1145596934	- .0045351893	+ 27.98562775
		- 1	+ .2686053276	- .1240495982	+ .0141126667	+ 27.38305653
		- 1	+ .0849001795	+ .1472022007	- .0031624769	+ 23.50238100
		- 1	+ .1949526047	+ .1213692134	- .0014607305	+ 36.22250847
			+ .1311998590	- .2386092916	+ .0186478560	- .60257122
			+ .1837051481	- .2712517989	+ .0172751436	+ 3.88067553
			+ .0736527229	- .2454188116	+ .0155733972	- 8.83945194
			+ 1	- 1.818670336	+ .1421332015	- 4.5927734
			+ 1	- 1.476560683	+ .0940373407	+ 21.1244789
			+ 1	- 3.332107788	+ .2114436043	- 120.0152770
				- 1.513437452	+ .0693104028	- 115.4225036
				- 1.855547105	+ .1174062636	- 141.1397559
				- 1	+ .0457966748	- 76.26512972
				- 1	+ .0632731248	- 76.06368791
					.0174764500 ρ_y	+ .20144181

ρ_y = + 11.52647191

Values of y-unknowns determined by consecutive substitutions:

ρ_y = + 11.52647191

λ_y = + 76.79300381

ω_y = + 133.4300903

μ = - 0.9064954247

ν = + 0.0411422244

v = + 0.0237535211

Example 2

Points (4), (5), and (6) are selected, and the camera coordinates are corrected by Δx and Δy. Then

$$\tan \eta_4 = -0.13292937 \qquad \tan \xi_4 = -0.47105766$$

$$\tan \eta_5 = +0.09745469 \qquad \tan \xi_5 = +0.28446034$$

$$\tan \eta_6 = +0.36473633 \qquad \tan \xi_6 = -0.06863802$$

$$\tan^2 \gamma_4 = 0.23956554 \qquad Q_4 = -2{,}999.627842$$

$$\tan^2 \gamma_5 = 0.09041510 \qquad Q_5 = -\ 522.233756$$

$$\tan^2 \gamma_6 = 0.13774377 \qquad Q_6 = -1{,}081.328882$$

or, solving for XL, YL, and ZL,

$$\tan \eta (XL) + \tan \xi (YL) - \tan^2 \gamma (ZL) = Q$$

$$(4) \quad -0.13292937 - 0.47105766 - 0.23956554 = -2{,}999.627842$$

$$(5) \quad +0.09745469 + 0.28446034 - 0.09041510 = -\ 522.233756$$

$$(6) \quad +0.36473633 - 0.06863802 - 0.13774377 = -1{,}081.328882$$

After successive divisions, subtractions, and substitutions,

$$XL = +1{,}000.01$$

$$YL = +\ 999.99$$

$$ZL = +9{,}999.95$$

and

$$\text{error } (XL) = +0.01$$

$$\text{error } (YL) = -0.01$$

$$\text{error } (ZL) = -0.05$$

Chapter IV

GENERAL ITERATIVE EQUATIONS FOR A SINGLE PHOTOGRAPH

A generalized iterative solution [11] results in the repeated simultaneous solution of six differential equations for six differential unknowns, since there are six basic elements to be determined. The six unknown elements are xp, yp, and f for interior orientation, and XL, YL, and ZL for exterior orientation. The differentials, therefore, are Δx, Δy, Δz, ΔX, ΔY, and ΔZ.

The utility of an iterative solution in the aerial evaluation of calibration data determined on the ground exists in the employment of the ground-derived interior orientation data for the first approximation. If the interior orientation data are valid in the air, the interior orientation differentials vanish with the first approximation. When both interior and exterior orientation data are completely unknown, the successive simultaneous solution of six differential equations provides a means of determining complete interior-exterior orientation data.

The generality of the differential solution for interior-exterior orientation is seen in the symmetrical simplification of the differential equations containing six differential unknowns when either the elements of interior orientation (xp, yp, f), or the elements of exterior orientation (XL, YL, ZL) are considered to be known. When the elements of exterior orientation are considered to be known, space calibration equations with unknown differentials Δx, Δy, and Δz result. When the elements of interior orientation are considered to be known, space resection equations with unknown differentials ΔX, ΔY, ΔZ result. The latter are not different from the solution published by Church [12].

A. *DERIVATION OF EQUATIONS.*

1. Interior-Exterior Orientation.

An equation is required that embraces both the space coordinates of an object and the camera coordinates of the conjugate image with respect to some fixed quantity. The law of cosines in plane trigonometry may be used to determine a ground length with the space and camera coordinates of a pair of objects defining the terminals of a known ground length, and with the cosine of the angle subtended by the corresponding pair of images. Assume the existence of two ground objects A and B whose conjugate images are a and b. Assume, further, that the focal length f of the the camera and the location of the principal point xp, yp, as well as the space coordinates of the lens XL, YL, ZL, are known. Then, with the law of cosines we may write:

$$AB^2 = LA^2 + LB^2 - 2\,LA \cdot LB \cdot \cos aLb$$

where

AB is the slope ground length defined by objects A and B, whose survey coordinates are known.

LA, LB are a pair of lines in space defined by L and A, and L and B respectively; these lines intersect at L, which is the camera lens.

$\angle aLb$ is the angle at L subtended by objects A and B, and conjugate images a and b.

The ground length is determined with the survey coordinates of A and B:

$$AB^2 = (XA-XB)^2 + (YA-YB)^2 + (ZA-ZB)^2$$

The lines in space are written with the sum of the squares of the differences in space coordinates:

$$LA^2 = (XL-XA)^2 + (YL-YA)^2 + (ZL-ZA)^2$$

$$LB^2 = (XL-XB)^2 + (YL-YB)^2 + (ZL-ZB)^2$$

The cosine of the subtended angle is computed with the analytic equation for an angle between two lines:

$$\cos aLb = \frac{(xa-xp)(xb-xp) + (ya-yp)(yb-yp) + f^2}{La \cdot Lb}$$

where

$$La = [(xa - xp)^2 + (ya - yp)^2 + f^2]^{1/2}$$

$$Lb = [(xb - xp)^2 + (yb - yp)^2 + f^2]^{1/2}$$

Substituting the right members of the above equations for various components of the first equation and simplifying the notation as follows,

$$(XL-XA) = XA \qquad (XL-XB) = XB$$

$$(YL-YA) = YA \qquad (YL-YB) = YB$$

$$(ZL-ZA) = ZA \qquad (ZL-ZB) = ZB$$

$$(xa - xp) = xa \qquad (xb - xp) = xb$$

$$(ya - yp) = ya \qquad (yb - yp) = yb$$

gives

$$AB^2 = [XA^2 + YA^2 + ZA^2] + [XB^2 + YB^2 + ZB^2] - \frac{2[XA^2 + YA^2 + ZA^2]^{1/2}[XB^2 + YB^2 + ZB^2]^{1/2}(xa \cdot xb + ya \cdot yb + f^2)}{(xa^2 + ya^2 + f^2)^{1/2}(xb^2 + yb^2 + f^2)^{1/2}}$$

This equation contains the unknown space and camera coordinates of the lens. The ground length AB is known. If approximate values of XL, YL, ZL, xp, yp, and f are employed, an approximate ground length AB^1 may be computed. The difference between AB and AB^1 is a linear differential that has a mathematical relation, in a differential sense, to the errors of the approximation of the space and camera coordinates. This provides the basis for differentiating AB with respect to XL, YL, ZL, xp, yp, and f. Differentiating, collecting coefficients of like differentials, and simplifying, yield a differential equation with linear coefficients of the form:

$$\begin{aligned}
AB^1\,\Delta(AB) = {} & \Delta X\,[XA^1(1 - \tfrac{LB}{LA}\cos aLb^1) + XB^1(1 - \tfrac{LA}{LB}\cos aLb^1)] \\
& + \Delta Y\,[YA^1(1 - \tfrac{LB}{LA}\cos aLb^1) + YB^1(1 - \tfrac{LA}{LB}\cos aLb^1)] \\
& + \Delta Z\,[ZA^1(1 - \tfrac{LB}{LA}\cos aLb^1) + ZB^1(1 - \tfrac{LA}{LB}\cos aLb^1)] \\
& - \Delta x\,[xa^1(1 - \tfrac{Lb}{La}\cos aLb^1) + xb^1(1 - \tfrac{La}{Lb}\cos aLb^1)]\,\frac{LA \cdot LB}{La \cdot Lb} \\
& - \Delta y\,[ya^1(1 - \tfrac{Lb}{La}\cos aLb^1) + yb^1(1 - \tfrac{La}{Lb}\cos aLb^1)]\,\frac{LA \cdot LB}{La \cdot Lb} \\
& - \Delta z\,[f^1(1 - \tfrac{Lb}{La}\cos aLb^1) + f^1(1 - \tfrac{La}{Lb}\cos aLb^1)]\,\frac{LA \cdot LB}{La \cdot Lb}
\end{aligned}$$

where

$$XA^1 = (XL^1 - XA) \qquad YA^1 = (YL^1 - YA) \qquad ZA^1 = (ZL^1 - ZA)$$

$$XB^1 = (XL^1 - XB) \qquad YB^1 = (YL^1 - YB) \qquad ZB^1 = (ZL^1 - ZB)$$

$$xa^1 = xa - xp^1 \qquad ya^1 = ya - yp^1$$

$$xb^1 = xb - xp^1 \qquad yb^1 = yb - yp^1$$

$$LA = (XA^{1^2} + YA^{1^2} + ZA^{1^2})^{1/2} \qquad La = (xa^{1^2} + ya^{1^2} + f^{1^2})^{1/2}$$

$$LB = (XB^{1^2} + YB^{1^2} + ZB^{1^2})^{1/2} \qquad Lb = (xb^{1^2} + yb^{1^2} + f^{1^2})^{1/2}$$

$$\cos aLb^1 = \frac{xa^1xb^1 + ya^1yb^1 + f^2}{La \cdot Lb}$$

$$\Delta (AB) = AB - AB^1$$

$$AB^{12} = LA^2 + LB^2 - 2\, LA \cdot LB \cos aLb^1$$

and XL^1, YL^1, ZL^1, xp^1, yp^1, and f^1 are the initial approximations of XL, YL, ZL, xp, yp, and f. The unknown differentials ΔX, ΔY, ΔZ, Δx, Δy, and Δz are linear corrections so that

$$XL = XL^1 + \Delta X$$

$$YL = YL^1 + \Delta Y$$

$$ZL = ZL^1 + \Delta Z$$

$$xp = xp^1 + \Delta x$$

$$yp = yp^1 + \Delta y$$

$$f = f^1 + \Delta z$$

approximately, and precisely in the nth solution where n is the number of approximations required for the differentials to vanish. Since there are six unknowns, six equations are required for a simultaneous determination. The cyclic permutations of the terms comprising the coefficients make it possible to write the coefficients for the remaining linear equations immediately with the space and camera coordinates of six objects,(*A*, *B*, *C*, *D*, *E*, and *G*), referred to an arbitrarily chosen origin, imaged on an aerial negative. Six differential equations are written:

$$A_1\Delta X + B_1\Delta Y + C_1\Delta Z + a_1\Delta x + b_1\Delta y + c_1\Delta z + Q_1 = 0$$

$$A_2\Delta X + B_2\Delta Y + C_2\Delta Z + a_2\Delta x + b_2\Delta y + c_2\Delta z + Q_2 = 0$$

$$A_3\Delta X + B_3\Delta Y + C_3\Delta Z + a_3\Delta x + b_3\Delta y + c_3\Delta z + Q_3 = 0$$

$$A_4\Delta X + B_4\Delta Y + C_4\Delta Z + a_4\Delta x + b_4\Delta y + c_4\Delta z + Q_4 = 0$$

$$A_5\Delta X + B_5\Delta Y + C_5\Delta Z + a_5\Delta x + b_5\Delta y + c_5\Delta z + Q_5 = 0$$

$$A_6\Delta X + B_6\Delta Y + C_6\Delta Z + a_6\Delta x + b_6\Delta y + c_6\Delta z + Q_6 = 0$$

where

$$A_1 = XA^1M_1 + XB^1N_1 \qquad B_1 = YA^1M_1 + YB^1N_1 \qquad C_1 = ZA^1M_1 + ZB^1N_1$$

$$A_2 = XB^1M_2 + XC^1N_2 \qquad B_2 = YB^1M_2 + YC^1N_2 \qquad C_2 = ZB^1M_2 + ZC^1N_2$$

$$\cdot \quad \cdot \quad \cdot \quad \cdot \qquad \cdot \quad \cdot \quad \cdot \quad \cdot \qquad \cdot \quad \cdot \quad \cdot \quad \cdot$$

$$A_6 = XG^1M_6 + XA^1N_6 \qquad B_6 = YG^1M_6 + YA^1N_6 \qquad C_6 = ZG^1M_6 + ZA^1N_6$$

$$a_1 = xa^1m_1 + xb^1n_1 \qquad b_1 = ya^1m_1 + yb^1n_1 \qquad c_1 = f^1\,(m_1 + n_1)$$

$$a_2 = xb^1m_2 + xc^1n_2 \qquad b_2 = yb^1m_2 + yc^1n_2 \qquad c_2 = f^1\,(m_2 + n_2)$$

$$\cdot \quad \cdot \quad \cdot \quad \cdot \qquad \cdot \quad \cdot \quad \cdot \quad \cdot \qquad \cdot \quad \cdot \quad \cdot \quad \cdot$$

$$a_6 = xg^1m_6 + xa^1n_6 \qquad b_6 = yg^1m_6 + ya^1n_6 \qquad c_6 = f^1\,(m_6 + n_6)$$

$$M_1 = 1 - \cos aLb^1\frac{LB}{LA} \qquad N_1 = 1 - \cos aLb^1\frac{LA}{LB}$$

$$M_2 = 1 - \cos bLc^1\frac{LC}{LB} \qquad N_2 = 1 - \cos bLc^1\frac{LB}{LC}$$

$$\cdot \quad \cdot \quad \cdot \quad \cdot \quad \cdot \qquad \cdot \quad \cdot \quad \cdot \quad \cdot \quad \cdot$$

$$M_6 = 1 - \cos gLa^1\frac{LA}{LG} \qquad N_6 = 1 - \cos gLa^1\frac{LG}{LA}$$

$$m_1 = \left(1 - \cos aLb^1\frac{Lb}{La}\right)\frac{LA\cdot LB}{La\cdot Lb} \qquad n_1 = \left(1 - \cos aLb^1\frac{La}{Lb}\right)\frac{LA\cdot LB}{La\cdot Lb}$$

$$m_2 = \left(1 - \cos bLc^1\frac{Lc}{Lb}\right)\frac{LB\cdot LC}{Lb\cdot Lc} \qquad n_2 = \left(1 - \cos bLc^1\frac{Lb}{Lc}\right)\frac{LB\cdot LC}{Lb\cdot Lc}$$

$$\cdot \quad \cdot \quad \cdot \quad \cdot \quad \cdot \quad \cdot \quad \cdot \qquad \cdot \quad \cdot \quad \cdot \quad \cdot \quad \cdot \quad \cdot \quad \cdot$$

$$m_6 = \left(1 - \cos gLa^1\frac{La}{Lg}\right)\frac{LG\cdot LA}{Lg\cdot La} \qquad n_6 = \left(1 - \cos gLa^1\frac{Lg}{La}\right)\frac{LG\cdot LA}{Lg\cdot La}$$

$$Q_1 = (AB - AB^1)\,AB^1$$

$$Q_2 = (BC - BC^1)\,BC^1$$

$$\cdot \quad \cdot \quad \cdot \quad \cdot \quad \cdot$$

$$Q_6 = (GA - GA^1)\,GA^1$$

$$\cos aLb^1 = (xa^1xb^1 + ya^1yb^1 + f^{1^2})/La \cdot Lb$$

$$\cos bLc^1 = (xb^1xc^1 + yb^1yc^1 + f^{1^2})/Lb \cdot Lc$$

. . . .

$$\cos gLa^1 = (xg^1xa^1 + yg^1ya^1 + f^{1^2})/Lg \cdot La$$

$$La = (xa^{1^2} + ya^{1^2} + f^{1^2})^{1/2}$$

$$Lb = (xb^{1^2} + yb^{1^2} + f^{1^2})^{1/2}$$

. . . . . .

$$Lg = (xg^{1^2} + yg^{1^2} + f^{1^2})^{1/2}$$

$$LA = (XA^{1^2} + YA^{1^2} + ZA^{1^2})^{1/2}$$

$$LB = (XB^{1^2} + YB^{1^2} + ZB^{1^2})^{1/2}$$

. . . . . .

$$LG = (XG^{1^2} + YG^{1^2} + ZG^{1^2})^{1/2}$$

$$AB = [(XA-XB)^2 + (YA-YB)^2 + (ZA-ZB)^2]^{1/2}$$

$$BC = [(XB-XC)^2 + (YB-YC)^2 + (ZB-ZC)^2]^{1/2}$$

. . . .

$$GA = [(XG-XA)^2 + (YG-YA)^2 + (ZG-ZA)^2]^{1/2}$$

$$AB^1 = [LA^2 + LB^2 - 2\, LA \cdot LB \cos aLb^1]^{1/2}$$

$$BC^1 = [LB^2 + LC^2 - 2\, LB \cdot LC \cos bLc^1]^{1/2}$$

. . . .

$$GA^1 = [LG^2 + LA^2 - 2\, LG \cdot LA \cos gLa^1]^{1/2}$$

The six equations are solved simultaneously. The solved-for differentials are applied to the approximate values of XL^1, YL^1, ZL^1, xp^1, yp^1, and f^1 to form a closer approximation of the unknowns. New coefficients are formed with the revised approximations, and the second set of simultaneous equations are solved for a second set of differentials that are expected to be smaller than those from the first solution. The solution is repeated with each new set of values until

$$AB = AB^1$$

$$BC = BC^1$$

$$\cdot \quad \cdot \quad \cdot$$

$$GA = GA^1$$

2. Interior Orientation.

Assume that the space coordinates *(XL, YL, ZL)* are known. Then the angles subtended by pairs of images may be determined explicitly and the differentials ΔX, ΔY, and ΔZ are equal to zero. This gives a simplification of the general equations with three differential unknowns Δx, Δy, and Δz:

$$AB^1 \; \Delta(AB) =$$

$$\Delta x \left[xa^1 \left(1 - \cos aLb^1 \frac{Lb}{La} \right) + xb^1 \left(1 - \cos aLb^1 \frac{La}{Lb} \right) \right] \frac{LA \cdot LB}{La \cdot Lb}$$

$$+ \; \Delta y \left[ya^1 \left(1 - \cos aLb^1 \frac{Lb}{La} \right) + yb^1 \left(1 - \cos aLb^1 \frac{La}{Lb} \right) \right] \frac{LA \cdot LB}{La \cdot Lb}$$

$$+ \; \Delta z \left[f^1 \left(1 - \cos aLb^1 \frac{Lb}{La} \right) + f^1 \left(1 - \cos aLb^1 \frac{La}{Lb} \right) \right] \frac{LA \cdot LB}{La \cdot Lb}$$

With shoran, distances from control points to the exposure station may be determined electronically, independent of the exposure camera. In such a case, *LA* and *LB* are considered to be known. With cine-theodolites the exposure station may be established by spatial intersection. In either case,

$$\cos aLb = \frac{LA^2 + LB^2 - AB^2}{2\, LA \cdot LB}$$

or

$$\cos aLb = \frac{(XL-XA)(XL-XB) + (YL-YA)(YL-YB) + (ZL-ZA)(ZL-ZB)}{LA \cdot LB}$$

When cameras are calibrated on the ground, the angular components of photographed objects or images in the image plane are generally observed with a surveyor's theodolite. Let θ_{ab} be the difference in the horizontal angles measured to images *a* and *b*; let V_a and V_b be the corresponding vertical angles. Then, with the law of cosines,

$$\cos aLb = \sin V_a \sin V_b + \cos V_a \cos V_b \cos \theta_{ab}$$

Suppose a star exposure is made. Then the angle subtended by two star images is similarly computed:

$$\cos aLb = \sin \delta_a \sin \delta_b + \cos \delta_a \cos \delta_b \cos (t_{ab})$$

where

δ_a, δ_b are the declinations of star images *a* and *b*, and
t_{ab} is the difference in right ascension, between stars *a* and *b*, converted to arc.

From this it may be inferred that the angles subtended by pairs of images at *L* are readily determined, whether the calibration observation is conducted on the ground or in the air. On the other hand, the space coordinates of *L* are likely to be known only through the use of shoran or cinetheodolites. This suggests that differentiating the cosine of the subtended angle, instead of the ground length, with respect to *xp*, *yp*, and *f* would extend the utility of the iterative equations for interior orientation to calibration observations conducted on the ground. The difference between the subtended angles determined from approximations of the interior orientation provides a differential that has a linear relation to the error of the interior orientation approximation.
Differentiating

$$\cos aLb = \frac{xa \cdot xb + ya \cdot yb + f^2}{La \cdot Lb}$$

gives a differential equation of the form:

$$- La \cdot Lb \sin aLb^1 \, \Delta(aLb) =$$

$$\Delta x \left[xa^1 \left(1 - \cos aLb^1 \frac{Lb}{La} \right) + xb^1 \left(1 - \cos aLb^1 \frac{La}{Lb} \right) \right]$$

$$+ \Delta y \left[ya^1 \left(1 - \cos aLb^1 \frac{Lb}{La} \right) + yb^1 \left(1 - \cos aLb^1 \frac{La}{Lb} \right) \right]$$

$$+ \Delta z \left[f^1 \left(1 - \cos aLb^1 \frac{Lb}{La} \right) + f^1 \left(1 - \cos aLb^1 \frac{La}{Lb} \right) \right]$$

It is fairly obvious that, if the differential is restricted to the subtended angle,

$$\frac{AB^1 \, \Delta(AB) \, La \cdot Lb}{LA \cdot LB} = La \cdot Lb \sin aLb^1 \, \Delta(aLb)$$

or

$$\frac{AB^1 \, \Delta(AB)}{LA \cdot LB} = \sin aLb^1 \;\; \Delta(aLb)$$

Since there are three differential unknowns, three differential equations are required for a unique determination of Δx, Δy, and Δz. With the camera-coordinate data of three images referred to an arbitrarily chosen origin and the angles subtended by the three images, the coefficients and constant terms of three differential interior-orientation equations are formed:

$$a_1\Delta x + b_1\Delta y + c_1\Delta z + q_1 = 0$$

$$a_2\Delta x + b_2\Delta y + c_2\Delta z + q_2 = 0$$

$$a_3\Delta x + b_3\Delta y + c_3\Delta z + q_3 = 0$$

where

$$a_1 = xa^1m_1 + xb^1n_1 \qquad b_1 = ya^1m_1 + yb^1n_1$$

$$a_2 = xb^1m_2 + xc^1n_2 \qquad b_2 = yb^1m_2 + yc^1n_2$$

$$a_3 = xc^1m_3 + xa^1n_3 \qquad b_3 = yc^1m_3 + ya^1n_3$$

$$c_1 = f^1(m_1 + n_1) \qquad q_1 = La \cdot Lb \sin aLb^1 \;\; \Delta(aLb)$$

$$c_2 = f^1(m_2 + n_2) \qquad q_2 = Lb \cdot Lc \sin bLc^1 \;\; \Delta(bLc)$$

$$c_3 = f^1(m_3 + n_3) \qquad q_3 = Lc \cdot La \sin cLa^1 \;\; \Delta(cLa)$$

$$m_1 = 1 - \cos aLb^1 \frac{Lb}{La} \qquad n_1 = 1 - \cos aLb^1 \frac{La}{Lb}$$

$$m_2 = 1 - \cos bLc^1 \frac{Lc}{Lb} \qquad n_2 = 1 - \cos bLc^1 \frac{Lb}{Lc}$$

$$m_3 = 1 - \cos cLa^1 \frac{La}{Lc} \qquad n_3 = 1 - \cos cLa^1 \frac{Lc}{La}$$

$$\Delta(aLb) = [(aLb) - (aLb)^1] \tan 1''$$

$$\Delta(bLc) = [(bLc) - (bLc)^1] \tan 1''$$

$$\Delta(cLa) = [(cLa) - (cLa)^1] \tan 1''$$

(aLb), (bLc), (cLa) are computed explicitly with the observed data and

$$\cos aLb^1 = (xa^1 xb^1 + ya^1 yb^1 + f^{1^2})/(La \cdot Lb)$$

$$\cos bLc^1 = (xb^1 xc^1 + yb^1 yc^1 + f^{1^2})/(Lb \cdot Lc)$$

$$\cos cLa^1 = (xc^1 xa^1 + yc^1 ya^1 + f^{1^2})/(Lc \cdot La)$$

where xa^1, xb^1, xc^1, ya^1, yb^1, yc^1, La, Lb, Lc, and f^1 have the same meaning as before. The solution is repeated with the revised values of xp, yp, and f until the basic equality is satisfied:

$$(aLb) = (aLb)^1$$

$$(bLc) = (bLc)^1$$

$$(cLa) = (cLa)^1$$

Explicit equations previously described are more efficient if the camera focal plane is autocollimated to a line of known direction angles. It should be pointed out here that the interior geometry of the camera may be determined explicitly with camera coordinates referred to an arbitrary origin and the subtended angles corresponding to four images, without recourse to autocollimation or special orientation imposed on the camera. This solution is based on cross ratios. It is described by Hotine [16] and McGaw [18]. It is omitted here because of a lack of symmetry and awkward reduction characterisitics.

3. Exterior Orientation.

a. Three-point solution.

There are numerous solutions to the problem of exterior orientation by explicit and iterative methods. The writer has developed several explicit and iterative methods and has tested all methods published in the English language. Among the names associated with various solutions are Church [13], Anderson [14], Underwood [15], Hotine [16], Hart [17], McGaw [18], and Miller [19]. None of the methods compare favorably in accuracy and computational efficiency to the one developed by Church. Church's solution is presented here as a special case of the general iterative solution to total orientation.

Assume that the elements of interior orientation (xp, yp, f) are known. Then the angles subtended by pairs of images may be precisely determined and the differentials Δx, Δy, and Δz are equal to zero. This results in a simplification of the general equations with three differential unknowns, ΔX, ΔY, and ΔZ:

$$AB^1 \; \Delta(AB) =$$

$$\Delta X \left[XA^1 \left(1 - \cos aLb \frac{LB}{LA}\right) + XB^1 \left(1 - \cos aLb \frac{LA}{LB}\right) \right]$$

$$+ \Delta Y \left[YA^1 \left(1 - \cos aLb \frac{LB}{LA}\right) + YB^1 \left(1 - \cos aLb \frac{LA}{LB}\right)\right]$$

$$+ \Delta Z \left[ZA^1 \left(1 - \cos aLb \frac{LB}{LA}\right) + ZB^1 \left(1 - \cos aLb \frac{LA}{LB}\right)\right]$$

The coefficients in this equation differ from the coefficients of the general equation only in the cosines of the subtended angles being known from the interior orientation data:

$$\cos aLb = \frac{xa \cdot xb + ya \cdot yb + f^2}{La \cdot Lb}$$

All other terms have the same meaning as in the general equation. Since the subtended angles are considered to be known, we may differentiate *(aLb)*, in place of *AB*, with respect to *XL*, *YL*, and *ZL*. Thus, approximating the values of *XL*, *YL*, and *ZL*, we may compute an approximate value of *(aLb)*:

$$\cos aLb^1 = \frac{(XL^1-XA)(XL^1-XB) + (YL^1-YA)(YL^1-YB) + (ZL^1-ZA)(ZL^1-ZB)}{LA \cdot LB}$$

Then, as in the preceding section,

$$\Delta(aLb) = [(aLb) - (aLb)^1] \tan 1''$$

provides a known differential which has a differential relation to the errors in the approximation of *XL*, *YL*, and *ZL*. Differentiating *(aLb)* with respect to the space coordinates of the lens gives an exterior differential equation similar to the interior differential equation:

$$- LA \cdot LB \sin aLb^1 \, \Delta(aLb) =$$

$$\Delta X \left[XA^1 \left(1 - \cos aLb^1 \frac{LB}{LA}\right) + XB^1 \left(1 - \cos aLb^1 \frac{LA}{LB}\right)\right]$$

$$+ \Delta Y \left[YA^1 \left(1 - \cos aLb^1 \frac{LB}{LA}\right) + YB^1 \left(1 - \cos aLb^1 \frac{LA}{LB}\right)\right]$$

$$+ \Delta Z \left[ZA^1 \left(1 - \cos aLb^1 \frac{LB}{LA}\right) + ZB^1 \left(1 - \cos aLb^1 \frac{LA}{LB}\right)\right]$$

This is the equation published by Church [13] for resection of the camera in space. Again, since there are three differential unknowns, three differential equations are required for a unique determination of ΔX, ΔY, and ΔZ. With ground-coordinate data of three imaged objects referred to an origin that is an approximation of the space coordinates of the lens, and the angles subtended by the three images, the coefficients and constant terms of three differential space-resection equations are formed:

$$A_1\Delta X + B_1\Delta Y + C_1\Delta Z + Q_1 = 0$$

$$A_2\Delta X + B_2\Delta Y + C_2\Delta Z + Q_2 = 0$$

$$A_3\Delta X + B_3\Delta Y + C_3\Delta Z + Q_3 = 0$$

where the coefficients are identical with those of the same notation in the general equations and

$$Q_1 = LA\cdot LB \sin aLb^1 \quad \Delta(aLb)$$

$$Q_2 = LB\cdot LC \sin bLc^1 \quad \Delta(bLc)$$

$$Q_3 = LC\cdot LA \sin cLa^1 \quad \Delta(cLa)$$

These equations, like the previous equations, are repeatedly solved with the revised coefficients and constant terms computed with each set of differential unknowns obtained from the preceding solution until the following analytic equations are satisfied:

$$\frac{xa\cdot xb + ya\cdot yb + f^2}{La\cdot Lb} = \frac{(XL-XA)(XL-XB)+(YL-YA)(YL-YB)+(ZL-ZA)(ZL-ZB)}{LA\cdot LB}$$

$$\frac{xb\cdot xc + yb\cdot yc + f^2}{Lb\cdot Lc} = \frac{(XL-XB)(XL-XC)+(YL-YB)(YL-YC)+(ZL-ZB)(ZL-ZC)}{LB\cdot LC}$$

$$\frac{xc\cdot xa + yc\cdot ya + f^2}{Lc\cdot La} = \frac{(XL-XC)(XL-XA)+(YL-YC)(YL-YA)+(ZL-ZC)(ZL-ZA)}{LC\cdot LA}$$

b. Two other iterative solutions.

Two iterative solutions to exterior orientation are given in this section that differ somewhat from the general iterative solution already described.

One method, designated the perspective ray method, determines the perspective ray lengths by iteration. The lengths are considered known when the conditions of iteration are satisfied.

The second method determines the differential corrections to assumed values of tilt, swing, and altitude, by iteration. Both solutions require the camera and object space coordinates of three points.

1. Perspective ray method [20].
   Reference is made to Figure 33.

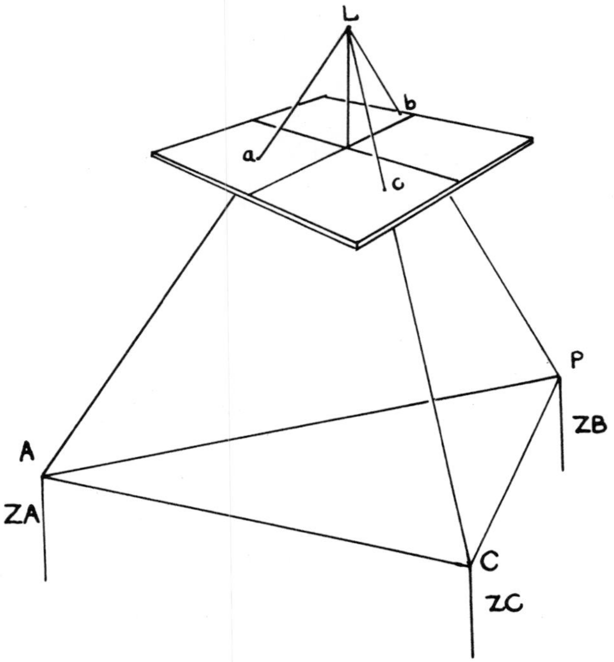

Fig. 33 Three-point space pyramid.

The sides *LB* and *LC* are expressed in terms of *LA*.

$$LB = LA \cos aLb + (D_{AB}^2 - LA^2)^{1/2} \sin aLb \quad . \; . \; . \; . \quad (1)$$

$$LC = LA \cos aLc + (D_{AC}^2 - LA^2)^{1/2} \sin aLc \quad . \; . \; . \; . \quad (2)$$

where

$$D_{AB} = AB/\sin aLb$$

$$D_{AC} = AC/\sin aLc$$

$$AB = [(XA-XB)^2 + (YA-YB)^2 + (ZA-ZB)^2]^{1/2}$$

$$AC = [(XA-XC)^2 + (YA-YC)^2 + (ZA-ZC)^2]^{1/2}$$

Similarly,

$$BC = [(XB-XC)^2 + (YB-YC)^2 + (ZB-ZC)^2]^{1/2}$$

and

$$\cos aLb = \frac{xa \cdot xb + ya \cdot yb + f^2}{La \cdot Lb}$$

$$\cos aLc = \frac{xa \cdot xc + ya \cdot yc + f^2}{La \cdot Lc}$$

Similarly,

$$\cos bLc = \frac{xb \cdot xc + yb \cdot yc + f^2}{Lb \cdot Lc}$$

Let us suppose a value of *LA* is approximated by the circle intersection method [10]. This method, illustrated in Figure 34, requires that

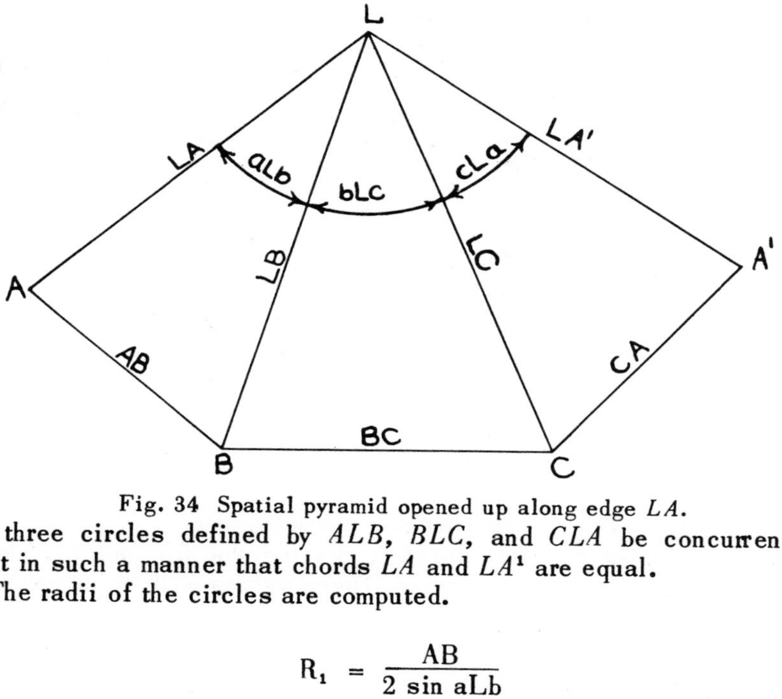

Fig. 34 Spatial pyramid opened up along edge *LA*.

the three circles defined by *ALB*, *BLC*, and *CLA* be concurrent at a point in such a manner that chords *LA* and LA^1 are equal.

The radii of the circles are computed.

$$R_1 = \frac{AB}{2 \sin aLb}$$

$$R_2 = \frac{BC}{2 \sin bLc}$$

$$R_3 = \frac{CA}{2 \sin cLa}$$

Circle *BLC* with its chord *BC* is laid off on a suitable piece of drafting paper at any desired scale. Then circles *ALB* and *CLA* with their chords AB and BC are constructed on any transparent material, such as acetate, at the scale of circle BLC. Points B of circle ALB and C of CLA are pinned to fixed circle BLC so that circles ALB and CLA may be rotated about these points. A point on circle BLC is quickly found that is concurrent to each of the two rotatable circles and that satisfies the equality

$$LA = LA^1$$

The numerical value of LA obtained by direct measurement will be as accurate as the combined accuracy of the drafting and given data. The procedure is illustrated in Figure 35.

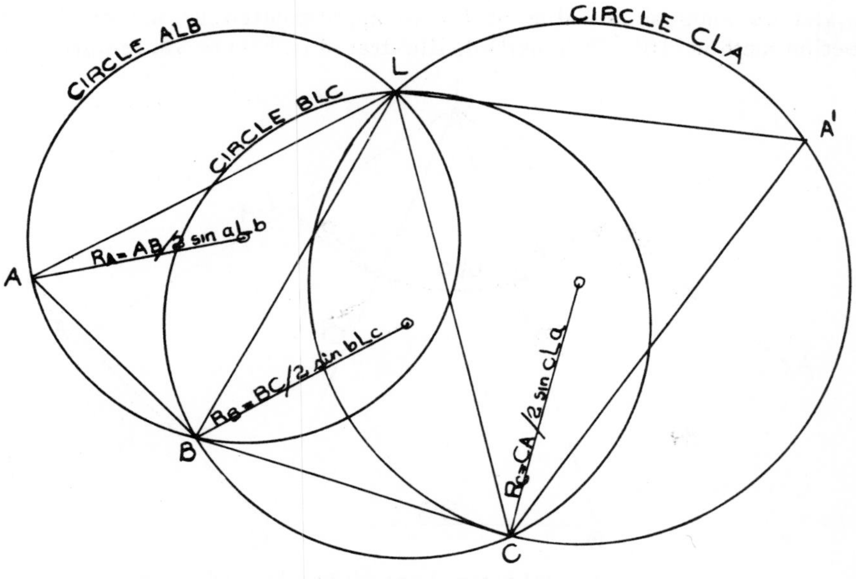

Fig. 35 Three circles concurrent at L.

Having an entrance value for LA, the lengths LB and LC may be computed with equations (1) and (2). These values will be in error as a direct function of the error in the approximate value of LA. Moreover, in the equation

$$\cos (bLc)^1 = \frac{LB^2 + LC^2 - BC^2}{2\,LB \cdot LC} \quad . \; . \; . \; . \; (3)$$

angle $(bLc)^1$ fails to agree with angle (bLc) computed with the camera data because of the error in the initial approximation of LA. It is evident that the error $\Delta(bLc)^1$ is a direct consequence of the error in the entrance value of LA.

Differentiating $(bLc)^1$ with respect to LB and LC in equation (3) we obtain the following:

$$- LB \cdot LC \sin (bLc)^1 \; \Delta(bLc)^1 + LB \cos (bLc)^1 \; \Delta LC$$

$$+ \; LC \cos (bLc)^1 \; \Delta LB = LB \cdot \Delta LB + LC \cdot \Delta LC \quad . \; . \; . \; . \; (4)$$

Now, differentiating *LA* with respect to *LB* and *LC* in equations (1) and (2) results in

$$\Delta LB = \left[\cos aLb - \frac{LA \sin aLb}{(D_{AB}{}^2 - LA^2)^{1/2}} \right] \Delta LA \quad . \; . \; . \; .(5)$$

$$\Delta LC = \left[\cos aLc - \frac{LA \sin aLc}{(D_{AC}{}^2 - LA^2)^{1/2}} \right] \Delta LA \quad . \; . \; . \; .(6)$$

Substituting in equation (4)

$$- LB \cdot LC \sin (bLc)^1 \; \Delta(bLc)'' \tan 1'' =$$

$$\Big\{ [LC - LB \cos (bLc)^1] \left[\cos aLc - \frac{LA \sin aLc}{(D_{AC}{}^2 - LA^2)^{1/2}} \right]$$

$$+ \; [LB - LC \cos (bLc)^1] \left[\cos aLb - \frac{LA \sin aLb}{(D_{AB}{}^2 - LA^2)^{1/2}} \right] \Big\} \Delta LA$$

Solving for ΔLA and expressing with abbreviated notation,

$$\Delta LA = \frac{q}{m \cdot k + n \cdot l}$$

where

$$q = - LB \cdot LC \sin (bLc)^1 \; \Delta(bLc)'' \tan 1''$$

$$m = [LC - LB \cos (bLc)^1]$$

$$n = [LB - LC \cos (bLc)^1]$$

$$k = \cos aLc - \frac{LA \sin aLc}{(D_{AC}{}^2 - LA^2)^{1/2}}$$

$$l = \cos aLb - \frac{LA \sin aLb}{(D_{AB}{}^2 - LA^2)^{1/2}}$$

and

$$\Delta(bLc) = (bLc) - (bLc)^1$$

Then

$$LA_1 = LA + \Delta LA$$

$$LB_1 = LB + \Delta LB$$

$$LC_1 = LC + \Delta LC$$

where ΔLB and ΔLC are computed with equations (5) and (6) respectively. LB and LC may also be computed with the last value of LA substituted in equations (1) and (2).

There are numerous approaches to the problem of space coordinates and angular orientation at this point. One of them is obtained by the differentiation of the perspective ray lengths with respect to the space coordinates of the lens:

$$(XA-XL^1)\Delta X + (YA-YL^1)\Delta Y + (ZA-ZL^1)\Delta Z = LA \cdot \Delta LA$$

$$(XB-XL^1)\Delta X + (YB-YL^1)\Delta Y + (ZB-ZL^1)\Delta Z = LB \cdot \Delta LB$$

$$(XC-XL^1)\Delta X + (YC-YL^1)\Delta Y + (ZC-ZL^1)\Delta Z = LC \cdot \Delta LC$$

where ΔX, ΔY, and ΔZ are differential corrections to assumed values of XL^1, YL^1, and ZL^1, and

$$\Delta LA = LA - LA^1$$

$$\Delta LB = LB - LB^1$$

$$\Delta LC = LC - LC^1$$

$$LA^1 = [(XA-XL^1)^2 + (YA-YL^1)^2 + (ZA-ZL^1)^2]^{1/2}$$

$$LB^1 = [(XB-XL^1)^2 + (YB-YL^1)^2 + (ZB-ZL^1)^2]^{1/2}$$

$$LC^1 = [(XC-XL^1)^2 + (YC-YL^1)^2 + (ZC-ZL^1)^2]^{1/2}$$

The equations are repeatedly solved until the differentials ΔLA, ΔLB, ΔLC vanish. Then

$$XL = XL^1 + \Delta X_1 + \Delta X_2 + \ldots + \Delta X_n$$

$$YL = YL^1 + \Delta Y_1 + \Delta Y_2 + \ldots + \Delta Y_n$$

$$ZL = ZL^1 + \Delta Z_1 + \Delta Z_2 + \ldots + \Delta Z_n$$

A second solution consists of three equations of the form:

$$XA(XL) + YA(YL) + ZA(ZL) + K = Q_A$$

$$XB(XL) + YB(YL) + ZB(ZL) + K = Q_B$$

$$XC(XL) + YC(YL) + ZC(ZL) + K = Q_C$$

where

$$K = -(XL^2 + YL^2 + ZL^2)/2$$

$$Q_A = (XA^2 + YA^2 + ZA^2 - LA^2)/2$$

$$Q_B = (XB^2 + YB^2 + ZB^2 - LB^2)/2$$

$$Q_C = (XC^2 + YC^2 + ZC^2 - LC^2)/2$$

The simultaneous solution is carried forward, neglecting K, for XL, YL, and ZL. Generally, the ZL coefficient is replaced with $Z\text{-}ZL^1$ and ZL with ΔZ, where ZL^1 is an estimate of ZL and ΔZ is the correction to ZL^1 so that $ZL = ZL^1 + \Delta Z$. Now tilt and swing may be determined with the simultaneous solution of the following equations:

$$\frac{(ZA-ZL)La}{LA} = xa \cos \gamma_x + ya \cos \gamma_y + f \cos \gamma_z$$

$$\frac{(ZB-ZL)Lb}{LB} = xb \cos \gamma_x + yb \cos \gamma_y + f \cos \gamma_z$$

$$\frac{(ZC-ZL)Lc}{LC} = xc \cos \gamma_x + yc \cos \gamma_y + f \cos \gamma_z$$

Solving for $\cos \gamma_x$, $\cos \gamma_y$, and $\cos \gamma_z$,

$$\tan s = \frac{\cos \gamma_x}{\cos \gamma_y}$$

$$\gamma_z = t$$

$$\tan Az = \frac{(X-XL)y^1 - (Y-YL)x^1}{(X-XL)x^1 + (Y-YL)y^1}$$

where

$$x^1 = x \cos s - y \sin s$$

$$y^1 = x \sin s \cos t + y \cos s \cos t - f \sin t$$

A value of $\tan Az$ may be obtained from the coordinate data of each point.

2. Orientation and altitude method [20].

An iterative method of determining the tilt, swing, and altitude of a camera in space that requires the camera and ground coordinates of three imaged control points is described in this section. After the tilt, swing, and altitude are determined, the datum coordinates of the exposure station and the azimuth of the principal line may be determined without iteration, if required. Tilt, swing, and altitude are all that are required for many photogrammetric operations.

Reference is again made to Figure 33. The slope ground lengths *AB*, *BC*, and *CA* defined by ground objects *A*, *B*, and *C* may be expressed with the following cosine formulae in terms of the length of the spatial pyramid edges and the cosine of the corresponding angles subtended at the lens.

$$AB^2 = LA^2 + LB^2 - 2\,LA \cdot LB \cos aLb$$

$$BC^2 = LB^2 + LC^2 - 2\,LB \cdot LC \cos bLc$$

$$CA^2 = LC^2 + LA^2 - 2\,LC \cdot LA \cos cLa$$

Angles *aLb*, *bLc*, and *cLa* are computed with the camera coordinates:

$$\cos aLb = \frac{xa \cdot xb + ya \cdot yb + f^2}{La \cdot Lb}$$

$$\cos bLc = \frac{xb \cdot xc + yb \cdot yc + f^2}{Lb \cdot Lc}$$

$$\cos cLa = \frac{xc \cdot xa + yc \cdot ya + f^2}{Lc \cdot La}$$

$$La = (xa^2 + ya^2 + f^2)^{1/2}$$

$$Lb = (xb^2 + yb^2 + f^2)^{1/2}$$

$$Lc = (xc^2 + yc^2 + f^2)^{1/2}$$

The slope line lengths are computed with the ground coordinates

$$AB^2 = (XA-XB)^2 + (YA-YB)^2 + (ZA-ZB)^2$$

$$BC^2 = (XB-XC)^2 + (YB-YC)^2 + (ZB-ZC)^2$$

$$CA^2 = (XC-XA)^2 + (YC-YA)^2 + (ZC-ZA)^2$$

The unknowns are the pyramid edges *LA*, *LB*, and *LC*. It is desired that the pyramid edges be expressed in terms of the altitude ZL and functions of tilt, t, and swing, s.

$$LA = (ZL-ZA) \sec \gamma_A$$

$$LB = (ZL-ZB) \sec \gamma_B$$

$$LC = (ZL-ZC) \sec \gamma_C$$

where

$$\sec \gamma_A = \frac{La}{za}, \qquad za = xa \sin s \sin t + ya \cos s \sin t + f \cos t$$

$$\sec \gamma_B = \frac{Lb}{zb}, \qquad zb = xb \sin s \sin t + yb \cos s \sin t + f \cos t$$

$$\sec \gamma_C = \frac{Lc}{zc}, \qquad zc = xc \sin s \sin t + yc \cos s \sin t + f \cos t$$

Substituting in the cosine formulae we obtain three equations in which ZL and functions of tilt and swing have symmetrical occurrence in each equation. Inasmuch as the number of unknowns exceeds the number of equations, a simultaneous solution is not possible in the present form. Differentiation of the apex angles with respect to ZL, t, and s yields three differential equations having three differential unknowns (ΔZ, Δt, Δs).

When the tilt and swing are known, the γ angles are known. Then expansion of the squared terms of any three of the cosine formulae gives a quadratic in ZL.

Values of ZL, t, and s are approximated. Substitution of the approximate values of ZL^1, t^1, and s^1 in the cosine formulae yields cosines of the apex angles whose errors with respect to the correct cosine functions obtained from the camera coordinates have an approximate linear relation to the errors in ZL^1, t^1, and s^1:

$$\cos a^1Lb^1 \doteq \frac{(ZL^1-ZA)^2 \sec^2\gamma_A{}^1 + (ZL^1-ZB)^2 \sec^2\gamma_B{}^1 - AB^2}{2(ZL^1-ZA)(ZL^1-ZB) \sec \gamma_A{}^1 \sec \gamma_B{}^1}$$

$$\cos b^1Lc^1 = \frac{(ZL^1-ZB)^2 \sec^2\gamma_B{}^1 + (ZL^1-ZC)^2 \sec^2\gamma_C{}^1 - BC^2}{2(ZL^1-ZB)(ZL^1-ZC) \sec \gamma_B{}^1 \sec \gamma_C{}^1}$$

$$\cos c^1La^1 = \frac{(ZL^1-ZC)^2 \sec^2\gamma_C{}^1 + (ZL^1-ZA)^2 \sec^2\gamma_A{}^1 - CA^2}{2(ZL^1-ZC)(ZL^1-ZA) \sec \gamma_C{}^1 \sec \gamma_A{}^1}$$

The differences between the approximate and correct values are the apex differentials:

$$\Delta(aLb) = aLb - a^1Lb^1$$

$$\Delta(bLc) = bLc - b^1Lc^1$$

$$\Delta(cLa) = cLa - c^1La^1$$

Differentiating ZL and γ with respect to the apex angles, we obtain

$$0 = 2\Big\{(ZL^1-ZA)\sec^2\gamma_A{}^1 + (ZL^1-ZB)\sec^2\gamma_B{}^1$$

$$-[(ZL^1-ZA)+(ZL^1-ZB)]\sec\gamma_A{}^1\sec\gamma_B{}^1\cos aLb\Big\}\Delta Z$$

$$+2[(ZL^1-ZA)^2\sec^2\gamma_A{}^1\tan\gamma_A{}^1\,\Delta\gamma_A + (ZL^1-ZB)^2\sec^2\gamma_B{}^1\tan\gamma_B{}^1\,\Delta\gamma_B$$

$$-(ZL^1-ZA)(ZL^1-ZB)\sec\gamma_A{}^1\sec\gamma_B{}^1\tan\gamma_A{}^1\cos aLb\,\Delta\gamma_A$$

$$-(ZL^1-ZA)(ZL^1-ZB)\sec\gamma_A{}^1\sec\gamma_B{}^1\tan\gamma_B{}^1\cos aLb\,\Delta\gamma_B$$

$$+(ZL^1-ZA)(ZL^1-ZB)\sec\gamma_A{}^1\sec\gamma_B{}^1\sin aLb\;\Delta(aLb)]$$

and by virtue of the cyclic form of the equations, similar expressions for the remaining two cosine formulae are obtained.
Now, since

$$\sec^2\gamma_A{}^1 = \frac{La^2}{za^2}$$

$$\sec^2\gamma_B{}^1 = \frac{Lb^2}{zb^2}$$

$$\sec^2\gamma_C{}^1 = \frac{Lc^2}{zc^2}$$

$$\sec\gamma_A{}^1\sec\gamma_B{}^1 = \frac{La\cdot Lb}{za\cdot zb}$$

$$\sec\gamma_B{}^1\sec\gamma_C{}^1 = \frac{Lb\cdot Lc}{zb\cdot zc}$$

$$\sec\gamma_C{}^1\sec\gamma_A{}^1 = \frac{Lc\cdot La}{zc\cdot za}$$

we may write

$$d(\sec^2\gamma_A{}^1) = 2\sec^2\gamma_A{}^1\tan\gamma_A{}^1\;\Delta\gamma = -2\sec^2\gamma_A{}^1\,\frac{dza}{za}$$

$$d(\sec^2\gamma_B{}^1) = 2\sec^2\gamma_B{}^1 \tan\gamma_B{}^1 \ \Delta\gamma = -2\sec^2\gamma_B{}^1 \frac{dzb}{zb}$$

$$d(\sec^2\gamma_C{}^1) = 2\sec^2\gamma_C{}^1 \tan\gamma_C{}^1 \ \Delta\gamma = -2\sec^2\gamma_C{}^1 \frac{dzc}{zc}$$

$$d(\sec\gamma_A{}^1 \sec\gamma_B{}^1) = \sec\gamma_A{}^1 \sec\gamma_B{}^1 (\tan\gamma_A{}^1 \ \Delta\gamma_A + \tan\gamma_B{}^1 \ \Delta\gamma_B)$$

$$= \sec\gamma_A{}^1 \sec\gamma_B{}^1 \left(\frac{dza}{za} + \frac{dzb}{zb}\right)$$

$$d(\sec\gamma_B{}^1 \sec\gamma_C{}^1) = \sec\gamma_B{}^1 \sec\gamma_C{}^1 (\tan\gamma_B{}^1 \ \Delta\gamma_B + \tan\gamma_C{}^1 \ \Delta\gamma_C)$$

$$= \sec\gamma_B{}^1 \sec\gamma_C{}^1 \left(\frac{dzb}{zb} + \frac{dzc}{zc}\right)$$

$$d(\sec\gamma_C{}^1 \sec\gamma_A{}^1) = \sec\gamma_C{}^1 \sec\gamma_A{}^1 (\tan\gamma_C{}^1 \ \Delta\gamma_C + \tan\gamma_A{}^1 \ \Delta\gamma_A)$$

$$= \sec\gamma_C{}^1 \sec\gamma_A{}^1 \left(\frac{dzc}{zc} + \frac{dza}{za}\right)$$

and, since

$$za = xa \sin s^1 \sin t^1 + ya \cos s^1 \sin t^1 + f \cos t^1$$

$$zb = xb \sin s^1 \sin t^1 + yb \cos s^1 \sin t^1 + f \cos t^1$$

$$zc = xc \sin s^1 \sin t^1 + yc \cos s^1 \sin t^1 + f \cos t^1$$

we may write

$$dza = (xa \cos s^1 - ya \sin s^1)\sin t^1 \ \Delta s + [(xa \sin s^1 + ya \cos s^1)\cos t^1 - f \sin t^1]\Delta t$$

$$dzb = (xb \cos s^1 - yb \sin s^1)\sin t^1 \ \Delta s + [(xb \sin s^1 + yb \cos s^1)\cos t^1 - f \sin t^1]\Delta t$$

$$dzc = (xc \cos s^1 - yc \sin s^1)\sin t^1 \ \Delta s + [(xc \sin s^1 + yc \cos s^1)\cos t^1 - f \sin t^1]\Delta t$$

From rotation equations,

$$xa^1 = xa \cos s^1 - ya \sin s^1$$

$$xb^1 = xb \cos s^1 - yb \sin s^1$$

$$xc^1 = xc \cos s^1 - yc \sin s^1$$

and

$$ya^{11} = [(xa \sin s^{1} + ya \cos s^{1})\cos t^{1} - f \sin t^{1}]$$

$$yb^{11} = [(xb \sin s^{1} + yb \cos s^{1})\cos t^{1} - f \sin t^{1}]$$

$$yc^{11} = [(xc \sin s^{1} + yc \cos s^{1})\cos t^{1} - f \sin t^{1}]$$

Therefore,

$$dza = xa^{1} \sin t^{1} \Delta s + ya^{11} \Delta t$$

$$dzb = xb^{1} \sin t^{1} \Delta s + yb^{11} \Delta t$$

$$dzc = xc^{1} \sin t^{1} \Delta s + yc^{11} \Delta t$$

However,

$$\tan \eta_a = \frac{xa^{1}}{za} \qquad \tan \xi_a = \frac{ya^{11}}{za}$$

$$\tan \eta_b = \frac{xb^{1}}{zb} \qquad \tan \xi_b = \frac{yb^{11}}{zb}$$

$$\tan \eta_c = \frac{xc^{1}}{zc} \qquad \tan \xi_c = \frac{yc^{11}}{zc}$$

Therefore,

$$\tan \gamma_A{}^{1} \Delta\gamma_A = -(\tan \eta_a \sin t^{1} \Delta s + \tan \xi_a \Delta t)$$

$$\tan \gamma_B{}^{1} \Delta\gamma_B = -(\tan \eta_b \sin t^{1} \Delta s + \tan \xi_b \Delta t)$$

$$\tan \gamma_C{}^{1} \Delta\gamma_C = -(\tan \eta_c \sin t^{1} \Delta s + \tan \xi_c \Delta t)$$

To simplify the notation, let

$$(ZL^{1} - ZA) = ZA^{1}$$

$$(ZL^{1} - ZB) = ZB^{1}$$

$$(ZL^{1} - ZC) = ZC^{1}$$

Substituting the simplified notation for the Z terms, the differential functions of t and s for the γ terms, and collecting common coefficients of ΔZ, Δt, and Δs result in three differential equations, with three differential unknowns, of the form

$$\Delta Z[ZA^1 \sec^2\gamma_A{}^1 + ZB^1 \sec^2\gamma_B{}^1 - (ZA^1 + ZB^1)\sec\gamma_A{}^1 \sec\gamma_B{}^1 \cos aLb]$$

$$+ \Delta s[ZA^1 \cdot ZB^1 \sec\gamma_A{}^1 \sec\gamma_B{}^1 \cos aLb\,(\tan\eta_a + \tan\eta_b)$$

$$- (ZA^{1^2} \sec^2\gamma_A{}^1 \tan\eta_a + ZB^{1^2} \sec^2\gamma_B{}^1 \tan\eta_b)]\sin t^1$$

$$+ \Delta t[ZA^1 \cdot ZB^1 \sec\gamma_A{}^1 \sec\gamma_B{}^1 \cos aLb\,(\tan\xi_a + \tan\xi_b)$$

$$- (ZA^{1^2} \sec^2\gamma_A{}^1 \tan\xi_a + ZB^{1^2} \sec^2\gamma_B{}^1 \tan\xi_b)]$$

$$+ [ZA^1 \cdot ZB^1 \sec\gamma_A{}^1 \sec\gamma_B{}^1 \sin aLb\,\Delta(aLb)] = 0$$

Division by $\sec\gamma_A{}^1 \cdot \sec\gamma_B{}^1$ gives:

$$\Delta Z\left[ZA^1 \frac{\sec\gamma_A{}^1}{\sec\gamma_B{}^1} + ZB^1 \frac{\sec\gamma_B{}^1}{\sec\gamma_A{}^1} - (ZA^1 + ZB^1)\cos aLb\right]$$

$$+ \Delta s\left[ZA^1\ ZB^1 \cos aLb\,(\tan\eta_a + \tan\eta_b)\right.$$

$$\left. - \left(ZA^{1^2} \frac{\sec\gamma_A{}^1}{\sec\gamma_B{}^1}\tan\eta_a + ZB^{1^2}\frac{\sec\gamma_B{}^1}{\sec\gamma_A{}^1}\tan\eta_b\right)\right]\sin t^1$$

$$+ \Delta t\left[ZA^1\ ZB^1 \cos aLb\,(\tan\xi_a + \tan\xi_b)\right.$$

$$\left. - \left(ZA^{1^2} \frac{\sec\gamma_A{}^1}{\sec\gamma_B{}^1}\tan\xi_a + ZB^{1^2}\frac{\sec\gamma_B{}^1}{\sec\gamma_A{}^1}\tan\xi_b\right)\right]$$

$$+ [ZA^1\ ZB^1\ \sin aLb\ \Delta(aLb)] = 0$$

Simplifying the coefficients and constant term notation further, let coefficients of

Δz be a_1, a_2, a_3,

Δs be b_1, b_2, b_3,

Δt be c_1, c_2, c_3, and the constant

terms be q_1, q_2, q_3,

The angular differentials (Δs, Δt, $\Delta(aLb)$, $\Delta(bLc)$, and $\Delta(cLa)$ are radian functions; division through by *tan 1"* converts the angular differentials to seconds of arc. ΔZ then, which is a linear value, divided by *tan 1"*, is designated *u*.

In terms of the simplified notation,

$$a_1\ u + b_1\ \Delta s + c_1\ \Delta t + q_1 = 0$$

$$a_2\ u + b_2\ \Delta s + c_2\ \Delta t + q_2 = 0$$

$$a_3\ u + b_3\ \Delta s + c_3\ \Delta t + q_3 = 0$$

Solving simultaneously for u, Δs, and Δt,

$$ZL = ZL^1 + u \cdot \tan 1''$$

$$s = s^1 + \Delta s$$

$$t = t^1 + \Delta t$$

The corrected values are substituted back in the cosine formulae and then if

$$aLb \neq a^1Lb^1$$

$$bLc \neq b^1Lc^1$$

$$cLa \neq c^1La^1$$

new coefficients are formed, and the solution repeated until the above inequality vanishes. Values for XL, YL, and azimuth may be determined by any number of direct equations described in the previous chapters.

c. Solutions for a spherical object space.

1. Concave object space.

It has been demonstrated in Chapter III, section A.4.c., that if the direction angles of two lines intersecting in a lens were known, the elements of angular orientation could be determined explicitly by use of spherical trigonometry. Now, when object space is made of star control points, the elements of angular orientation so determined become spherical coordinates of the camera principal point; that is, tilt corresponds to latitude, azimuth corresponds to longitude, and swing corresponds to geodetic azimuth. Therefore, with the camera and astronomic data of two star images, the latitude and longitude of the principal point may be determined. However, while these formulae are straightforward, they do involve a great many steps. Frequently iteration is employed in the interest of greater speed, even when there is no reduction in given data. Furthermore, iteration equations are adapted to Least Squares adjustment when the data exceed the minimum. Consider the law of cosines:

$$\cos \gamma = \sin \varphi \sin \delta + \cos \varphi \cos \delta \cos (\lambda - GHA)$$

Now $\lambda - \text{GHA} = \text{LHA}$ (converted to arc)

and
$$\cos\gamma = \frac{f}{(x^2 + y^2 + f^2)^{1/2}}$$

Let a value of φ and λ be assumed and a corresponding value of γ_a be computed.

$$\cos\gamma_a = \sin\varphi_a \sin\delta + \cos\varphi_a \cos\delta \cos(\lambda_a - \text{GHA})$$

γ differs from γ_a:

$$\gamma - \gamma_a = \Delta\gamma$$

since φ_a and λ_a are in error. Differentiating γ with respect to φ and λ gives

$$-\sin\gamma\, d\gamma =$$

$$(\sin\delta\cos\varphi_a - \cos\delta\sin\varphi_a\cos\text{LHA})\Delta\varphi - (\cos\varphi_a\cos\delta\sin\text{LHA})\Delta\lambda$$

Now,

$$\frac{\sin\delta\cos\varphi_a - \cos\delta\sin\varphi_a\cos\text{LHA}}{\sin\gamma_a} = \cos\text{Az}$$

$$\frac{\cos\varphi_a\cos\delta\sin\text{LHA}}{\sin\gamma_a} = \sin\text{Az}\,\cos\varphi_a$$

Therefore, division by $\sin\gamma\cdot\tan 1''$ gives

$$d\gamma'' = \cos\text{Az}\,\Delta\varphi'' + \sin\text{Az}\cos\varphi_a\,\Delta\lambda''$$

Solving two such equations simultaneously gives $\Delta\varphi$ and $\Delta\lambda$. Then

$$\varphi = \varphi_a + \Delta\varphi'' \qquad \lambda = \lambda_a + \Delta\lambda''$$

The solution is repeated until $d\gamma = 0$. If there are n images on the exposures whose camera and astronomic coordinates are known, n observation equations may be converted to a normal equation in $\Delta\varphi''$ and a normal equation in $\Delta\lambda''$, whereby Least Squares values may be obtained.

This is the application of the two-point iterative solution to the determination of the spherical coordinates of the principal point. The same solution may be employed to determine the elements of angular orientation when two vertical angles on imaged objects have been measured with a theodolite, or the space coordinates of the camera station and two imaged objects are known. The solution may also be employed to determine the relative orientation of two overlapping exposures without conjugate principal points or the absolute orientation of one when the absolute orientation of the other is known. In any case, let *a* and *b* denote objects, or conjugate images on the exposure whose orientation is known, and a^1 and b^1 denote images on the exposure whose orientation is to be determined. The zenith angles may be observed with a theodolite, or obtained from survey data as follows:

$$\cos \gamma_A = \frac{ZA-ZL}{LA}$$

$$\cos \gamma_B = \frac{ZB-ZL}{LB}$$

$$LA = [(XA-XL)^2 + (YA-YL)^2 + (ZA-ZL)^2]^{1/2}$$

$$LB = [(XB-XL)^2 + (YB-YL)^2 + (ZB-ZL)^2]^{1/2}$$

or, for purposes of relative orientation,

$$\cos \gamma_a = \frac{f}{La}$$

$$\cos \gamma_b = \frac{f}{Lb}$$

or, if the absolute orientation of the reference exposure is known,

$$\cos \gamma_a = \frac{xa}{La} \cos \gamma_{x_1} + \frac{ya}{La} \cos \gamma_{y_1} + \frac{f}{La} \cos \gamma_{z_1}$$

$$\cos \gamma_b = \frac{xb}{Lb} \cos \gamma_{x_1} + \frac{yb}{Lb} \cos \gamma_{y_1} + \frac{f}{Lb} \cos \gamma_{z_1}$$

where, in each case,

$$La = (xa^2 + ya^2 + f^2)^{1/2}$$

$$Lb = (xb^2 + yb^2 + f^2)^{1/2}$$

and γ_{x_1}, γ_{y_1}, γ_{z_1}, are the direction angles of the reference exposure referred to the *Z* axis. γ_a and γ_b are the known differential data, however they are obtained. Then the tilt and swing on the exposure whose orientation is assumed and the zenith angle of images a^1 and b^1 referred to the principal point are computed.

$$\cos \gamma_a{}^1 = \frac{f}{(xa^{1^2} + ya^{1^2} + f^2)^{\frac{1}{2}}}$$

$$\cos \gamma_b{}^1 = \frac{f}{(xb^{1^2} + yb^{1^2} + f^2)^{\frac{1}{2}}}$$

With an assumed value of s^1

$$s_a{}^1 = \theta_a - s^1$$

$$s_b{}^1 = \theta_b - s^1$$

a value of $\cos \gamma_a$ and $\cos \gamma_b$ are computed with these data:

$$\cos \gamma_{a_1} = \cos \gamma_a{}^1 \cos \gamma_{z_1}{}^1 + \sin \gamma_a{}^1 \sin \gamma_{z_1}{}^1 \cos s_a{}^1$$

$$\cos \gamma_{b_1} = \cos \gamma_b{}^1 \cos \gamma_{z_1}{}^1 + \sin \gamma_b{}^1 \sin \gamma_{z_1}{}^1 \cos s_b{}^1$$

These values are in error as a function of the error in s^1 and $\gamma_z{}^1$

$$\gamma_a - \gamma_{a_1} = d\gamma_{a_1}{}''$$

$$\gamma_b - \gamma_{b_1} = d\gamma_{b_1}{}''$$

These errors provide known differentials from which the differentials $d\gamma_z{}''$ and ds'' may be determined by the simultaneous solution of two differential equations.

$$d\gamma_a{}'' = \frac{(\cos \gamma_a{}^1 \sin \gamma_{z_1}{}^1 - \sin \gamma_a{}^1 \cos \gamma_{z_1}{}^1 \cos s_a{}^1) d\gamma_z{}''}{\sin \gamma_a}$$

$$+ (\sin \gamma_a{}^1 \sin \gamma_{z_1}{}^1 \sin s_a{}^1) ds''$$

$$d\gamma_b{}'' = \frac{(\cos \gamma_b{}^1 \sin \gamma_{z_1}{}^1 - \sin \gamma_b{}^1 \cos \gamma_{z_1}{}^1 \cos s_b{}^1) d\gamma_z{}''}{\sin \gamma_b}$$

$$+ (\sin \gamma_b{}^1 \sin \gamma_{z_1}{}^1 \sin s_b{}^1) ds''$$

These equations are repeatedly formed, with the assumed values revised from the previous solutions, until

$$\gamma_a = \gamma_{a_1} + d\gamma_{a_1}{}'' + d\gamma_{a_2}{}'' + \ldots + d\gamma_{a_n}{}''$$

$$\gamma_b = \gamma_{b_1} + d\gamma_{b_1}{}'' + d\gamma_{b_2}{}'' + \ldots + d\gamma_{b_n}{}''$$

Then

$$s = s^1 + ds_1'' + ds_2'' + \ldots + ds_n''$$

$$\gamma_z = \gamma_z^1 + d\gamma_{z_1}'' + d\gamma_{z_2}'' + \ldots + d\gamma_{z_n}''$$

2. Convex object space.

Thus far, only concave spherical object space has been considered insofar as the celestial sphere is concentric with the camera station. Conceivably, exposures made from altitudes of a hundred miles, or possibly a thousand miles, present a convex spherical object space. The geometry of a convex spherical object space is illustrated in Figure 36.

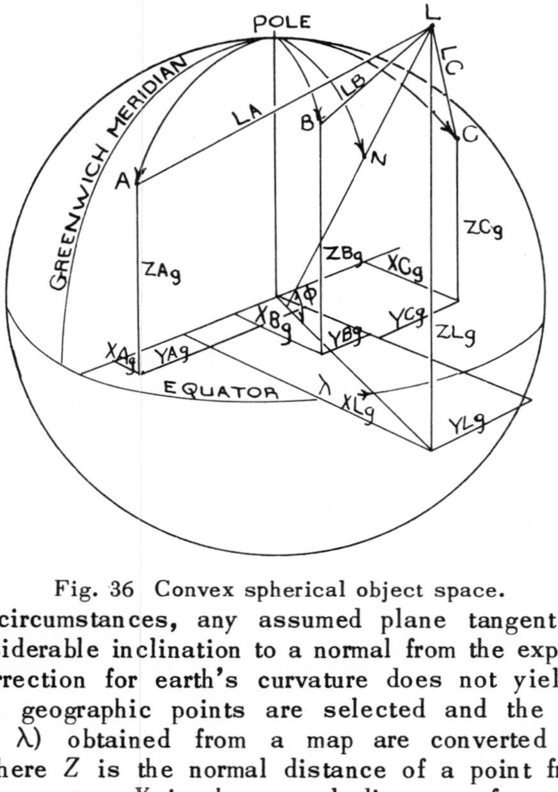

Fig. 36 Convex spherical object space.

Under these circumstances, any assumed plane tangent to the earth may have considerable inclination to a normal from the exposure camera, whereupon correction for earth's curvature does not yield the correct normal. Three geographic points are selected and the spherical coordinates (φ, λ) obtained from a map are converted to Cartesian coordinates where Z is the normal distance of a point from the plane of the earth's equator, X is the normal distance of a point from the Greenwich meridional plane, and Y is the normal distance from the meridional plane which is 90° east and west of Greenwich.

For any point,

$$X_g = \left[\frac{a}{(1 - e^2 \sin^2 \varphi)^{1/2}} + Z\right] \cos \varphi \sin \lambda$$

$$Y_g = \left[\frac{a}{(1 - e^2 \sin^2 \varphi)^{1/2}} + Z\right] \cos \varphi \cos \lambda$$

$$Z_g = \left[\frac{a}{(1 - e^2 \sin^2 \varphi)^{1/2}} + Z \right] \sin \varphi$$

where *g* denotes geodetic Cartesian coordinates, and *Z* is the sea-level elevation of a point. *a* and *b* are the semi-major and semi-minor axes of the earth, after Hayford, and

$$e^2 = \frac{a^2 - b^2}{a^2}$$

Assume now the transformed Cartesian coordinates are employed to resect the position of the camera in space by iteration. The solved-for XL_g, YL_g, and ZL_g are obviously in the same system. Reference is made to Figure 37.

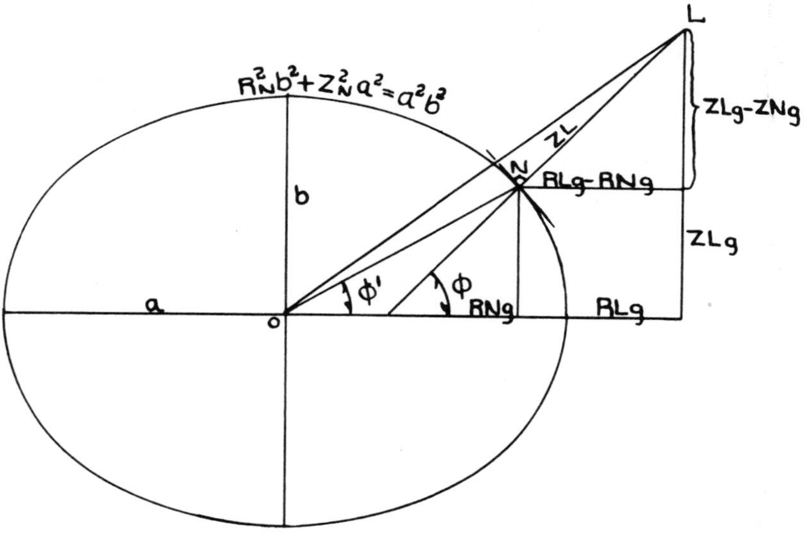

Fig. 37 Meridional section of the earth.

A straight line from the center of the earth to a point defines the geocentric latitude φ^1 when the point lies on the surface of the geoid corresponding to *N*. The geographic latitude is the angle a normal to the ellipsoidal surface from a point *L* makes with the equator. It may be seen in Figure 37 that the line *LO* passed north of *N* an amount that is dependent on the magnitude of *ZL*. From the reciprocal of the first derivative of an ellipse we obtain

$$\tan \varphi = \frac{a^2}{b^2} \cdot \frac{ZN_g}{RN_g}$$

where ZN_g and RN_g are the nadir geodetic coordinates of the exposure station and

$$RN_g = (XN_g^2 + YN_g^2)^{1/2}$$

$$RL_g = (XL_g^2 + YL_g^2)^{1/2}$$

The slope of line *LN*, which is the distance *ZL*, may be expressed:

$$\tan \varphi = \frac{ZL_g - ZN_g}{RL_g - RN_g}$$

or

$$\frac{ZL_g - ZN_g}{RL_g - RN_g} = \frac{a^2}{b^2} \cdot \frac{ZN_g}{RN_g}$$

Cross-multiplying gives:

$$ZL_g \cdot RN_g \cdot b^2 - ZN_g \cdot RN_g \cdot b^2 = RL_g \cdot ZN_g \cdot a^2 - RN_g \cdot ZN_g \cdot a^2$$

or

$$RN_g[(ZL_g - ZN_g)b^2 + ZN_g \cdot a^2] = RL_g \cdot ZN_g \cdot a^2$$

or

$$RN_g[b^2 \cdot ZL_g + ZN_g(a^2 - b^2)] = RL_g \cdot ZN_g \cdot a^2 \quad . \; . \; . \quad (1)$$

From

$$RN_g^2 \cdot b^2 + ZN_g^2 \cdot a^2 = a^2 b^2,$$

$$RN_g^2 = \frac{a^2}{b^2}(b^2 - ZN_g^2) \quad . \; . \; . \; . \; . \; . \; . \quad (2)$$

Squaring (1) and substituting (2) in (1),

$$a^2(b^2 - ZN_g^2)[b^2 ZL_g + ZN_g(a^2 - b^2)]^2 = RL_g^2 \cdot ZN_g^2 \cdot a^2 b^2$$

Expanding the squares and collecting coefficients of common powers of ZN_g, and dividing through by $(a^2 - b^2)^2$ give

$$ZN_g^4 + ZN_g^3 \frac{(2b^2 ZL_g)}{(a^2 - b^2)} + ZN_g^2 \frac{[b^4 ZL_g^2 + a^2 b^2 RL_g^2 - b^2(a^2 - b^2)^2]}{(a^2 - b^2)^2}$$

$$- ZN_g \frac{(2b^4 ZL_g)}{(a^2 - b^2)} - \frac{b^6 ZL_g^2}{(a^2 - b^2)^2} = 0$$

which is a quartic in ZN_g. This equation is readily solved by Ferrari's solution of a biquadratic or Newton's method of iteration, especially since a good approximation of ZN_g may be obtained. According to Descartes' rule of signs, the equation has one real root which is the desired value of ZN_g.

Then

$$RN_g = \frac{a}{b}(b^2 - ZN_g^2)^{1/2}$$

and

$$\tan \varphi_0 = \frac{(ZL_g - ZN_g)}{(RL_g - RN_g)} = \frac{a^2}{b^2} \cdot \frac{ZN_g}{RN_g}$$

$$ZL = [(ZL_g - ZN_g)^2 + (RL_g - RN_g)^2]^{1/2}$$

and, of course, $\tan \lambda_0$ is obtained precisely from the initial space coordinates:

$$\tan \lambda_0 = \frac{XL_g}{YL_g}$$

In order to compute the angular orientation with respect to the direction of gravity by any of the equations enumerated in the six groups, or a two-point solution, the control points must be converted to a local tangent plane, normal to ZL, at sea level. The values X_g, Y_g, Z_g employed as control are transformed to a local tangent plane by rotations through λ_0 and φ_0, and translations through Y_o and Z_o:

$$Z_o = \frac{a(1 - e^2)\sin \varphi_0}{(1 - e^2 \sin^2 \varphi_0)^{1/2}}$$

$$Y_o = \frac{a \cos \varphi_0}{(1 - e^2 \sin^2 \varphi_0)^{1/2}}$$

$$Y^1 = (X_g - XL)\sin \lambda_0 + (Y_g - YL)\cos \lambda_0$$

$$Z^1 = Z_g - Z_o$$

Then

$$X = X_g \cos \lambda_0 - Y_g \sin \lambda_0$$

$$Y = Z^1 \cos \varphi_0 - Y^1 \sin \varphi_0$$

$$Z = Z^1 \sin \varphi_0 + Y^1 \cos \varphi_0$$

The angular orientation of the camera determined with these transformed data will refer, in tilt and azimuth, to the local direction of gravity and to the local meridian. The coordinates so defined are free from the effects of earth's curvature.

4. Iterative Equations for Variations in the Given Data.

The differential vanishes for any quantity considered to be correct or known. The number of equations required for a unique simultaneous solution is therefore reduced by the number of quantities considered to be known. Occasionally, the focal length is known, but the plate perpendicular is not recoverable owing to the absence of fiducial marks. Still other times, the fiducial marks are imaged but the numerical value of the focal length is not available. The latter results in an equation containing five unknown differentials:

$$A\ \Delta X + B\ \Delta Y + C\ \Delta Z + a\ \Delta x + b\ \Delta y + Q = 0$$

Five equations of the above form are required for a unique solution.

In the second situation, Δx and Δy are equal to zero. This results in an equation containing four unknown differentials:

$$A\ \Delta X + B\ \Delta Y + C\ \Delta Z + c\ \Delta z + Q = 0$$

Four equations of the above form are required for a unique solution.

Summarizing, the differential equations described herein may be employed to determine all, or any combination of, elements of interior and exterior orientation.

B. *NUMERICAL EXAMPLES OF GENERAL ITERATIVE EQUATIONS.*

Following are the given data used for the numerical examples:

Camera Coordinates

Referred to the principal point

Point	x(mm.)	y(mm.)
1	− 52.321	+ 50.622
2	+ 5.311	+ 60.801
3	+ 61.962	+ 12.679
4	+ 38.660	− 46.962
5	− 36.962	− 55.981
6	− 62.631	− 1.519
7	+ 56.782	+ 61.651
8	+ 10.981	+ 40.981

Focal length = 170 mm.

Ground Coordinates

Referred to an arbitrary X and Y origin
and to mean sea-level datum

Point	X(ft.)	Y(ft.)	Z(ft.)
1	+ 1,309.54	+ 4,507.91	600
2	+ 3,561.68	+ 2,041.00	200
3	+ 2,641.91	− 2,121.93	500
4	− 875.54	− 2,650.82	400
5	− 3,459.68	+ 742.34	350
6	− 1,499.43	+ 3,461.14	700
7	+ 5,126.60	− 547.29	100
8	+ 2,678.75	+ 1,155.57	300

(For purposes of this numerical test, the ground coordinates are made to be in error by these amounts:

$$\Delta X = + 60 \text{ ft.}$$

$$\Delta Y = + 80 \text{ ft.}$$

and these are the corrections to the ground coordinates which should be obtained when solving for the exterior orientation.)

1. Interior-Exterior Orientation.

Given Data: the camera coordinates of six points (points 1, 2, 3, 4, 5, and 6) referred to an arbitrary origin, and the ground coordinates of the same points also referred to an arbitrary origin. (For purposes of the solution an origin other than the principal point has been employed. This origin has the coordinates 2 mm. in x and 3 mm. in y; therefore, the camera coordinates referred to the principal point have been translated by these amounts.)

Camera Coordinates

Referred to an origin other than the principal point

Point	x(mm.)	y(mm.)
1	− 50.321	+ 53.622

2	+ 7.311	+ 63.801
3	+ 63.962	+ 15.679
4	+ 40.660	− 43.962
5	− 34.962	− 52.981
6	− 60.631	+ 1.481

Letting XL^1 and YL^1 be 0, the convention $XL^1 - X$, $YL^1 - Y$, and $ZL^1 - Z$ alters only the signs of the X and Y coordinates and changes Z by a constant. Points 1, 2, 3, 4, 5, and 6 are designated a, b, c, d, e, and g for images, and A, B, C, D, E, and G for objects.

Equations.

$$A_1\Delta X + B_1\Delta Y + C_1\Delta Z + a_1\Delta x + b_1\Delta y + c_1\Delta z + Q_1 = 0$$

$$A_2\Delta X + B_2\Delta Y + C_2\Delta Z + a_2\Delta x + b_2\Delta y + c_2\Delta z + Q_2 = 0$$

$$A_3\Delta X + B_3\Delta Y + C_3\Delta Z + a_3\Delta x + b_3\Delta y + c_3\Delta z + Q_3 = 0$$

$$A_4\Delta X + B_4\Delta Y + C_4\Delta Z + a_4\Delta x + b_4\Delta y + c_4\Delta z + Q_4 = 0$$

$$A_5\Delta X + B_5\Delta Y + C_5\Delta Z + a_5\Delta x + b_5\Delta y + c_5\Delta z + Q_5 = 0$$

$$A_6\Delta X + B_6\Delta Y + C_6\Delta Z + a_6\Delta x + b_6\Delta y + c_6\Delta z + Q_6 = 0$$

Coefficients

$A_1 = XA^1M_1 + XB^1N_1$ $\quad$ $B_1 = YA^1M_1 + YB^1N_1$ $\quad$ $C_1 = ZA^1M_1 + ZB^1N_1$

$A_2 = XB^1M_2 + XC^1N_2$ $\quad$ $B_2 = YB^1M_2 + YC^1N_2$ $\quad$ $C_2 = ZB^1M_2 + ZC^1N_2$

. . . . $\quad$ . . . . $\quad$ . . . .

$A_6 = XG^1M_6 + XA^1N_6$ $\quad$ $B_6 = YG^1M_6 + YA^1N_6$ $\quad$ $C_6 = ZG^1M_6 + ZA^1N_6$

$a_1 = xa^1m_1 + xb^1n_1$ $\quad$ $b_1 = ya^1m_1 + yb^1n_1$ $\quad$ $c_1 = f^1(m_1 + n_1)$

$a_2 = xb^1m_2 + xc^1n_2$ $\quad$ $b_2 = yb^1m_2 + yc^1n_2$ $\quad$ $c_2 = f^1(m_2 + n_2)$

. . . . $\quad$ . . . . $\quad$ . . . .

$a_6 = xg^1m_6 + xa^1n_6$ $\quad$ $b_6 = yg^1m_6 + ya^1n_6$ $\quad$ $c_6 = f^1(m_6 + n_6)$

where

$$M_1 = 1 - \cos aLb^1 \frac{LB}{LA} \qquad N_1 = 1 - \cos aLb^1 \frac{LA}{LB}$$

$$M_2 = 1 - \cos bLc^1 \frac{LC}{LB} \qquad N_2 = 1 - \cos bLc^1 \frac{LB}{LC}$$

. . . .

$$M_6 = 1 - \cos gLa^1 \frac{LA}{LG} \qquad N_6 = 1 - \cos gLa^1 \frac{LG}{LA}$$

$$m_1 = \left(1 - \cos aLb^1 \frac{Lb}{La}\right) \frac{LA \cdot LB}{La \cdot Lb} \qquad n_1 = \left(1 - \cos aLb^1 \frac{La}{Lb}\right) \frac{LA \cdot LB}{La \cdot Lb}$$

$$m_2 = \left(1 - \cos bLc^1 \frac{Lc}{Lb}\right) \frac{LB \cdot LC}{Lb \cdot Lc} \qquad n_2 = \left(1 - \cos bLc^1 \frac{Lb}{Lc}\right) \frac{LB \cdot LC}{Lb \cdot Lc}$$

. . . .

$$m_6 = \left(1 - \cos gLa^1 \frac{La}{Lg}\right) \frac{LG \cdot LA}{Lg \cdot La} \qquad n_6 = \left(1 - \cos gLa^1 \frac{Lg}{La}\right) \frac{LG \cdot LA}{Lg \cdot La}$$

$$\cos aLb^1 = (xa^1 xb^1 + ya^1 yb^1 + f^{1^2})/La \cdot Lb$$

$$\cos bLc^1 = (xb^1 xc^1 + yb^1 yc^1 + f^{1^2})/Lb \cdot Lc$$

. . . .

$$\cos gLa^1 = (xg^1 xa^1 + yg^1 ya^1 + f^{1^2})/Lg \cdot La$$

$$La = (xa^{1^2} + ya^{1^2} + f^{1^2})^{1/2}$$

$$Lb = (xb^{1^2} + yb^{1^2} + f^{1^2})^{1/2}$$

. . . . . .

$$Lg = (xg^{1^2} + yg^{1^2} + f^{1^2})^{1/2}$$

$$LA = (XA^{1^2} + YA^{1^2} + ZA^{1^2})^{1/2}$$

$$LB = (XB^{1^2} + YB^{1^2} + ZB^{1^2})^{1/2}$$

. . . .

$$LG = (XG^{1^2} + YG^{1^2} + ZG^{1^2})^{1/2}$$

<u>Constant terms</u>

$$Q_1 = (AB - AB^1)AB^1$$

$$Q_2 = (BC - BC^1)BC^1$$

$$. \quad . \quad . \quad . \quad .$$

$$Q_6 = (GA - GA^1)GA^1$$

where

$$AB = [(XA - XB)^2 + (YA - YB)^2 + (ZA - ZB)^2]^{1/2}$$

$$BC = [(XB - XC)^2 + (YB - YC)^2 + (ZB - ZC)^2]^{1/2}$$

$$. \quad . \quad . \quad . \quad . \quad . \quad . \quad . \quad . \quad . \quad .$$

$$GA = [(XG - XA)^2 + (YG - YA)^2 + (ZG - ZA)^2]^{1/2}$$

$$AB^1 = (LA^2 + LB^2 - 2\,LA{\cdot}LB \cos aLb^1)^{1/2}$$

$$BC^1 = (LB^2 + LC^2 - 2\,LB{\cdot}LC \cos bLc^1)^{1/2}$$

$$. \quad . \quad . \quad . \quad . \quad . \quad . \quad . \quad . \quad . \quad .$$

$$GA^1 = (LG^2 + LA^2 - 2\,LG{\cdot}LA \cos gLa^1)^{1/2}$$

To be determined: Δx, Δy, f, ΔX, ΔY, and ZL,

where

$$\Delta x = \Delta x_1 + \Delta x_2 + . \; . \; . + \Delta x_n$$

$$\Delta y = \Delta y_1 + \Delta y_2 + . \; . \; . + \Delta y_n$$

$$f = f^1 + \Delta z_1 + \Delta z_2 + . \; . \; . + \Delta z_n$$

$$\Delta X = \Delta X_1 + \Delta X_2 + . \; . \; . + \Delta X_n$$

$$\Delta Y = \Delta Y_1 + \Delta Y_2 + . \; . \; . \quad \Delta Y_n$$

$$ZL = ZL^1 + \Delta Z_1 + \Delta Z_2 + . \; . \; . + \Delta Z_n$$

and f^1 is the first approximation of the focal length
ZL^1 is the first approximation of the altitude.

Compute true ground lengths.

AB = 3,364.19

BC = 4,273.87

CD = 3,558.40

DE = 4,265.42

EG = 3,370.01

GA = 2,999.34

First approximation.

f^1 = 169 mm.	ZL^1 = 9,900 ft.
La = 184.306	LA = 10,417.59
Lb = 180.790	LB = 10,532.87
Lc = 181.378	LC = 9,992.11
Ld = 179.296	LD = 9,901.69
Le = 180.528	LE = 10,184.45
Lg = 179.553	LG = 9,943.23

$\cos aLb^1$ = .94878992

$\cos bLc^1$ = .91575946

$\cos cLd^1$ = .93702856

$\cos dLe^1$ = .91042794

$\cos eLg^1$ = .94409795

$\cos gLa^1$ = .95765832

Approximate ground lengths.

AB^1 = 3,354.33

$BC^1 = 4{,}245.50$

$CD^1 = 3{,}531.12$

$DE^1 = 4{,}259.74$

$EG^1 = 3{,}373.45$

$GA^1 = 2{,}999.48$

The coefficients and constant terms are listed in Example 3.

$m_1 = 228.235270$	$n_1 = 107.882667$
$m_2 = 260.815515$	$n_2 = 279.902836$
$m_3 = 224.312890$	$n_3 = 158.472142$
$m_4 = 259.568805$	$n_4 = 298.428077$
$m_5 = 190.571424$	$n_5 = 158.631429$
$m_6 = 53.194523$	$n_6 = 209.830190$
$M_1 = 0.04071117$	$N_1 = 0.06159408$
$M_2 = .13125537$	$N_2 = .03468135$
$M_3 = .07145103$	$N_3 = .05441441$
$M_4 = .06357329$	$N_4 = .11484902$
$M_5 = .07826303$	$N_5 = .03299860$
$M_6 = .00334522$	$N_6 = .08594825$

Form six differential equations:

$A(\Delta X_1)$	+	$B(\Delta Y_1)$	+	$C(\Delta Z_1)$	+	$a(\Delta x_1)$	+	$b(\Delta y_1)$	+	$c(\Delta z_1)$	=	Q
− 272.69131	−	309.23581	+	976.07646	−	10,696.29684	+	19,121.45369	+	56,803.93135	+	33,065.67495
− 559.11463	−	194.30081	+	1,599.18178	+	19,809.97643	+	21,028.88724	+	91,381.40132	+	120,429.22590
− 141.12520	+	295.85689	+	1,188.57658	+	20,790.97836	−	3,449.75050	+	64,690.67041	+	96,313.41667
+ 453.00182	+	83.26433	+	1,700.75440	+	120.42518	−	27,222.18175	+	94,301.47306	+	24,180.86393
+ 320.24413	−	172.31055	+	1,050.99906	−	16,280.74030	−	9,861.73147	+	59,015.28216	−	11,614.79145
− 117.56859	−	375.86870	+	768.54270	−	13,784.10212	+	11,330.29554	+	44,451.17650	−	428.92605

After successive divisions and subtractions, we obtain:

$\Delta z_1 = -\ 0.9$

$\Delta y_1 = +\ 4.0$

$\Delta x_1 = +\ 2.6$

$\Delta Z_1 = +\ 91.$

$\Delta Y_1 = +\ 72.$

Example 3

$\Delta X_1 = +\ 119.$

Second approximation.

Camera coordinates after first adjustment

Point	x_1(mm.)	y_1(mm)
a	− 52.921	+ 49.622
b	+ 4.711	+ 59.801
c	+ 61.362	+ 11.679
d	+ 38.060	− 47.962
e	− 37.562	− 56.981
g	− 63.231	− 2.519

$f_1^1 = 169.9$ mm.

where

$$x_1 = x - \Delta x_1$$
$$y_1 = y - \Delta y_1$$
$$f_1^1 = f^1 - \Delta z_1$$

Ground coordinates after first adjustment

Point	X_1(ft.)	Y_1(ft.)	Z_1(ft.)
A	− 1,190.54	− 4,435.91	9391
B	− 3,442.68	− 1,969.00	9791
C	− 2,522.91	+ 2,193.93	9491
D	+ 994.54	+ 2,722.82	9591
E	+ 3,578.68	− 670.34	9691
G	+ 1,618.43	− 3,389.14	9291

$ZL_1^1 = 9{,}991$ ft.

where

$$X_1 = X + \Delta X_1$$
$$Y_1 = Y + \Delta Y_1$$
$$ZL_1^1 = ZL^1 + \Delta Z_1$$

The coefficients and constant terms are listed in Example 4.

Form second set of six differential equations:

$A(\Delta X_2)$	+	$B(\Delta Y_2)$	+	$C(\Delta Z_2)$	+	$a(\Delta x_2)$	+	$b(\Delta y_2)$	+	$c(\Delta z_2)$	=	Q
− 259.006750	−	302.738624	+	983.861874	−	12,668.03251	+	17,654.99178	+	57,313.62039	+	5,759.75638
− 539.696064	−	166.430156	+	1,625.473313	+	19,020.78678	+	19,059.57664	+	93,778.42342	+	5,079.36317
− 110.005277	+	306.133442	+	1,195.981947	+	19,383.87770	−	6,613.64650	+	65,711.39515	+	7,983.13158
+ 465.390520	+	91.898448	+	1,679.222619	−	2,824.81504	−	29,035.03510	+	92,870.51633	+	9,775.43719
+ 333.427594	−	148.061792	+	1,035.042423	−	16,349.44195	−	11,666.12653	+	57,622.80763	+	4,114.80426
− 96.153397	−	364.311009	+	772.619489	−	14,615.24711	+	9,097.48237	+	44,454.48184	+	4,898.70087

After successive divisions and subtractions:

$$\Delta z_2 = -\ 0.126$$

$$\Delta y_2 = -\ 1.014$$

$$\Delta x_2 = -\ 0.599$$

$$\Delta Z_2 = +\ 10.30$$

$$\Delta Y_2 = +\ 7.49$$

$$\Delta X_2 = -\ 59.46$$

Example 4

Third approximation.

Camera coordinates after second adjustment

Point	x_2(mm.)	y_2(mm.)
a	− 52.322	+ 50.636
b	+ 5.310	+ 60.815
c	+ 61.961	+ 12.693
d	+ 38.659	− 46.948
e	− 36.963	− 55.967
g	− 62.632	− 1.505

$$f_2^1 = 170.026 \text{ mm.}$$

where

$$x_2 = x_1 - \Delta x_2$$

$$y_2 = y_1 - \Delta y_2$$

$$f_2^1 = f_1^1 - \Delta z_2$$

Ground coordinates after second adjustment

Point	X_2(ft.)	Y_2(ft.)	Z_2(ft.)
A	− 1,250.00	− 4,428.42	9,401.30
B	− 3,502.14	− 1,961.51	9,801.30
C	− 2,582.37	+ 2,201.42	9,501.30
D	+ 935.08	+ 2,730.31	9,601.30
E	+ 3,519.22	− 662.85	9,651.30
G	+ 1,558.97	− 3,381.65	9,301.30

$$ZL_2^1 = 10{,}001.30 \text{ ft.}$$

where

$$X_2 = X_1 + \Delta X_2$$

$$Y_2 = Y_1 + \Delta Y_2$$

$$ZL_2 = ZL_1^1 + \Delta Z_2$$

Constant terms for third approximation:

$$Q_1 = +100.9248$$

$$Q_2 = +128.2152$$

$$Q_3 = +142.3344$$

$$Q_4 = +42.6541$$

$$Q_5 = +101.0994$$

$$Q_6 = +89.9793$$

These Q values are found to be too small for further computation, since the true and approximate ground lengths are nearly identical.

$$AB - AB^1 = +0.03$$

$$BC - BC^1 = +0.03$$

$$CD - CD^1 = +0.04$$

$$DE - DE^1 = +0.01$$

$$EG - EG^1 = +0.03$$

$$GA - GA^1 = +0.03$$

Then

$$\Delta X = \Delta X_1 + \Delta X_2 = +59.54 \text{ ft.}$$

$$\Delta Y = \Delta Y_1 + \Delta Y_2 = +79.49 \text{ ft.}$$

$$ZL = ZL^1 + \Delta Z_1 + \Delta Z_2 = 10{,}001.30 \text{ ft.}$$

$$\Delta x = -\Delta x_1 - \Delta x_2 = -2.001 \text{ mm.}$$

$$\Delta y = -\Delta y_1 - \Delta y_2 = -2.986 \text{ mm.}$$

$$f = f^1 - \Delta z_1 - \Delta z_2 = 170.026 \text{ mm.}$$

2. Interior Orientation.

Given Data: the camera coordinates of three points (points 1, 3, and 5) referred to an arbitrary origin, and the vertex angles obtained by direct measurement. Points 1, 3, and 5 are designated *a*, *b*, and *c*.

Measured vertex angles

$$aLb = 38^\circ\ 22'\ 02''$$

$$bLc = 38^\circ\ 37'\ 07''$$

$$cLa = 34^\circ\ 03'\ 33''$$

Equations.

$$a_1\Delta x + b_1\Delta y + c_1\Delta z + q_1 = 0$$

$$a_2\Delta x + b_2\Delta y + c_2\Delta z + q_2 = 0$$

$$a_3\Delta x + b_3\Delta y + c_3\Delta z + q_3 = 0$$

Coefficients

$$a_1 = xa^1m_1 + xb^1n_1 \qquad b_1 = ya^1m_1 + yb^1n_1 \qquad c_1 = f^1(m_1 + n_1)$$

$$a_2 = xb^1m_2 + xc^1n_2 \qquad b_2 = yb^1m_2 + yc^1n_2 \qquad c_2 = f^1(m_2 + n_2)$$

$$a_3 = xc^1m_3 + xa^1n_3 \qquad b_3 = yc^1m_3 + ya^1n_3 \qquad c_3 = f^1(m_3 + n_3)$$

where

$$m_1 = 1 - \cos aLb^1 \frac{Lb}{La} \qquad n_1 = 1 - \cos aLb^1 \frac{La}{Lb}$$

$$m_2 = 1 - \cos bLc^1 \frac{Lc}{Lb} \qquad n_2 = 1 - \cos bLc^1 \frac{Lb}{Lc}$$

$$m_3 = 1 - \cos cLa^1 \frac{La}{Lc} \qquad n_3 = 1 - \cos cLa^1 \frac{Lc}{La}$$

Constant terms

$$q_1 = La\cdot Lb \ \sin aLb^1\Delta(aLb)$$

$$q_2 = Lb\cdot Lc \ \sin bLc^1\Delta(bLc)$$

$$q_3 = Lc\cdot La \ \sin cLa^1\Delta(cLa)$$

where

$$\Delta(aLb) = [(aLb) - (aLb)^1] \tan 1''$$

$$\Delta(bLc) = [(bLc) - (bLc)^1] \tan 1''$$

$$\Delta(cLa) = [(cLa) - (cLa)^1] \tan 1''$$

To be determined : Δx, Δy, and f,
where

$$\Delta x = \Delta x_1 + \Delta x_2 + \ldots + \Delta x_n$$

$$\Delta y = \Delta y_1 + \Delta y_2 + \ldots + \Delta y_n$$

$$f = f^1 + \Delta z_1 + \Delta z_2 + \ldots + \Delta z_n$$

and f^1 is the initial approximation of the focal length.
First approximation.

$$f^1 = 169 \text{ mm.}$$

$La = 184.306$ $\qquad$ $\cos aLb^1 = .78324625$

$Lb = 181.378$ $\qquad$ $\cos bLc^1 = .77859264$

$Lc = 180.528$ $\qquad$ $\cos cLa^1 = .82589373$

$aLb^1 = 38° \; 26' \; 28''$ $\qquad$ $\sin aLb^1 = .62170994$

$bLc^1 = 38° \; 52' \; 05''$ $\qquad$ $\sin bLc^1 = .62752906$

$cLa^1 = 34° \; 19' \; 15''$ $\qquad$ $\sin cLa^1 = .56382639$

$m_1 = 0.22919497$ $\qquad$ $n_1 = 0.20411172$

$m_2 = .22505636$ $\qquad$ $n_2 = .21774118$

$m_3 = .15682420$ $\qquad$ $n_3 = .19103411$

$$\Delta(aLb) = -266'' \cdot \tan 1'' = -0.00129010$$

$$\Delta(bLc) = -898'' \cdot \tan 1'' = -.00435530$$

$$\Delta(cLa) = -942'' \cdot \tan 1'' = -.00456870$$

Form three differential equations:

	$a(\Delta x_1)$		$b(\Delta y_1)$		$c(\Delta z_1)$	=	$-q$
+	1.52207375	+	15.70385664	+	73.22883061	=	+ 26.81229884
+	6.78238776	−	8.00748679	+	74.83278426	=	+ 89.49130104
−	15.09591513	+	1.93492811	+	58.78805439	=	+ 85.70787551

$$\Delta z_1 = +1.052$$

$$\Delta y_1 = -3.008$$

$$\Delta x_1 = -1.966$$

Second approximation.

Camera coordinates after first adjustment

Point	x_1(mm.)	y_1(mm.)
a	− 52.287	+ 50.614
b	+ 61.996	+ 12.671
c	− 36.928	− 55.989

$$f_1^1 = 170.052 \text{ mm.}$$

where

$$x_1 = x + \Delta x_1$$

$$y_1 = y + \Delta y_1$$

$$f_1^1 = f^1 + \Delta z_1$$

La = 184.969	$\cos aLb^1$ = .78415874
Lb = 181.443	$\cos bLc^1$ = .78144137
Lc = 182.801	$\cos cLa^1$ = .82853338
aLb^1 = 38° 21' 25"	$\sin aLb^1$ = .62055869
bLc^1 = 38° 36' 26"	$\sin bLc^1$ = .62397810

$cLa^1 = 34° \ 03' \ 06''$ $\qquad$ $\sin cLa^1 = .55994026$

$m_1 = 0.23078573$ $\qquad$ $n_1 = 0.20060644$

$m_2 = .21271303$ $\qquad$ $n_2 = .22436083$

$m_3 = .16164106$ $\qquad$ $n_3 = .18117703$

$$\Delta(aLb) = +37'' \cdot \tan 1'' = +.00017945$$

$$\Delta(bLc) = +41'' \cdot \tan 1'' = +.00019885$$

$$\Delta(cLa) = +27'' \cdot \tan 1'' = +.00013095$$

Form a second set of three differential equations:

$a(\Delta x_2)$	+ $b(\Delta y_2)$	+ $c(\Delta z_2)$	= $-q$
+ 0.36970339	+ 14.22287314	+ 73.35910129	= − 3.73736725
+ 4.90216028	− 9.86645171	+ 74.32528404	= − 4.11542226
− 15.44228443	+ 0.11997289	+ 58.29690185	= − 2.47926709

$$\Delta z_2 = -0.052$$

$$\Delta y_2 = +0.007$$

$$\Delta x_2 = -0.036$$

Third approximation.

Camera coordinates after second adjustment

Point	x_2(mm.)	y_2(mm.)
a	− 52.323	+ 50.621
b	+ 61.960	+ 12.678
c	− 36.964	− 55.982

$$f_2^1 = 170.000 \text{ mm.}$$

$La = 184.933$ $\qquad$ $\cos aLb^1 = .78404763$ $\qquad$ $aLb^1 = 38° \ 22' \ 02''$

$Lb = 181.383$ $\cos bLc^1 = .78131740$ $bLc^1 = 38° 37' 07''$

$Lc = 182.758$ $\cos cLa^1 = .82846018$ $cLa^1 = 34° 03' 33''$

Now,

$$aLb = aLb^1$$

$$bLc = bLc^1$$

$$cLa = cLa^1$$

$$\Delta(aLb) = \Delta(bLc) = \Delta(cLa) = 0$$

Then the residuals q_1, q_2, and q_3 vanish. Therefore,

$$\Delta x = \Delta x_1 + \Delta x_2 = -2.002 \text{ mm.}$$

$$\Delta y = \Delta y_1 + \Delta y_2 = -3.001 \text{ mm.}$$

$$f = f^1 + \Delta z_1 + \Delta z_2 = 170.000 \text{ mm.}$$

3. Exterior Orientation.

Given Data: the camera coordinates of three points (points 1, 3, and 5) referred to the principal point, the ground coordinates of these points referred to an arbitrary origin, and the camera focal length.

Equations.

$$A_1\Delta X + B_1\Delta Y + C_1\Delta Z + Q_1 = 0$$

$$A_2\Delta X + B_2\Delta Y + C_2\Delta Z + Q_2 = 0$$

$$A_3\Delta X + B_3\Delta Y + C_3\Delta Z + Q_3 = 0$$

Coefficients

$A_1 = XA^1M_1 + XB^1N_1$ $B_1 = YA^1M_1 + YB^1N_1$ $C_1 = ZA^1M_1 + ZB^1N_1$

$A_2 = XB^1M_2 + XC^1N_2$ $B_2 = YB^1M_2 + YC^1N_2$ $C_2 = ZB^1M_2 + ZC^1N_2$

$A_3 = XC^1M_3 + XA^1N_3$ $B_3 = YC^1M_3 + YA^1N_3$ $C_3 = ZC^1M_3 + ZA^1N_3$

where

$$M_1 = 1 - \cos aLb^1 \frac{LB}{LA} \qquad N_1 = 1 - \cos aLb^1 \frac{LA}{LB}$$

$$M_2 = 1 - \cos bLc^1 \frac{LC}{LB} \qquad N_2 = 1 - \cos bLc^1 \frac{LB}{LC}$$

$$M_3 = 1 - \cos cLa^1 \frac{LA}{LC} \qquad N_3 = 1 - \cos cLa^1 \frac{LC}{LA}$$

Constant terms

$$Q_1 = LA \cdot LB \ \sin aLb^1 \Delta(aLb)$$

$$Q_2 = LB \cdot LC \ \sin bLc^1 \Delta(bLc)$$

$$Q_3 = LC \cdot LA \ \sin cLa^1 \Delta(cLa)$$

where

$$\Delta(aLb) = [(aLb) - (aLb)^1] \tan 1''$$

$$\Delta(bLc) = [(bLc) - (bLc)^1] \tan 1''$$

$$\Delta(cLa) = [(cLa) - (cLa)^1] \tan 1''$$

To be determined: ΔX, ΔY, and ZL,
where

$$\Delta X = \Delta X_1 + \Delta X_2 + \ldots + \Delta X_n$$

$$\Delta Y = \Delta Y_1 + \Delta Y_2 + \ldots + \Delta Y_n$$

$$ZL = ZL^1 + \Delta Z_1 + \Delta Z_2 + \ldots + \Delta Z_n$$

and ZL^1 is the first approximation of the altitude.

The true angles subtended at L by points A, B, and C are computed with the camera coordinates.

$$\cos aLb = .78404807$$

$$\cos bLc = .78131740$$

$$\cos cLa = .82845927$$

$$aLb = 38^\circ\ 22'\ 02''$$

$$bLc = 38^\circ\ 37'\ 07''$$

$$cLa = 34^\circ\ 03'\ 33''$$

First approximation.

$$ZL^1 = 9{,}900 \text{ ft.}$$

$$LA = 10{,}417.59 \qquad \cos aLb^1 = .78116371$$

$$LB = 9{,}992.11 \qquad \cos bLc^1 = .77684202$$

$$LC = 10{,}184.45 \qquad \cos cLa^1 = .82594705$$

$$aLb^1 = 38^\circ\ 37'\ 58'' \qquad \sin aLb^1 = .62432659$$

$$bLc^1 = 39^\circ\ 01'\ 40'' \qquad \sin bLc^1 = .62969709$$

$$cLa^1 = 34^\circ\ 18'\ 55'' \qquad \sin cLa^1 = .56374631$$

$$M_1 = 0.25074077 \qquad N_1 = 0.18557327$$

$$M_2 = .20820471 \qquad N_2 = .23782885$$

$$M_3 = .15514543 \qquad N_3 = .19253733$$

$$\Delta(aLb) = -\ 956'' \cdot \tan 1'' = -\ 0.00463660$$

$$\Delta(bLc) = -\ 1{,}473'' \cdot \tan 1'' = -\ .00714405$$

$$\Delta(cLa) = -\ 922'' \cdot \tan 1'' = -\ .00447170$$

Form three differential equations:

$$A(\Delta X_1) + B(\Delta Y_1) + C(\Delta Z_1) = -Q$$

$$-\ 818.62 - 736.54 + 4{,}076.28 = +\ 301{,}325.51$$

$$+\ 272.75 + 265.25 + 4{,}228.39 = +\ 457{,}794.79$$

$$+\ 284.62 - 983.11 + 3{,}272.24 = +\ 267{,}461.33$$

$$\Delta Z_1 = +\ 100$$

$$\Delta Y_1 = +\ 77$$

$$\Delta X_1 = +\ 59$$

Second approximation.

Ground coordinates after first adjustment

Point	X(ft.)	Y(ft.)	Z(ft.)
A	− 1,250.54	− 4,430.91	9400
B	− 2,582.91	+ 2,198.93	9500
C	+ 3,518.68	− 665.34	9650

$LA = 10{,}466.94$ $\qquad \cos aLb^1 = .78407879$

$LB = 10{,}087.45$ $\qquad \cos bLc^1 = .78130828$

$LC = 10{,}293.02$ $\qquad \cos cLa^1 = .82848313$

$aLb^1 = 38^\circ\ 21'\ 52''$ $\qquad \sin aLb^1 = .62066133$

$bLc^1 = 38^\circ\ 37'\ 10''$ $\qquad \sin bLc^1 = .62414479$

$cLa^1 = 34^\circ\ 03'\ 24''$ $\qquad \sin cLa^1 = .56001256$

$M_1 = 0.24434850$ $\qquad N_1 = 0.18642450$

$M_2 = .20276978$ $\qquad N_2 = .23429567$

$M_3 = .15751826$ $\qquad N_3 = .18528288$

$$\Delta(aLb) = +\ 10'' \cdot \tan 1'' = +\ 0.00004850$$

$$\Delta(bLc) = -\ 3'' \cdot \tan 1'' = -\ .00001455$$

$$\Delta(cLa) = +\ 0'' \cdot \tan 1'' = +\ .00004365$$

Form a second set of three differential equations:

$$A(\Delta X_2) + B(\Delta Y_2) + C(\Delta Z_2) = -Q$$

$$-\ 787.0852785 - 672.7517864 + 4{,}067.908650 = -\ 3{,}178.320333$$

$$+\ 300.6753957 + 289.9902713 + 4{,}187.266126 = +\ 942.915458$$

$$+\ 322.5526983 - 925.7749649 + 3{,}261.710281 = -\ 2{,}633.568270$$

$$\Delta Z_2 = -0.06$$

$$\Delta Y_2 = +3.01$$

$$\Delta X_2 = +1.13$$

Third approximation.

Ground coordinates after second adjustment

Point	X(ft.)	Y(ft.)	Z(ft.)
A	- 1,249.41	- 4,427.90	9,399.94
B	- 2,581.78	+ 2,201.94	9,499.94
C	+ 3,519.81	- 662.33	9,649.94

LA = 10,465.48	cos aLb¹ = .78404890	aLb¹ = 38° 22' 02"
LB = 10,087.76	cos bLc¹ = .78131756	bLc¹ = 38° 37' 07"
LC = 10,293.16	cos cLa¹ = .82845885	cLa¹ = 34° 03' 33"

Now,

$$aLb = aLb^1$$

$$bLc = bLc^1$$

$$cLa = cLa^1$$

$$\Delta(aLb) = \Delta(bLc) = \Delta(cLa) = 0$$

Then the residuals Q_1, Q_2, and Q_3 vanish. Therefore,

$$\Delta X = \Delta X_1 + \Delta X_2 = +60.13 \text{ ft.}$$

$$\Delta Y = \Delta Y_1 + \Delta Y_2 = +80.01 \text{ ft.}$$

$$ZL = ZL^1 + \Delta Z_1 + \Delta Z_2 = 9{,}999.94 \text{ ft.}$$

Chapter V

ORIENTATION OF MULTIPLE CAMERA STATIONS

A. *GENERAL.*

Thus far, all equations have dealt with the single exposure station and each case involved data in addition to the camera data. The ultimate objective of photogrammetric orientation data is to define the space coordinates of points beyond those employed in the determination of the camera orientation. This is the simplest concept of control extension. A point cannot be located unless its images are conjugate to two exposures. If the location of the point requires that the space coordinates of conjugate images be obtained, then the relative orientation of the two exposures having conjugate images must be determined. Given two exposures with conjugate images, the spatial configuration of the object space defined by the system of images may be determined without a dimension in object space being known. These exposures are presumably from different camera stations.

Other applications involve the determination of the relative and absolute orientation of one exposure with respect to another when the exposures are made at the same camera station. This section embraces the equations for the determination of the angular orientation of two overlapping exposures made from the same camera station and different camera stations. The former is considered first, inasmuch as it involves the less complicated equations. Both considerations are basically a preliminary to control extension.

B. *RELATIVE AND ABSOLUTE ORIENTATION OF OVERLAPPING EXPOSURES FROM THE SAME STATION.*

1. Introduction [21].

Successive overlapping exposures at the same camera station are made in terrestrial photographic surveys. Three exposures are made at the same camera station in trimetrogon photographic surveys.

In the former case, the principal points are not usually conjugate. The determination of relative and absolute orientation is extremely simple when the principal points are conjugate. The equations for relative and absolute orientation are given for conjugate principal points and for nonconjugate principal points.

Terrestrial photogrammetric surveys are generally conducted with tripod-mounted cameras equipped with horizontal and vertical circles, whereby the camera's orientation data are read directly. Other times, theodolites and various hand-held cameras are employed. It is the latter combination in which there is an economy in (1) reducing the required zenith angle measurement to a single exposure, and (2) reducing the horizontal sidelap to 10 percent, in which case the principal points are nonconjugate.

In both the preceding and succeeding sections, equations are given for the determination of orientation data that require the camera coordinates and the zenith angles of two images. Thus, observation of the zenith angles of two images and measurements of the corresponding photographic coordinates provide the minimum data for an analytical determination of the camera orientation. If the orientation of one exposure is known, the orientation of the remaining exposures may be calculated successively by the same equations.

In trimetrogon photography, it is supposed that the orientation of either oblique may be determined with the numerical values of the camera's interior geometry and measurements of the images of the apparent horizons. If the orientation of either oblique exposure is known, the orientation of the overlapping near vertical and the interlocking angle may also be calculated by the equations presented in this section.

2. Derivation.

a. When the principal points are conjugate.

Assume that the orientation of the reference exposure (the exposure to which all other exposures will be referred) has been determined by any means whatsoever. The principal points are located and transferred to their conjugate positions by matching detail. With the orientation data of the reference exposure and coordinates of the second principal point on the reference exposure, the interlocking angle γ_{p_2}, the tilt of the second exposure γ_{z_2}, and the dihedral angle Az between adjacent principal planes are computed.

$$\cos \gamma_{p_2} = \frac{f}{(xp_2^2 + yp_2^2 + f^2)^{1/2}} = \frac{f}{Lp_2}$$

$$\cos \gamma_{z_2} = \cos \alpha_{p_2} \cos \gamma_{x_1} + \cos \beta_{p_2} \cos \gamma_{y_1} + \cos \gamma_{p_2} \cos \gamma_{z_1}$$

where

$$\cos \alpha_{p_2} = \frac{xp_2}{Lp_2}$$

$$\cos \beta_{p_2} = \frac{yp_2}{Lp_2}$$

$$\cos \gamma_{p_2} = \frac{f}{Lp_2}$$

$$\cos \gamma_{x_1} = \sin s_1 \sin t_1$$

$$\cos \gamma_{y_1} = \cos s_1 \ \sin t_1$$

$$\cos \gamma_{z_1} = \cos t_1$$

and swing s_2 follows immediately:

$$s_2 = s^1 \pm \theta$$

where

$$\cos \theta = \frac{\cos \gamma_{z_1} - \cos \gamma_{p_2} \ \cos \gamma_{z_2}}{\sin \gamma_{p_2} \ \sin \gamma_{z_2}}$$

$$\tan s^1 = \frac{xp_1}{yp_1}$$

$$\cos Az^1 = \frac{\cos \gamma_{p_2} - \cos \gamma_{z_1} \ \cos \gamma_{z_2}}{\sin \gamma_{z_1} \ \sin \gamma_{z_2}}$$

These formulae are repeated between exposures 2 and 3, 3 and 4, and so on, until the reference exposure is reached. The angle Az^1 is defined by two adjacent principal planes at the exposure station. The sum of the Az^1 angles is equal to $360° \pm e$ (closure error) around the horizon on terrestrial exposures.

$$Az_{1,2}^1 + Az_{2,3}^1 + \ldots + Az_{n,1}^1 = 360° \pm e$$

b. When the principal points are not conjugate.

Assume as in the previous paragraph that the orientation of the initial exposure has been determined by any means whatsoever. Two conjugate image coordinates are required to determine the orientation of the adjacent exposure. Functions of the zenith angles are computed with the orientation data of the reference exposure and the coordinates of the pair of images on the reference exposure:

$$\cos \gamma_A = \frac{xa^1 \cos \gamma_{x_1} + ya^1 \cos \gamma_{y_1} + f \cos \gamma_{z_1}}{La^1}$$

$$\cos \gamma_B = \frac{xb^1 \cos \gamma_{x_1} + yb^1 \cos \gamma_{y_1} + f \cos \gamma_{z_1}}{Lb^1}$$

where

$$\cos \gamma_{x_1} = \sin s_1 \ \sin t_1$$

$$\cos \gamma_{y_1} = \cos s_1 \ \sin t_1$$

$$\cos \gamma_{z_1} = \cos t_1$$

$$La^1 = (xa^{1^2} + ya^{1^2} + f^2)^{1/2}$$

$$Lb^1 = (xb^{1^2} + yb^{1^2} + f^2)^{1/2}$$

Similarly, the angles subtended by the images *a*, *b*, and the principal point on the adjacent exposure are required:

$$\cos aLb = \cos \alpha_a \ \cos \alpha_b + \cos \beta_a \ \cos \beta_b + \cos \gamma_a \ \cos \gamma_b$$

where

$$\cos \alpha_a = \frac{xa}{La}$$

$$\cos \alpha_b = \frac{xb}{Lb}$$

$$\cos \beta_a = \frac{ya}{La}$$

$$\cos \beta_b = \frac{yb}{Lb}$$

$$\cos \gamma_a = \frac{f}{La}$$

$$\cos \gamma_b = \frac{f}{Lb}$$

$$La = (xa^2 + ya^2 + f^2)^{1/2}$$

$$Lb = (xb^2 + yb^2 + f^2)^{1/2}$$

or

$$\cos aLb = \cos \alpha_A \ \cos \alpha_B + \cos \beta_A \ \cos \beta_B + \cos \gamma_A \ \cos \gamma_B$$

where

$$\cos \alpha_A = \frac{xa^1}{La^1}$$

$$\cos \alpha_B = \frac{xb^1}{Lb^1}$$

$$\cos \beta_A = \frac{ya^1}{La^1}$$

$$\cos \beta_B = \frac{yb^1}{Lb^1}$$

$$\cos \gamma_A = \frac{f}{La^1}$$

$$\cos \gamma_B = \frac{f}{Lb^1}$$

Angles γ_A, γ_B, γ_a, γ_b, and aLb are spherical sides of spherical triangles apb and anb. Spherical angles a_o and b_o are also needed. Angles a_o and b_o are obtained from the relation

$$a_o = a_n - a_f$$

$$b_o = b_n - b_f$$

Angles a_f, a_n, b_f, and b_n are computed with functions of the spherical sides

$$\cos a_f = \frac{\cos \gamma_b - \cos aLb \cos \gamma_a}{\sin aLb \sin \gamma_a}$$

$$\cos a_n = \frac{\cos \gamma_B - \cos aLb \cos \gamma_A}{\sin aLb \sin \gamma_A}$$

$$\cos b_f = \frac{\cos \gamma_a - \cos aLb \cos \gamma_b}{\sin aLb \sin \gamma_b}$$

$$\cos b_n = \frac{\cos \gamma_A - \cos aLb \cos \gamma_B}{\sin aLb \sin \gamma_B}$$

With these functions, tilt, swing, relative azimuth, and the "interlocking" angle or relative tilt are computed with the law of cosines.

$$\cos \gamma_{z_2} = \cos \gamma_A \cos \gamma_a + \sin \gamma_A \sin \gamma_a \cos a_o$$

Also

$$\cos \gamma_{z_2} = \cos \gamma_B \cos \gamma_b + \sin \gamma_B \sin \gamma_b \cos b_o$$

$$\gamma_{z_2} = t_2$$

$$\cos s_a = \frac{\cos \gamma_A - \cos \gamma_{z_2} \cos \gamma_a}{\sin \gamma_{z_2} \sin \gamma_a}$$

$$\cos s_b = \frac{\cos \gamma_B - \cos \gamma_{z_2} \cos \gamma_b}{\sin \gamma_{z_2} \sin \gamma_b}$$

$$\tan \theta_a = \frac{xa}{ya}$$

$$\tan \theta_b = \frac{xb}{yb}$$

$$s_2 = s_a \pm \theta_a = 180° - (s_b \pm \theta_b)$$

$$Az_2 = Az_1 \pm \Delta A$$

where

$$\Delta A = \varphi_{a_2} \pm \varphi_{a_1} = \varphi_{b_2} \pm \varphi_{b_1}$$

$$\cos \varphi_{a_2} = \frac{\cos \gamma_{a_2} - \cos t_2 \cos \gamma_A}{\sin t_2 \sin \gamma_A}$$

$$\cos \varphi_{a_1} = \frac{\cos \gamma_{a_1} - \cos t_1 \cos \gamma_A}{\sin t_1 \sin \gamma_A}$$

$$\cos \varphi_{b_2} = \frac{\cos \gamma_{b_2} - \cos t_2 \cos \gamma_B}{\sin t_2 \sin \gamma_B}$$

$$\cos \varphi_{b_1} = \frac{\cos \gamma_{b_1} - \cos t_1 \cos \gamma_B}{\sin t_1 \sin \gamma_B}$$

and

$$\cos t_{1,2} = \cos t_1 \cos t_2 + \sin t_1 \sin t_2 \cos \Delta A$$

where $t_{1,2}$ is the interlocking angle.

This solution is identical with the solution for computing the elements of angular orientation when the space coordinates are known for the lens and two point-objects on a single exposure, or the object-space direction angles are known for two images on a single exposure. The essential differences are the fact that in this solution the zenith angles are determined from the orientation data of the reference exposure instead of the space coordinates of the lens and the two point-objects, and the fact that no interlocking angle is involved on the single exposure.

The equations, as in the case of the conjugate principal points, are repeated between exposures 2 and 3, 3 and 4, and so on, until the reference exposure is reached. Similarly, ΔA is the dihedral angle between adjacent principal planes. The sum of the ΔA angles is also equal to $360° \pm e$ on terrestrial exposures.

C. *ORIENTATION OF OVERLAPPING EXPOSURES MADE FROM DIFFERENT CAMERA STATIONS* [22].

1. Introduction.

Relative orientation by analytical means has maximum application in photogrammetric control extension. Generally, the absolute orientation of the initial exposure is determined with the space and camera coordinates of three or more imaged objects as the given data. Then the camera coordinates of eight or more images on the initial exposure that are conjugate to the succeeding exposure are mathematically rectified to be collinear with the object-space-coordinate system. The relative orientation of the first and second exposures is then determined with the rectified camera coordinates of eight images on the initial exposure and with the conjugate camera coordinates of eight images on the succeeding exposure. The solved-for direction cosines of the two exposures with respect to each other are combined mathematically to determine the absolute orientation of the second exposure. These data are in turn employed to rectify the coordinates of the second exposure without ground control. Thereafter, rectification, relative orientation, and absolute orientation are repeated from exposure station to exposure station, independent of object-space data, except for that data given at the first camera station.

2. Derivation of Equations for Relative and Absolute Orientation.

The introduction of an arbitrary datum that is parallel to the line connecting the two exposure stations (commonly referred to as the air base) results in the following equality between the η angles of conjugate images:

$$\eta_1 = \eta_2$$

$$\tan \eta_1 = \tan \eta_2$$

where subscripts 1 and 2 denote the first and second exposure stations. The tangent equality provides the basis for the relative orientation equations. The geometry of the arbitrary datum referred to the two exposure stations is illustrated in Figure 38.

With no other restrictions, the rotational angle of the arbitrary datum about the air base may assume any magnitude whatsoever without impairing the equality of η_1 and η_2. To remove this ambiguity, the plane defined by the two exposure stations and the Y axis of the arbitrary datum is made to coincide with the principal point of one of the exposures. This rotational angle is readily imposed by assigning a value of zero to the appropriate direction cosine of one of the exposure stations.

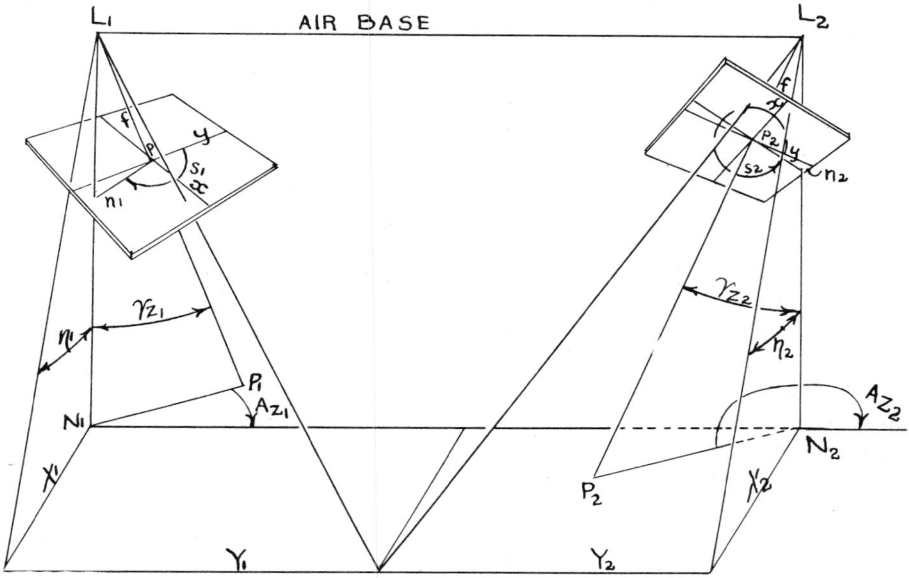

Fig. 38 Relative orientation.

From previous developments, the tangent-η values defined by any arbitrary object-space-coordinate system may be expressed in terms of the corresponding camera coordinates and the appropriate direction cosines.

Initially, the camera coordinates of eight images on the first exposure that are conjugate to the second exposure are rectified with the direction cosines of the first exposure. These direction cosines are determined, by methods described in the previous section, with the aid of ground data and refer to the standard coordinate system.

$$x_1^1 = \left(\frac{x_1 \cos \alpha_{x_1} + y_1 \cos \alpha_{y_1} + f \cos \alpha_{z_1}}{x_1 \cos \gamma_{x_1} + y_1 \cos \gamma_{y_1} + f \cos \gamma_{z_1}} \right) f$$

$$y_1^1 = \left(\frac{x_1 \cos \beta_{x_1} + y_1 \cos \beta_{y_1} + f \cos \beta_{z_1}}{x_1 \cos \gamma_{x_1} + y_1 \cos \gamma_{y_1} + f \cos \gamma_{z_1}} \right) f$$

Then

$$\tan \eta_1 = \frac{x_1^1 \cos \alpha_{x_1}^1 + y_1^1 \cos \alpha_{y_1}^1 + f \cos \alpha_{z_1}^1}{x_1^1 \cos \gamma_{x_1}^1 + y_1^1 \cos \gamma_{y_1}^1 + f \cos \gamma_{z_1}^1}$$

$$\tan \eta_2 = \frac{x_2 \cos \alpha_{x_2}^1 + y_2 \cos \alpha_{y_2}^1 + f \cos \alpha_{z_2}^1}{x_2 \cos \gamma_{x_2}^1 + y_2 \cos \gamma_{y_2}^1 + f \cos \gamma_{z_2}^1}$$

The primed coordinates denote rectified coordinates and the primed direction angles denote direction angles referred to an arbitrary datum.

Since $\tan \eta_1 = \tan \eta_2$,

$$\frac{x_1' \cos \alpha_{x_1}' + y_1' \cos \alpha_{y_1}' + f_1 \cos \alpha_{z_1}'}{x_1' \cos \gamma_{x_1}' + y_1' \cos \gamma_{y_1}' + f_1 \cos \alpha_{z_1}'} = \frac{x_2 \cos \alpha_{x_2}' + y_2 \cos \alpha_{y_2}' + f_2 \cos \alpha_{z_2}'}{x_2 \cos \gamma_{x_2}' + y_2 \cos \gamma_{y_2}' + f_2 \cos \gamma_{z_2}'}$$

Therefore,

$$(x_1' \cos \alpha_{x_1}' + y_1' \cos \alpha_{y_1}' + f_1 \cos \alpha_{z_1}')(x_2 \cos \gamma_{x_2}' + y_2 \cos \gamma_{y_2}' + f_2 \cos \gamma_{z_2}') =$$

$$(x_2 \cos \alpha_{x_2}' + y_2 \cos \alpha_{y_2}' + f_2 \cos \alpha_{z_2}')(x_1' \cos \gamma_{x_1}' + y_1' \cos \gamma_{y_1}' + f_1 \cos \gamma_{z_1}')$$

Generally, $f_1 = f_2$, though not necessarily. Now, to fix the rotational angle of the datum plane, $\cos \alpha z_1'$ is arbitrarily set equal to zero. This effectively makes the azimuth (Az_1) of the first exposure station zero and orients f in the principal plane of the arbitrary datum.
Expanding,

$$x_1' x_2 \cos \alpha_{x_1}' \cos \gamma_{x_2}' + x_1' y_2 \cos \alpha_{x_1}' \cos \gamma_{y_2}' + x_1' f \cos \alpha_{x_1}' \cos \gamma_{z_2}' +$$

$$y_1' x_2 \cos \alpha_{y_1}' \cos \gamma_{x_2}' + y_1' y_2 \cos \alpha_{y_1}' \cos \gamma_{y_2}' + y_1' f \cos \alpha_{y_1}' \cos \gamma_{z_2}' +$$

$$f x_2 \cos \alpha_{z_1}' \cos \gamma_{x_2}' + f y_2 \cos \alpha_{z_1}' \cos \gamma_{y_2}' + f^2 \cos \alpha_{z_1}' \cos \gamma_{z_2}'$$

$$= x_2 x_1' \cos \alpha_{x_2}' \cos \gamma_{x_1}' + x_2 y_1' \cos \alpha_{x_2}' \cos \gamma_{y_1}' + x_2 f \cos \alpha_{x_2}' \cos \gamma_{z_1}' +$$

$$y_2 x_1' \cos \alpha_{y_2}' \cos \gamma_{x_1}' + y_2 y_1' \cos \alpha_{y_2}' \cos \gamma_{y_1}' + y_2 f \cos \alpha_{y_2}' \cos \gamma_{z_1}' +$$

$$f x_1' \cos \alpha_{z_2}' \cos \gamma_{x_1}' + f y_1' \cos \alpha_{z_2}' \cos \gamma_{y_1}' + f^2 \cos \alpha_{z_2}' \cos \gamma_{z_1}'$$

Collecting and letting $\cos \alpha_{z_1} = 0$,

$$+ x_1' x_2 (\cos \alpha_{x_1}' \cos \gamma_{x_2}' - \cos \alpha_{x_2}' \cos \gamma_{x_1}')$$

$$+ y_1' x_2 (\cos \alpha_{y_1}' \cos \gamma_{x_2}' - \cos \alpha_{x_2}' \cos \gamma_{y_1}')$$

$$+ f x_2 (- \cos \alpha_{x_2}' \cos \gamma_{z_1}')$$

$$+ x_1' y_2 (\cos \alpha_{x_1}' \cos \gamma_{y_2}' - \cos \alpha_{y_2}' \cos \gamma_{x_1}')$$

$$+ y_1' y_2 (\cos \alpha_{y_1}' \cos \gamma_{y_2}' - \cos \alpha_{y_2}' \cos \gamma_{y_1}')$$

$$+ f y_2 (- \cos \alpha_{y_2}' \cos \gamma_{z_1}')$$

$$+ x_1' f (\cos \alpha_{x_1}' \cos \gamma_{z_2}' - \cos \alpha_{z_2}' \cos \gamma_{x_1}')$$

$$+ \; y_1^1 \; f \; (\cos \alpha_{y_1}^{\;1} \; \cos \gamma_{z_2}^{\;1} \; - \; \cos \alpha_{z_2}^{\;1} \; \cos \gamma_{y_1}^{\;1})$$

$$+ \quad f^2 \; (- \cos \alpha_{z_2}^{\;1} \; \cos \gamma_{z_1}^{\;1}) \; = \; 0$$

The unknowns are in parentheses. In order to obtain a constant term, let any one of the unknowns be a common devisor m and let the resulting quotients be v, μ, ν, λ, φ, ρ, τ, and ω. Arbitrarily letting $x_1^1 x_2$ be the constant term, a linear equation results:

$$x_1^1 x_2 \; = \; y_1^1 x_2 v \; + \; f x_2 \mu \; + \; x_1^1 y_2 \nu \; + \; y_1^1 y_2 \lambda \; + \; f y_2 \varphi \; + \; x_1^1 f \rho \; + \; y_1^1 f \tau \; + \; f^2 \omega$$

The camera coordinates of eight conjugate images are required to form the coefficients and constant terms of eight linear equations which, solved simultaneously, yield the unknown functions specified above. These functions are further equated for the direction cosines of the X^1 and Z^1 axes of the arbitrary datum (α_x^1, α_y^1, α_z^1, γ_x^1, γ_y^1, γ_z^1) referred to the coordinate axes of the camera stations. Use is made of the fact that the sum of the squares of the direction cosines of a line in space is equal to unity, and that the sum of the products of corresponding direction cosines enclosing a 90° angle is equal to zero. These two geometric properties make it possible to equate directly for m:
Let

$$\Sigma \; = \; (v^2 \; + \; \mu^2 \; + \; \nu^2 \; + \; \lambda^2 + \; \varphi^2 + \; \rho^2 \; + \; \tau^2 \; + \; \omega^2 \; + \; 1) \; = \; \frac{2}{m^2}$$

Then

$$m \; = \sqrt{\frac{2}{\Sigma}}$$

Proof of the equation $\Sigma = 2/m^2$ is seen from examination of the expanded squares of the solved-for functions:

$$1 \; = [\cos^2\alpha_{x_1}^{\;1} \cos^2\gamma_{x_2}^{\;1} + \cos^2\alpha_{x_2}^{\;1} \cos^2\gamma_{x_1}^{\;1} - 2 \cos \alpha_{x_1}^{\;1} \cos \gamma_{x_1}^{\;1} (\cos \alpha_{x_2}^{\;1} \cos \gamma_{x_2}^{\;1})]/m^2$$

$$v^2 = [\cos^2\alpha_{y_1}^{\;1} \cos^2\gamma_{x_2}^{\;1} + \cos^2\alpha_{x_2}^{\;1} \cos^2\gamma_{y_1}^{\;1} - 2 \cos \alpha_{y_1}^{\;1} \cos \gamma_{y_1}^{\;1} (\cos \alpha_{x_2}^{\;1} \cos \gamma_{x_2}^{\;1})]/m^2$$

$$\mu^2 = [\cos^2\alpha_{z_1}^{\;1} \cos^2\gamma_{x_2}^{\;1} + \cos^2\alpha_{x_2}^{\;1} \cos^2\gamma_{z_1}^{\;1} - 2 \cos \alpha_{z_1}^{\;1} \cos \gamma_{z_1}^{\;1} (\cos \alpha_{x_2}^{\;1} \cos \gamma_{x_2}^{\;1})]/m^2$$

$$\nu^2 = [\cos^2\alpha_{x_1}^{\;1} \cos^2\gamma_{y_2}^{\;1} + \cos^2\alpha_{y_2}^{\;1} \cos^2\gamma_{x_1}^{\;1} - 2 \cos \alpha_{x_1}^{\;1} \cos \gamma_{x_1}^{\;1} (\cos \alpha_{y_2}^{\;1} \cos \gamma_{y_2}^{\;1})]/m^2$$

$$\lambda^2 = [\cos^2\alpha_{y_1}^{\;1} \cos^2\gamma_{y_2}^{\;1} + \cos^2\alpha_{y_2}^{\;1} \cos^2\gamma_{y_1}^{\;1} - 2 \cos \alpha_{y_1}^{\;1} \cos \gamma_{y_1}^{\;1} (\cos \alpha_{y_2}^{\;1} \cos \gamma_{y_2}^{\;1})]/m^2$$

$$\varphi^2 = [\cos^2\alpha_{z_1}^{\;1} \cos^2\gamma_{y_2}^{\;1} + \cos^2\alpha_{y_2}^{\;1} \cos^2\gamma_{z_1}^{\;1} - 2 \cos \alpha_{z_1}^{\;1} \cos \gamma_{z_1}^{\;1} (\cos \alpha_{y_2}^{\;1} \cos \gamma_{y_2}^{\;1})]/m^2$$

$$\rho^2 = [\cos^2\alpha_{x_1}^{\;1} \cos^2\gamma_{z_2}^{\;1} + \cos^2\alpha_{z_2}^{\;1} \cos^2\gamma_{x_1}^{\;1} - 2 \cos \alpha_{x_1}^{\;1} \cos \gamma_{x_1}^{\;1} (\cos \alpha_{z_2}^{\;1} \cos \gamma_{z_2}^{\;1})]/m^2$$

$$\tau^2 = [\cos^2\alpha_{y_1}{}^1 \cos^2\gamma_{z_2}{}^1 + \cos^2\alpha_{z_2}{}^1 \cos^2\gamma_{y_1}{}^1 - 2\cos\alpha_{y_1}{}^1 \cos\gamma_{y_1}{}^1 (\cos\alpha_{z_2}{}^1 \cos\gamma_{z_2}{}^1)]/m^2$$

$$\omega^2 = [\cos^2\alpha_{z_1}{}^1 \cos^2\gamma_{z_2}{}^1 + \cos^2\alpha_{z_2}{}^1 \cos^2\gamma_{z_1}{}^1 - 2\cos\alpha_{z_1}{}^1 \cos\gamma_{z_1}{}^1 (\cos\alpha_{z_2}{}^1 \cos\gamma_{z_2}{}^1)]/m^2$$

The sum of the first and second columns is equal to 2 divided by m^2, while the sum of the third column is equal to zero. Equally obvious are the following identities:

$$m^2(\mu^2 + \varphi^2 + \omega^2) = \cos^2\gamma_{z_1}{}^1$$

$$\frac{m\,\mu}{\cos\gamma_{z_1}{}^1} = \cos\alpha_{z_2}{}^1$$

$$\frac{m\,\varphi}{\cos\gamma_{z_1}{}^1} = \cos\alpha_{x_2}{}^1$$

$$\frac{m\,\omega}{\cos\gamma_{z_1}{}^1} = \cos\alpha_{z_2}{}^1$$

$$m^2(1 + v^2 + \mu^2) - \cos^2\alpha_{x_2}{}^1 = \cos^2\gamma_{x_2}{}^1$$

$$m^2(\nu^2 + \lambda^2 + \varphi^2) - \cos^2\alpha_{y_2}{}^1 = \cos^2\gamma_{y_2}{}^1$$

$$m^2(\rho^2 + \tau^2 + \omega^2) - \cos^2\alpha_{z_2}{}^1 = \cos^2\gamma_{z_2}{}^1$$

$$1 - m^2(1 + v^2 + \mu^2) = \cos^2\beta_{x_2}{}^1$$

$$1 - m^2(\nu^2 + \lambda^2 + \varphi^2) = \cos^2\beta_{y_2}{}^1$$

$$1 - m^2(\rho^2 + \tau^2 + \omega^2) = \cos^2\beta_{z_2}{}^1$$

This completes the relative direction cosines of the second exposure. $\cos\gamma_{z_1}{}^1$ has been determined and $\cos\alpha_{z_1}{}^1$ is zero. With a similar application of the sum-of-the-squares property we obtain:

$$1 - m^2(1 + \nu^2 + \rho^2) = \cos^2\beta_{x_1}{}^1$$

$$1 - m^2(v^2 + \lambda^2 + \tau^2) = \cos^2\beta_{y_1}{}^1$$

$$1 - m^2(\mu^2 + \varphi^2 + \omega^2) = \cos^2\beta_{z_1}{}^1$$

and then when $\cos\alpha_{z_1}{}^1 = 0$,

$$\cos\alpha_{x_1}{}^1 = \frac{\cos\beta_{y_1}{}^1}{\cos\gamma_{z_1}{}^1}$$

$$\cos \alpha_{y_1}{}^1 = \frac{\cos \beta_{x_1}{}^1}{\cos \gamma_{z_1}{}^1}$$

$$\cos \alpha_{z_1}{}^1 = 0$$

$$\cos \gamma_{x_1}{}^1 = \cos \alpha_{y_1}{}^1 \cos \beta_{z_1}{}^1$$

$$\cos \gamma_{y_1}{}^1 = \cos \alpha_{x_1}{}^1 \cos \beta_{z_1}{}^1$$

$$\cos \gamma_{z_1}{}^1 = \cos \gamma_{z_1}{}^1 \text{ (already determined)}$$

and this completes the relative direction cosines of the first exposure. Check for computational errors may be made by substitution of all combinations in the unity- and zero-direction-cosine equations.

The rectified camera coordinates are collinear with the object-space standard coordinate system. Therefore, the angles enclosed between each axis of the rectified system and each axis of the unrectified system are the direction angles of the second exposure (unrectified system) with respect to the standard or geodetic coordinate system. Thus, the nine relative direction cosines of each exposure are combined mathematically to determine the nine direction cosines of the leading exposure referred to the standard or geodetic coordinate system.

$$\cos \alpha_{x_2} = \cos \alpha_{x_1}{}^1 \cos \alpha_{x_2}{}^1 + \cos \beta_{x_1}{}^1 \cos \beta_{x_2}{}^1 + \cos \gamma_{x_1}{}^1 \cos \gamma_{x_2}{}^1$$

$$\cos \alpha_{y_2} = \cos \alpha_{x_1}{}^1 \cos \alpha_{y_2}{}^1 + \cos \beta_{x_1}{}^1 \cos \beta_{y_2}{}^1 + \cos \gamma_{x_1}{}^1 \cos \gamma_{y_2}{}^1$$

$$\cos \alpha_{z_2} = \cos \alpha_{x_1}{}^1 \cos \alpha_{z_2}{}^1 + \cos \beta_{x_1}{}^1 \cos \beta_{z_2}{}^1 + \cos \gamma_{x_1}{}^1 \cos \gamma_{z_2}{}^1$$

$$\cos \beta_{x_2} = \cos \alpha_{y_1}{}^1 \cos \alpha_{x_2}{}^1 + \cos \beta_{y_1}{}^1 \cos \beta_{x_2}{}^1 + \cos \gamma_{y_1}{}^1 \cos \gamma_{x_2}{}^1$$

$$\cos \beta_{y_2} = \cos \alpha_{y_1}{}^1 \cos \alpha_{y_2}{}^1 + \cos \beta_{y_1}{}^1 \cos \beta_{y_2}{}^1 + \cos \gamma_{y_1}{}^1 \cos \gamma_{y_2}{}^1$$

$$\cos \beta_{z_2} = \cos \alpha_{y_1}{}^1 \cos \alpha_{z_2}{}^1 + \cos \beta_{y_1}{}^1 \cos \beta_{z_2}{}^1 + \cos \gamma_{y_1}{}^1 \cos \gamma_{z_2}{}^1$$

$$\cos \gamma_{x_2} = 0 + \cos \beta_{z_1}{}^1 \cos \beta_{x_2}{}^1 + \cos \gamma_{z_1}{}^1 \cos \gamma_{x_2}{}^1$$

$$\cos \gamma_{y_2} = 0 + \cos \beta_{z_1}{}^1 \cos \beta_{y_2}{}^1 + \cos \gamma_{z_1}{}^1 \cos \gamma_{y_2}{}^1$$

$$\cos \gamma_{z_2} = 0 + \cos \beta_{z_1}{}^1 \cos \beta_{z_2}{}^1 + \cos \gamma_{z_1}{}^1 \cos \gamma_{z_2}{}^1$$

With these direction cosines, eight images on exposure two which are conjugate to exposure three are rectified:

$$x_2{}^1 = \left(\frac{x_2 \cos \alpha_{x_2} + y_2 \cos \alpha_{y_2} + f \cos \alpha_{z_2}}{x_2 \cos \gamma_{x_2} + y_2 \cos \gamma_{y_2} + f \cos \gamma_{z_2}} \right) f$$

$$y_2{}^1 = \left(\frac{x_2 \cos \beta_{x_2} + y_2 \cos \beta_{y_2} + f \cos \beta_{z_2}}{x_2 \cos \gamma_{x_2} + y_2 \cos \gamma_{y_2} + f \cos \gamma_{z_2}} \right) f$$

These rectified coordinates are combined with the unrectified coordinates of exposure three to form relative orientation equations of exposures two and three. The procedure of rectification, relative orientation, and absolute orientation is continued from overlap to overlap, without recourse to object-space control other than that employed to determine the space coordinates and absolute orientation of the first exposure.

3. Alternate Solution to Absolute Orientation of Overlapping Exposures.

Assume that the direction cosines of the initial exposure have been computed directly with functions of tilt, swing, and azimuth. The absolute direction cosines of the adjacent exposure are required. Five conjugate images are selected for definition and geometric distribution only; they require no ground control. The five images on exposure one are rectified to be collinear with the survey coordinates.

$$xa_1{}^1 = \left(\frac{xa_1 \cos \alpha_{x_1} + ya_1 \cos \alpha_{y_1} + f \cos \alpha_{z_1}}{xa_1 \cos \gamma_{x_1} + ya_1 \cos \gamma_{y_1} + f \cos \gamma_{z_1}} \right) f$$

$$xb_1{}^1 = \left(\frac{xb_1 \cos \alpha_{x_1} + yb_1 \cos \alpha_{y_1} + f \cos \alpha_{z_1}}{xb_1 \cos \gamma_{x_1} + yb_1 \cos \gamma_{y_1} + f \cos \gamma_{z_1}} \right) f$$

. . . .

$$xe_1{}^1 = \left(\frac{xe_1 \cos \alpha_{x_1} + ye_1 \cos \alpha_{y_1} + f \cos \alpha_{z_1}}{xe_1 \cos \gamma_{x_1} + ye_1 \cos \gamma_{y_1} + f \cos \gamma_{z_1}} \right) f$$

where, as before, the primes denote rectification, the lower case letters denote images, and the numerical subscripts denote exposures. The direction cosines are functions of the angular orientation of the first exposure and are known. Now

$$\tan \eta_1 = \tan \eta_2$$

but these refer to an arbitrary system of coordinates and therefore yield arbitrary direction cosines as demonstrated in the first derivation. Furthermore,

$$\tan \eta_1{}^1 \neq \tan \eta_2{}^1$$

where

$$\tan \eta_1{}^1 = \frac{x_1{}^1}{f}$$

$$\tan \eta_2{}^1 = \frac{x_2 \cos \alpha_{x_2} + y_2 \cos \alpha_{y_2} + f \cos \alpha_{z_2}}{x_2 \cos \gamma_{x_2} + y_2 \cos \gamma_{y_2} + f \cos \gamma_{z_2}}$$

But if a constant, K_x, is subtracted from x^1, and f is modified by another constant, K_z,

$$\frac{x_1{}^1 - K_x}{K_z} = \tan \eta_1{}^{11} \equiv \tan \eta_2{}^1$$

Therefore,

$$\frac{x_1{}^1 - K_x}{K_z} = \frac{x_2 \cos \alpha_{x_2} + y_2 \cos \alpha_{y_2} + f \cos \alpha_{z_2}}{x_2 \cos \gamma_{x_2} + y_2 \cos \gamma_{y_2} + f \cos \gamma_{z_2}}$$

The unknowns are the absolute direction cosines of exposure two and the constants K_x and K_z. Cross-multiplying,

$$x_1{}^1 x_2 \cos \gamma_{x_2} + x_1{}^1 y_2 \cos \gamma_{y_2} + x_1{}^1 f \cos \gamma_{z_2}$$

$$- x_2(K_x \cos \gamma_{x_2}) - y_2(K_x \cos \gamma_{y_2}) - f(K_x \cos \gamma_{z_2})$$

$$= x_2(K_z \cos \alpha_{x_2}) + y_2(K_z \cos \alpha_{y_2}) + f(K_z \cos \alpha_{z_2})$$

Collecting unknowns of common coefficients,

$$x_1{}^1 x_2 (\cos \gamma_{x_2}) + x_1{}^1 y_2 (\cos \gamma_{y_2}) + x_1{}^1 f (\cos \gamma_{z_2})$$

$$- x_2 (K_x \cos \gamma_{x_2} + K_z \cos \alpha_{x_2}) - y_2 (K_x \cos \gamma_{y_2} + K_z \cos \alpha_{y_2})$$

$$- f (K_x \cos \gamma_{z_2} + K_z \cos \alpha_{z_2}) = 0$$

Division by $(K_x \cos \gamma_{x_2} + K_z \cos \alpha_{x_2})$ yields five linear equations of the form

$$xa_1{}^1 xa_2 (v) + xa_1{}^1 ya_2 (\mu) + xa_1{}^1 f(\nu) - ya_2(m) - f(n) = xa_2$$

$$xb_1{}^1 xb_2 (v) + xb_1{}^1 yb_2 (\mu) + xb_1{}^1 f(\nu) - yb_2(m) - f(n) = xb_2$$

. . . .

$$xe_1{}^1 xe_2 (v) + xe_1{}^1 ye_2 (\mu) + xe_1{}^1 f(\nu) - ye_2(m) - f(n) = xe_2$$

where

$$v = \frac{\cos \gamma_{x_2}}{L}$$

$$\mu = \frac{\cos \gamma_{y_2}}{L}$$

$$\nu = \frac{\cos \gamma_{z_2}}{L}$$

$$m = \frac{K_x \cos \gamma_{y_2} + K_z \cos \alpha_{y_2}}{L}$$

$$n = \frac{K_x \cos \gamma_{z_2} + K_z \cos \alpha_{z_2}}{L}$$

and

$$L = K_x \cos \gamma_{x_2} + K_z \cos \alpha_{x_2}$$

Simultaneous solution of these five equations yields the above unknowns. Then

$$L = \frac{1}{(v^2 + \mu^2 + \nu^2)^{1/2}}$$

$$\cos \gamma_{x_2} = v \cdot L$$

$$\cos \gamma_{y_2} = \mu \cdot L$$

$$\cos \gamma_{z_2} = \nu \cdot L$$

$$K_x = (v + m\mu + n\nu)L^2$$

$$K_z = [(m^2 + n^2 + 1)L^2 - K_x^2]^{1/2}$$

$$\cos \alpha_{x_2} = \frac{L - K_x \cos \gamma_{x_2}}{K_z}$$

$$\cos \alpha_{y_2} = \frac{Lm - K_x \cos \gamma_{y_2}}{K_z}$$

$$\cos \alpha_{z_2} = \frac{Ln - K_x \cos \gamma_{z_2}}{K_z}$$

Also

$$\cos \beta_{x_2} = (1 - \cos^2\alpha_{x_2} - \cos^2\gamma_{x_2})^{1/2}$$

$$\cos \beta_{y_2} = (1 - \cos^2\alpha_{y_2} - \cos^2\gamma_{y_2})^{1/2}$$

$$\cos \beta_{z_2} = (1 - \cos^2\alpha_{z_2} - \cos^2\gamma_{z_2})^{1/2}$$

which are the nine direction cosines of the second exposure obtained directly with only five images and without subsequent reductions.

A similar expression could have been written for the y^1 values:

$$\frac{y_1^1 + K_y}{K_z} = \frac{x_2 \cos \beta_{x_2} + y_2 \cos \beta_{y_2} + f \cos \beta_{z_2}}{x_2 \cos \gamma_{x_2} + y_2 \cos \gamma_{y_2} + f \cos \gamma_{z_2}}$$

where K_y is the constant of y^1 and K_z is the same as before.

$$y_1^1 = \left(\frac{x_1 \cos \beta_{x_1} + y_1 \cos \beta_{y_1} + f \cos \beta_{z_1}}{x_1 \cos \gamma_{x_1} + y_1 \cos \gamma_{y_1} + f \cos \gamma_{z_1}} \right) f$$

The solution is the same, except the α functions and β functions are interchanged. The previous solution not employing K_x, K_y, or K_z involved the solution of eight simultaneous equations for the relative direction cosines. These values were later combined with the absolute direction cosines of the first exposure to obtain the absolute direction cosines of the second exposure. The former solution involves eight sets of data and two distinct computational operations to determine the absolute orientation of the second exposure. The alternate solution determines the absolute orientation of the second exposure with five sets of data in one operation.

D. *SPACE COORDINATES OF UNKNOWN POINTS* [23].

1. General.

Determination of the space coordinates of images beyond the initial exposure resolves into two similar computations. The first computation is the determination of the space coordinates of the second exposure with the camera coordinates of two images, the direction cosines of the second exposure, and the corresponding space coordinates of control points common to both.

The second computation is the determination of new space coordinates on exposure two which are common to exposures one, two, and three.

Thereafter, the operation is repeated from overlapping station to overlapping station until the last exposure is reached. It is clear that the exposures must overlap approximately 60 percent, plus or minus 5 percent, to provide an area of imagery that is common to three exposures, or a trilap. Aside from the accuracy of results obtained with geometric distribution of images, very little overlap is required for the relative orientation equation. A closure error is generally present if the end exposure has ground control which has been predetermined. The photogrammetrically established control may be adjusted to reduce the closure error to zero. This may be done with several adjustment equations, the most practical of which is a quadratic in X, Y, and Z set equal to the corresponding closure error (ΔX, ΔY, and ΔZ).

2. Space Coordinates of Leading Exposure.

The leading exposure is taken to be the exposure immediately adjacent to the exposure whose space coordinates are known, and which has ground control common to both exposures. Assume control points A and B are imaged (a_2, b_2) on exposure two. The standard tangent functions referred to the object-space-coordinate system are computed with the camera coordinates of a_2 and b_2 and the direction cosines of exposure two.

$$\tan \eta_{a_2} = \frac{xa_2 \cos \alpha_{x_2} + ya_2 \cos \alpha_{y_2} + f \cos \alpha_{z_2}}{xa_2 \cos \gamma_{x_2} + ya_2 \cos \gamma_{y_2} + f \cos \gamma_{z_2}}$$

$$\tan \eta_{b_2} = \frac{xb_2 \cos \alpha_{x_2} + yb_2 \cos \alpha_{y_2} + f \cos \alpha_{z_2}}{xb_2 \cos \gamma_{x_2} + yb_2 \cos \gamma_{y_2} + f \cos \gamma_{z_2}}$$

$$\tan \xi_{a_2} = \frac{xa_2 \cos \beta_{x_2} + ya_2 \cos \beta_{y_2} + f \cos \beta_{z_2}}{xa_2 \cos \gamma_{x_2} + ya_2 \cos \gamma_{y_2} + f \cos \gamma_{z_2}}$$

$$\tan \xi_{b_2} = \frac{xb_2 \cos \beta_{x_2} + yb_2 \cos \beta_{y_2} + f \cos \beta_{z_2}}{xb_2 \cos \gamma_{x_2} + yb_2 \cos \gamma_{y_2} + f \cos \gamma_{z_2}}$$

Then, since tangent functions are directed line segments of object space coordinates,

$$\tan \eta = \frac{X - XL}{Z - ZL}$$

$$\tan \xi = \frac{Y - YL}{Z - ZL}$$

or

$$XL_2 - \tan \eta_{a_2} \; ZL_2 = (XA - \tan \eta_{a_2} \; ZA)$$

$$XL_2 - \tan \eta_{b_2} \; ZL_2 = (XB - \tan \eta_{b_2} \; ZB)$$

$$YL_2 - \tan \xi_{a_2} \; ZL_2 = (YA - \tan \xi_{a_2} \; ZA)$$

$$YL_2 - \tan \xi_{b_2} \; ZL_2 = (YB - \tan \xi_{b_2} \; ZB)$$

or

$$XL_2 - \tan\theta_{a_2} \; YL_2 = (XA - \tan\theta_{a_2} \; YA)$$

$$XL_2 - \tan\theta_{b_2} \; YL_2 = (XB - \tan\theta_{b_2} \; YB)$$

where

$$\tan\theta = \frac{\tan\eta}{\tan\xi}$$

The unknowns are XL_2, YL_2, and ZL_2. Solution of any pair gives two of the space coordinates of the lens, whereby the third coordinate may be obtained by substitution of one of the solved-for unknowns in the appropriate remaining pair.

3. Space Coordinates of New Points.

The space coordinates of points imaged in the area of trilap of exposures one, two, and three are determined with intersection equations employing the direction cosines and space coordinates of exposures one and two. Two control points are the number necessary to determine subsequently the space coordinates of exposure three. Each control point is determined in the same manner. Consider one point, say *C*.

$$\tan\eta_{c_1} = \frac{xc_1 \cos\alpha_{x_1} + yc_1 \cos\alpha_{y_1} + f \cos\alpha_{z_1}}{xc_1 \cos\gamma_{x_1} + yc_1 \cos\gamma_{y_1} + f \cos\gamma_{z_1}}$$

$$\tan\eta_{c_2} = \frac{xc_2 \cos\alpha_{x_2} + yc_2 \cos\alpha_{y_2} + f \cos\alpha_{z_2}}{xc_2 \cos\gamma_{x_2} + yc_2 \cos\gamma_{y_2} + f \cos\gamma_{z_2}}$$

$$\tan\xi_{c_1} = \frac{xc_1 \cos\beta_{x_1} + yc_1 \cos\beta_{y_1} + f \cos\beta_{z_1}}{xc_1 \cos\gamma_{x_1} + yc_1 \cos\gamma_{y_1} + f \cos\gamma_{z_1}}$$

$$\tan\xi_{c_2} = \frac{xc_2 \cos\beta_{x_2} + yc_2 \cos\beta_{y_2} + f \cos\beta_{z_2}}{xc_2 \cos\gamma_{x_2} + yc_2 \cos\gamma_{y_2} + f \cos\gamma_{z_2}}$$

Then, as before,

$$XC - \tan\eta_{c_1} \; ZC = (XL_1 - \tan\eta_{c_1} \; ZL_1)$$

$$XC - \tan\eta_{c_2} \; ZC = (XL_2 - \tan\eta_{c_2} \; ZL_2)$$

$$YC - \tan\xi_{c_1} \; ZC = (YL_1 - \tan\xi_{c_1} \; ZL_1)$$

$$YC - \tan\xi_{c_2} \; ZC = (YL_2 - \tan\xi_{c_2} \; ZL_2)$$

$$XC - \tan\theta_{c_1}\ YC = (XL_1 - \tan\theta_{c_1}\ YL_1)$$

$$XC - \tan\theta_{c_2}\ YC = (XL_2 - \tan\theta_{c_2}\ YL_2)$$

These equations are identical to the previous equations, except that the unknowns in the previous equations are constant terms in these, and conversely. Equations of this form are solved for each point. The basic procedure of determining the space coordinates of the leading camera station followed by the determination of new points is repeated until the end exposure is reached.

E. *NUMERICAL EXAMPLE OF RELATIVE AND ABSOLUTE ORIENTATION EQUATIONS.*

1. Rectification of Image Coordinates on the First Exposure with Direction Cosines of the First Exposure.

For example,

$$xd_1^{\,1} = \left(\frac{xd_1 \cos\alpha_{x_1} + yd_1 \cos\alpha_{y_1} + f \cos\alpha_{z_1}}{xd_1 \cos\gamma_{x_1} + yd_1 \cos\gamma_{y_1} + f \cos\gamma_{z_1}}\right) f = -63.957$$

The rectified coordinates on the first exposure and the unrectified coordinates on the second exposure of eight conjugate points are employed.

Image Coordinates

	Exposure I Rectified coordinates		Exposure II Original coordinates	
	$x_1^{\,1}$	$y_1^{\,1}$	x_2	y_2
d	- 63.957	- 79.322	- 86.920	- 45.633
e	- 18.716	+ 1.594	+ 3.338	- 67.735
f	- 5.972	+ 79.806	+ 81.335	- 60.731
g	- 31.655	- 46.883	- 46.698	- 68.259
h	- 124.900	- 66.836	- 91.713	+ 18.570
i	- 108.174	- 18.319	- 38.942	+ 8.584
j	- 65.165	+ 37.984	+ 26.196	- 10.876
k	- 61.024	+ 81.020	+ 68.721	- 4.423

$f = 152.000$

2. Relative Orientation Equations.

Eight relative orientation equations are formed, and solved simultaneously.

$$(f^2\omega) + yd_1{}^1 xd_2(v) + xd_2(f\mu) + xd_1{}^1 yd_2(\nu) + yd_1{}^1 yd_2(\lambda) + yd_2(f\varphi) + xd_1{}^1(f\rho) + yd_1{}^1 (f\tau) = xd_1{}^1 xd_2$$

$$(f^2\omega) + ye_1{}^1 xe_2(v) + xe_2(f\mu) + xe_1{}^1 ye_2(\nu) + ye_1{}^1 ye_2(\lambda) + ye_2(f\varphi) + xe_1{}^1(f\rho) + ye_1{}^1 (f\tau) = xe_1{}^1 xe_2$$

. . . .

$$(f^2\omega) + yk_1{}^1 xk_2(v) + xk_2(f\mu) + xk_1{}^1 yk_2(\nu) + yk_1{}^1 yk_2(\lambda) + yk_2(f\varphi) + xk_1{}^1(f\rho) + yk_1{}^1 (f\tau) = xk_1{}^1 xk_2$$

Solving the equations for $(f^2\omega)$, (v), $(f\mu)$, (ν), (λ), $(f\varphi)$, $(f\rho)$, and $(f\tau)$,

$$\omega = \frac{f^2\omega}{f^2} \qquad \mu = \frac{f\mu}{f} \qquad \varphi = \frac{f\varphi}{f} \qquad \rho = \frac{f\rho}{f} \qquad \tau = \frac{f\tau}{f}$$

and

$$m = \sqrt{\frac{2}{\Sigma}}$$

where

$$\Sigma = (v^2 + \mu^2 + \nu^2 + \lambda^2 + \varphi^2 + \rho^2 + \tau^2 + \omega^2 + 1)$$

3. Relative Direction Cosines.

The relative direction cosines of exposures one and two are determined with the equations shown in section C.2. of this chapter.

Relative Orientation of Exposures I and II

$$\cos \alpha_{x_1}{}^1 = +0.16494428 \qquad \cos \alpha_{x_2}{}^1 = +0.99530589$$

$$\cos \alpha_{y_1}{}^1 = +0.98630289 \qquad \cos \alpha_{y_2}{}^1 = +0.09613955$$

$$\cos \alpha_{z_1}{}^1 = 0 \qquad \cos \alpha_{z_2}{}^1 = +0.01110732$$

$$\cos \beta_{x_1}{}^1 = -0.98615739 \qquad \cos \beta_{x_2}{}^1 = -0.09606468$$

$$\cos \beta_{y_1}{}^1 = +0.16491995 \qquad \cos \beta_{y_2}{}^1 = +0.99534965$$

$$\cos \beta_{z_1}{}^1 = +0.01717615 \qquad \cos \beta_{z_2}{}^1 = -0.00709000$$

$\cos \gamma_{x_1}{}^1 = +0.01694089$ $\cos \gamma_{x_2}{}^1 = -0.01140280$

$\cos \gamma_{y_1}{}^1 = -0.00283311$ $\cos \gamma_{y_2}{}^1 = +0.00602200$

$\cos \gamma_{z_1}{}^1 = +0.99985248$ $\cos \gamma_{z_2}{}^1 = +0.99991685$

4. Absolute Direction Cosines of the Second Exposure.

The absolute direction cosines of the second exposure are determined with the equations also shown in section C.2.

Absolute Orientation of Second Exposure

$$\cos \alpha_{x_2} = +0.24871173$$

$$\cos \alpha_{y_2} = -0.96561173$$

$$\cos \alpha_{z_2} = +0.02576343$$

$$\cos \beta_{x_2} = +0.96586240$$

$$\cos \beta_{y_2} = +0.25895867$$

$$\cos \beta_{z_2} = +0.00695302$$

$$\cos \gamma_{x_2} = -0.01305114$$

$$\cos \gamma_{y_2} = +0.02311739$$

$$\cos \gamma_{z_2} = +0.99964756$$

Chapter VI

PHOTOGRAMMETRICALLY DEFINED OBJECT-SPACE WITHOUT OBJECT-SPACE CONTROL POINTS

The analytical equations developed thus far are based on the premise that none of the elements of exterior orientation are recorded instrumentally. Both the determination of exterior orientation and reciprocal orientation are substantially simplified when some of the elements are determined instrumentally or recorded automatically.

The most common example of simplification of data reduction is seen in terrestrial exposures made with goniometric cameras from known exposure stations. The elements of angular orientation are read or recorded automatically on graduated circles that are an integral part of the goniometric camera. The data reduction is reduced to simple transformations and space-intersection equations when the six elements of orientation are known.

The stable platform of a terrestrial exposure makes it practical for the elements of exterior orientation to be measured directly or recorded automatically.

The unstable platform of an airborne exposure makes it impractical for the elements of exterior orientation to be measured directly, at least, by the same method. Various types of airborne instrumentation have been developed to provide some of the equivalent elements of exterior orientation. The reason for the development of airborne instruments for this purpose is to:

(1) simplify the data reduction, but more important to

(2) provide a means of metrically defining a surface or a phenomenon with respect to dimension, position, and orientation where no object-space control is identifiable or may be established.

To emphasize the true significance of the second objective, the bulk of the object space cannot be photogrammetrically defined, for the lack of object-space control, without automatic instrumentation.

The following airborne instrumentation has been employed to provide various elements of exterior orientation at the moment of exposure:

(1) Horizon cameras.
(2) High-oblique cameras.
(3) Star zenith cameras.

(4) Sun zenith cameras.
(5) Statoscopes.
(6) Profile recorders.
(7) Radio altimeters.
(8) Gyro-stabilized cameras.
(9) Shoran.

No one of these airborne instruments frees the exposure camera from object-space control.

The horizon camera, oblique camera, star zenith camera, sun zenith camera, and gyro provide elements of angular orientation, while altimetric devices and shoran provide dimensional elements of exterior orientation. Strictly speaking, only altimetric devices provide truly airborne dimensional data inasmuch as the shoran data is a combination of airborne instrumentation and ground instrumentation located at known points.

In order to define object space with respect to position, orientation, and dimension, without recourse to ground control, airborne instrumentation is required that is capable of providing a dimension, position, and/or angular orientation data.

Of the instruments listed, the first four, the auxiliary orientation cameras, are photogrammetric in nature. They are briefly defined and described in the succeeding paragraphs. This means the auxiliary orientation cameras. The simplification in data reduction when any of these devices is employed will be demonstrated. A system for defining object space with respect to dimension, position, and orientation, without ground control, will be outlined in terms of a combination of the devices listed and the necessary equations related to reduction of data with the combination outlined.

A. *AUXILIARY ORIENTATION CAMERAS.*

1. Horizon Cameras [24].

A horizon camera is oriented to image the apparent horizon, the measurements of which provide data for a direct determination of the tilt and swing of the nadir camera. The nadir camera photographs terrain, while the horizon camera photographs only the apparent horizon.

This method of aerial surveying has been employed for over 20 years in Finland. The Finns employ two horizon cameras considerably smaller than the nadir camera. The two cameras, with their optical axes approximately collinear with the x and y fiducial axes of the nadir camera, are rigidly interlocked and tripped synchronously. From measurements made on images of the horizon the tilt and swing can be computed in duplicate without ground control. There are two possible arrangements for x and y cameras: one arrangement images the x and y horizon on the border of the nadir exposure while the other images the x and y horizon and the terrain on three distinct exposures. The former attached arrangement and the latter detached arrangement are shown in Figure 39.

The detached camera is less desirable in that three separate pictures result for each exposure. It is sometimes difficult to correlate the three pictures for each exposure station.

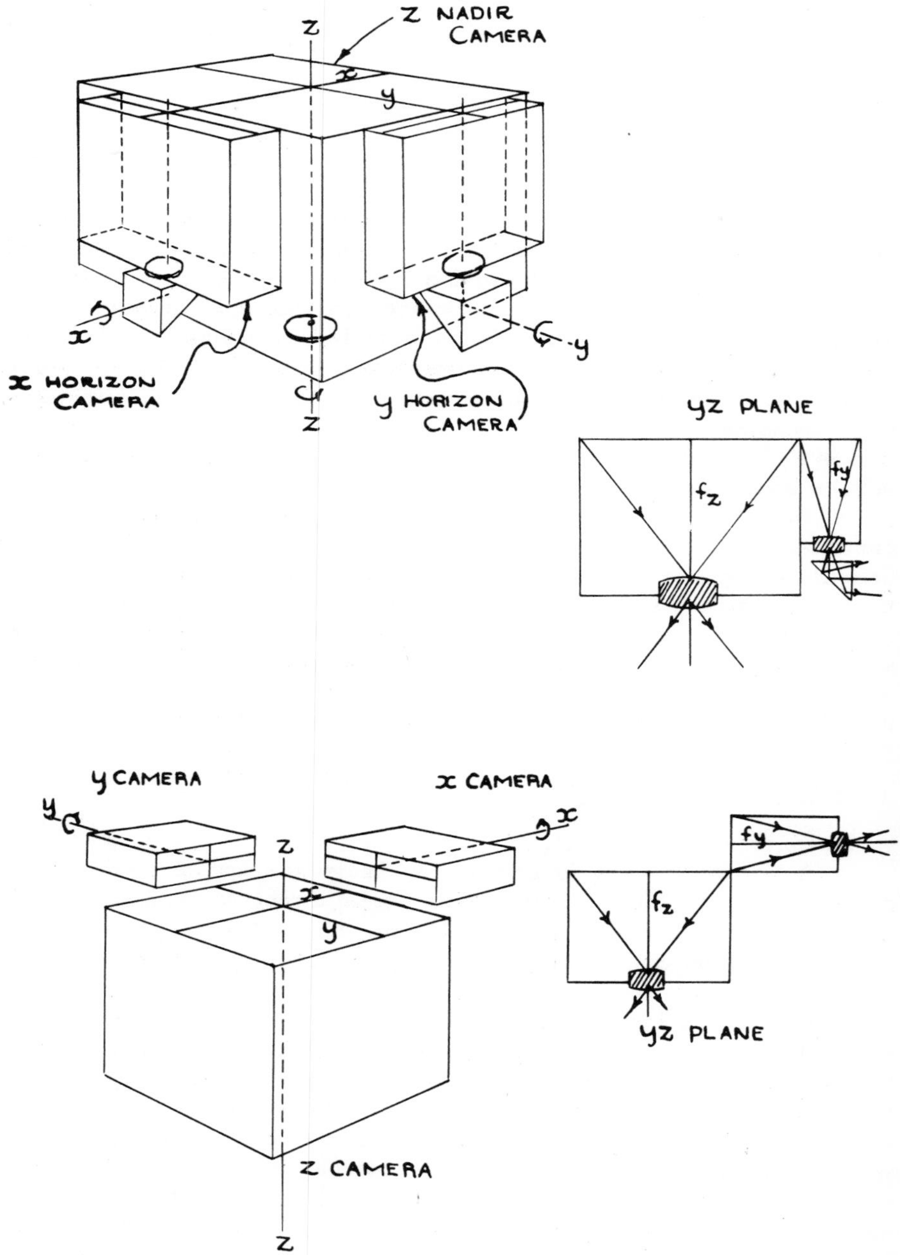

Fig. 39 Detached horizon cameras.

a. Tilt and swing with two horizon cameras.

The components of tilt uncorrected for the dip of the horizon (Δ) are computed with simple formulae:

$$\tan t_x^1 = \frac{v_x}{f_x} \qquad \tan t_y^1 = \frac{v_y}{f_y}$$

where v_x and v_y are the perpendicular distances from the x and y camera principal points to the apparent horizons, and f_x and f_y are the corresponding focal lengths. The tilt and swing are computed with sine functions of the components of tilt corrected for the dip (Δ) of the apparent horizon:

$$\tan t = (\sin^2 t_x + \sin^2 t_y)^{1/2}$$

$$\tan s = \frac{\sin t_x}{\sin t_y}$$

These equations are illustrated in Figure 40.

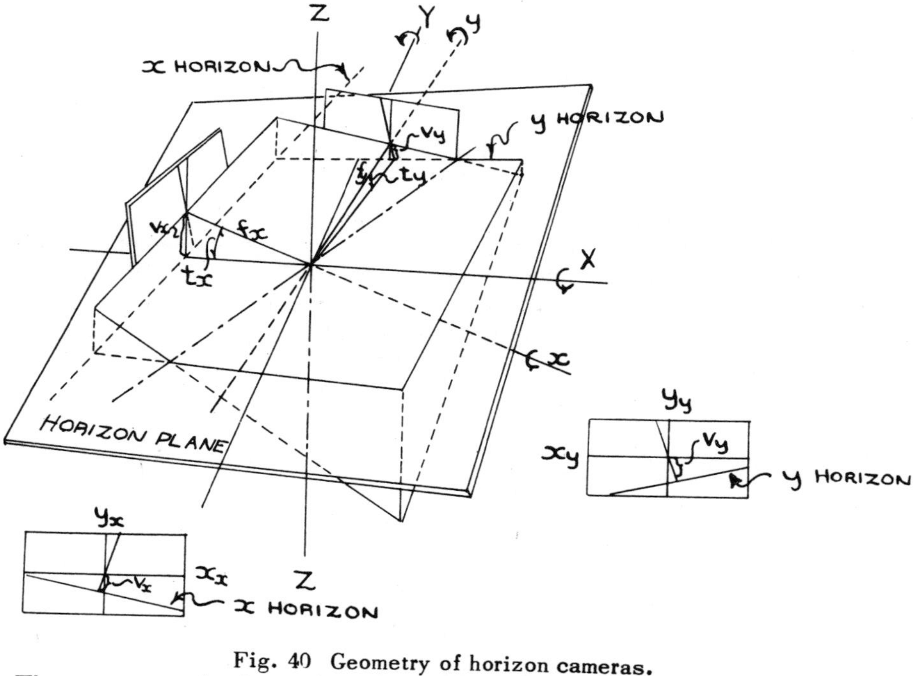

Fig. 40 Geometry of horizon cameras.

The apparent horizon dips below the true horizon because of the altitude of the aircraft, and hence the term dip angle (Δ). The dip angle is computed as a function of aircraft altitude:

$$\Delta'' = 59\,(ZL)^{1/2}, \text{ approximately,}$$

and

$$t_x = t_x^1 + \Delta'' \qquad\qquad t_y = t_y^1 + \Delta''$$

It is possible for the apparent horizon to be below the principal point on one camera and above on the other, or the converse. The signs of the v values define the quadrant in which the photographic nadir lies. The v is minus below the principal point and plus above the principal point. The quadrant in which the photographic nadir lies is the quadrant in which the terminal side of the swing angle lies since swing is measured clockwise from the positive y axis to the photographic nadir.

Assuming that the x and y horizon cameras are oriented respectively in the direction of positive x and y of the nadir camera, the terminal side of the swing angle will fall in the following quadrant according to the four possible sign variations of v_x and v_y.

Sign variation		Quadrant
$+ v_x$	$+ v_y$	I
$+ v_x$	$- v_y$	II
$- v_x$	$- v_y$	III
$- v_x$	$+ v_y$	IV

b. Tilt and swing with one horizon camera.

Tilt and swing may be determined from measurements on either horizon camera. Consider the x horizon camera. The x axis of this camera is considered to be parallel to both the y axis of the nadir camera and the optical axis of the y horizon camera. The following relations are evident from Figure 41.

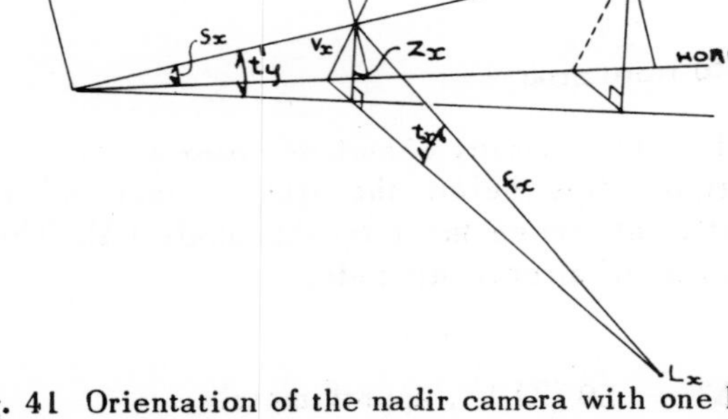

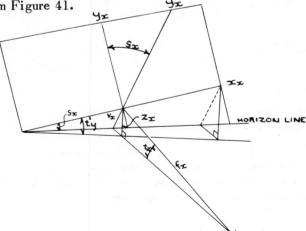

Fig. 41 Orientation of the nadir camera with one horizon camera.

$$\sin t_y = \frac{z_x}{l} \cdot \frac{f \sin t_x{}^1}{\frac{v_x}{\sin s_x}} = \sin t_x{}^1 \cdot \cot t_x{}^1 \cdot \sin s_x$$

$$\sin t_y = \cos t_x{}^1 \cdot \sin s_x$$

$$\sin t = \frac{\sin t_x}{\sin s}$$

$$\tan s = \frac{\tan t_x}{\sin s_x}$$

Now consider the *y* horizon camera.

$$\sin t_x = \cos t_y \cdot \sin s_y$$

$$\sin t = \frac{\sin t_y}{\cos s}$$

$$\tan s = \frac{\sin s_y}{\tan t_y}$$

2. High-Oblique Cameras [25].

a. General.

The essential difference between the horizon cameras and the high-oblique cameras, hereafter referred to as the trimetrogon cameras, is the fact that in the latter system the oblique cameras are mounted so their optical axes are inclined approximately 60° to the optical axis of the nadir camera.

Object detail is included with the image of the horizon on the high-oblique cameras. The trimetrogon cameras are mounted on opposite sides of the nadir camera with their optical axes normal to the line of flight. The tricamera in some instances consists of three cartographic cameras with 6-inch cones and metrogon lenses. The 60° tilts of the high-oblique cameras result in a 14° overlap between the fields of coverage of oblique and vertical cameras. With the aircraft in level flight, the oblique cameras cover approximately 7° above the true horizon. All three cameras are interconnected so as to make exposures simultaneously and thus cover a strip of ground, extending from horizon to horizon, normal to the direction of flight. In practice, the relative tilts and swings of the oblique cameras may vary with the vertical camera from exposure to exposure owing to the approximate settings of the tricamera installation.

b. Tilt and swing.

The tilt and swing of the left and right obliques are determined in the same manner as the tilt and swing of the *x* and *y* horizon cameras.

The geometry of the tricamera installation is illustrated in Figure 42.

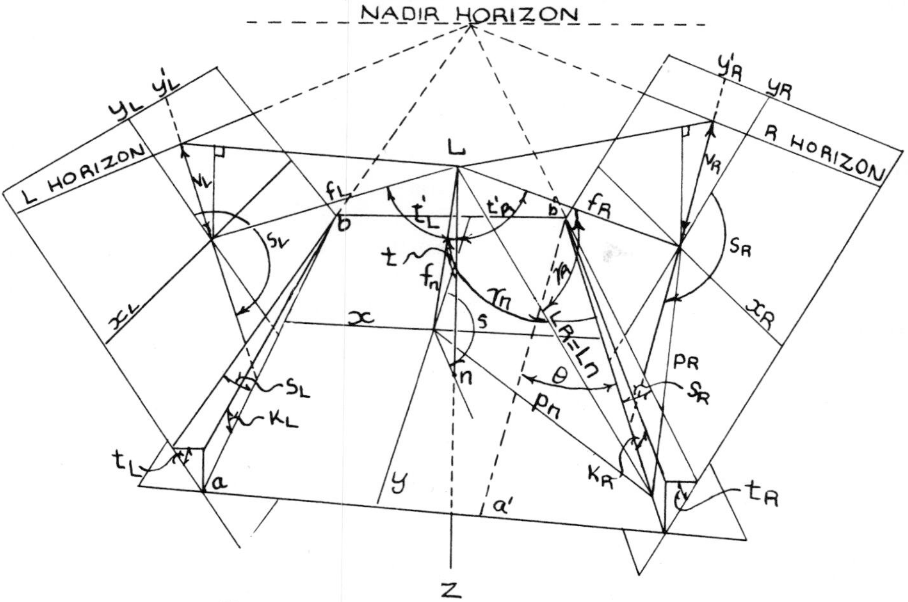

Fig. 42 Geometry of tricamera installation.

$$\tan t_L{}^1 = \frac{f_L}{v_L} \qquad \tan t_R{}^1 = \frac{f_R}{v_R}$$

$$\sin s_L = \frac{x_L}{v_L} \qquad \sin s_R = \frac{x_R}{v_R}$$

where v_L and v_R are the measured distances normal to the horizon from principal points, and x_L and x_R are measured distances normal to the y axis from the points where the principal line cuts the horizon line. The computed tilts of the oblique cameras are corrected for the dip (Δ) of the apparent horizon as before:

$$t_L = t_L{}^1 + \Delta''$$

$$t_R = t_R{}^1 + \Delta''$$

Owing to the fact that the left and right oblique image planes have no orthogonal relation to the nadir camera, the components so obtained cannot be converted directly to orientation functions of the nadir camera. The angular orientation of the nadir camera may be determined graphically or analytically. There are many published papers and reports on the trimetrogon system, all of which describe in detail graphical methods of determining the angular orientation of the nadir camera. There are two practical analytical solutions: One solution requires the camera coordinates of three conjugate images on the left or right oblique and nadir exposures. The other requires the camera coordinates of two conjugate images measured on the left or right oblique and nadir exposures. The advantage of either analytical solution over the commonly known graphical solutions lies on the fact that either oblique yields a complete solution and that the images need only be conjugate and are not required to fall on the intersection line. With conjugate-coordinate data from either oblique and the near vertical and the orientation data of either oblique, three linear equations are written:

$$xa \cos \gamma_x + ya \cos \gamma_y + f \cos \gamma_z = La \cos \gamma_a^1$$

$$xb \cos \gamma_x + yb \cos \gamma_y + f \cos \gamma_z = Lb \cos \gamma_b^1$$

$$xc \cos \gamma_x + yc \cos \gamma_y + f \cos \gamma_z = Lc \cos \gamma_c^1$$

where the unknowns are $\cos \gamma_x$, $\cos \gamma_y$, and $\cos \gamma_z$ and the coefficients are the camera coordinates from the near vertical. The constant terms are products of orientation and camera data from the oblique, and only camera data from the near vertical. From the near vertical are obtained:

$$La = (xa^2 + ya^2 + f_n^2)^{1/2}$$

$$Lb = (xb^2 + yb^2 + f_n^2)^{1/2}$$

$$Lc = (xc^2 + yc^2 + f_n^2)^{1/2}$$

and from the oblique are obtained:

$$\cos \gamma_a^1 = (xa_1 \sin s_1 \sin t_1 + ya_1 \cos s_1 \sin t_1 + f_1 \cos t_1)/La_1$$

$$\cos \gamma_b^1 = (xb_1 \sin s_1 \sin t_1 + yb_1 \cos s_1 \sin t_1 + f_1 \cos t_1)/Lb_1$$

$$\cos \gamma_c^1 = (xc_1 \sin s_1 \sin t_1 + yc_1 \cos s_1 \sin t_1 + f_1 \cos t_1)/Lc_1$$

where

$$La_1 = (xa_1^2 + ya_1^2 + f_1^2)^{1/2}$$

$$Lb_1 = (xb_1^2 + yb_1^2 + f_1^2)^{1/2}$$

$$Lc_1 = (xc_1^2 + yc_1^2 + f_1^2)^{1/2}$$

The subscript one (1) denotes the right or left exposure. These equations are identical to those described in Chapter III, section A.4.a., for determining the tilt and swing of an exposure from three known points or direction angles when the space coordinates have been determined; only the application is different.

A more accurate value of tilt and swing of the near vertical may be determined by subjecting *n* observation equations of the form just described to the method of Least Squares. This suggestion is made on the supposition that more precise near-vertical orientation data will result from a solution involving conjugate camera coordinates and orientation data from both obliques simultaneously than will result from either oblique singly. Let it be supposed that six points on the near vertical are selected: three that are conjugate with the left oblique and three that are conjugate with the right oblique. Let the letters *a*, *b*, and *c* denote the left oblique and letters *d*, *e*, and *g* denote the right oblique. With these data *n* observation equations are formed just as three are formed for a unique solution:

$$xa \cos \gamma_x + ya \cos \gamma_y + f \cos \gamma_z = La \cos \gamma_a$$

$$xb \cos \gamma_x + yb \cos \gamma_y + f \cos \gamma_z = Lb \cos \gamma_b$$

$$\cdot \quad \cdot \quad \cdot \quad \cdot \quad \cdot \quad \cdot \quad \cdot \quad \cdot \quad \cdot \quad \cdot \quad \cdot$$

$$xg \cos \gamma_x + yg \cos \gamma_y + f \cos \gamma_z = Lg \cos \gamma_g$$

These six observation equations are employed to form three normal equations in the usual manner:

$$[x \cdot x] \cos \gamma_x + [x \cdot y] \cos \gamma_y + [x \cdot f] \cos \gamma_z = [x \cdot L \cos \gamma]$$

$$[x \cdot y] \cos \gamma_x + [y \cdot y] \cos \gamma_y + [y \cdot f] \cos \gamma_z = [y \cdot L \cos \gamma]$$

$$[x \cdot f] \cos \gamma_x + [y \cdot f] \cos \gamma_y + [f \cdot f] \cos \gamma_z = [f \cdot L \cos \gamma]$$

The coefficients and constant terms are sums of the products of the terms enclosed in brackets. Simultaneous solution of these equations yields the most probable values of $\cos \gamma_x$, $\cos \gamma_y$, and $\cos \gamma_z$ exhibited by the camera coordinates of the two obliques and the near vertical, and the previously determined orientation data of the two obliques. In any case,

$$\tan s = \frac{\cos \gamma_x}{\cos \gamma_y}$$

and

$$\cos t = \cos \gamma_z$$

Two conjugate-image coordinates are required to determine the orientation of the adjacent exposures. The functions of the zenith angles are computed with the reference exposure whose orientation is known. The reference exposure is either oblique while the adjacent exposure is the near vertical. This solution is described in the preceding chapter under relative orientation of two exposures at the same camera station when their principal points are not conjugate. It, as the one just outlined, gives tilt, swing, interlocking angle, and relative azimuth.

3. Zenith Cameras.

The purpose of the airborne zenith camera is to provide zenithal exposures of the celestial sphere that are synchronized with nadir exposures of terrain. The zenith-nadir camera is illustrated in Figure 43.

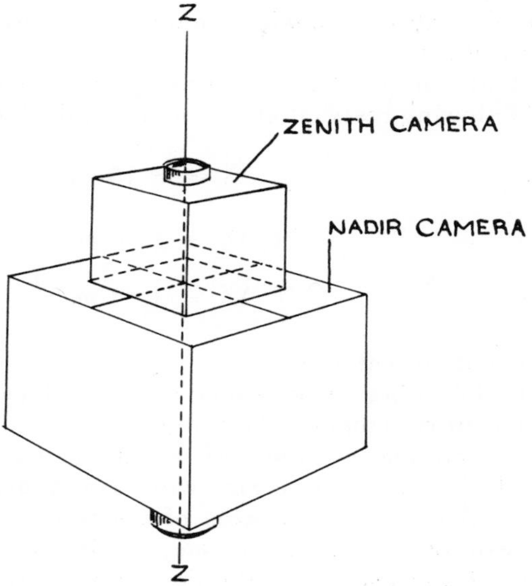

Fig. 43 Zenith-nadir camera.

Theoretically, the absolute position, azimuth, and orientation of the nadir camera can be determined from measurements made on the zenith camera exposure, provided that the relative orientation of the zenith and nadir cameras has been determined and provided that at least two celestial bodies have been imaged. The most direct results are obtained when the optical and fiducial axes of the two cameras are collinear. The interlocking angle between the zenith and nadir cameras being fixed, the same geometry applies that is incorporated in the oblique and horizon camera systems.

The airborne zenith camera may be employed for photographing the sun or stars. The sun zenith camera developed by Santoni of Italy in 1920 has the advantage of daylight exposures of terrain but the disadvantage of a single astronomic control image which is that of the sun. A star application of Santoni's camera has the disadvantage of requiring special illumination of the terrain synchronized with each camera exposure, and the advantage of recording multiple astronomic star-control images. The latter advantages make possible a determination of tilt, swing, and azimuth with the camera and astronomic coordinates of stars as given data. The sun zenith camera can provide only azimuth data.

a. Description of Santoni's sun zenith camera.

"Two known points on the ground for each photogram were sufficient with my method, instead of the three needed for the ordinary pyramidal vertex. In fact, the third egde of the pyramid was replaced by the solar ray, which form an edge of known direction, according to the hour at which the photograph was taken." [26] Originally Santoni developed the idea of the solar camera as a means of space resection requiring two known points per exposure (1919). In 1930 he conceived the idea of control extension where two known points are required at the flight ends only.

A test of Santoni's solar camera over a course of 100 kilometers gave the following residual errors on a single check point:

$$\Delta X = -15 \text{ m.}$$

$$\Delta Y = +46 \text{ m.}$$

$$\Delta Z = +14 \text{ m.}$$

b. Absolute orientation.

The following exact equation derived by the writer is different from the equations proposed by Santoni.

The observation consists of simultaneous zenithal and nadir exposures of the sky and terrain with zenith and nadir cameras locked together so that the *x, y, z* axes of the two cameras are collinear. The zenithal exposure images the sun, while the nadir exposure images, along with the terrain beneath the aircraft, two objects whose space coordinates *(X, Y, Z)* are known. This is shown in Figure 44.

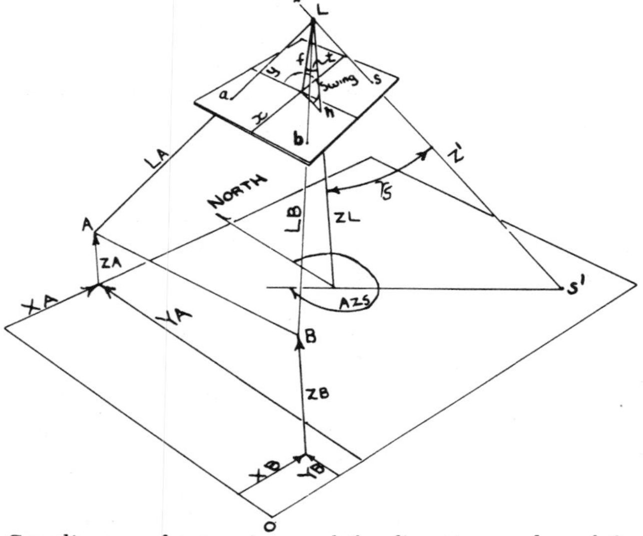

Fig. 44 Coordinates of two points and the direction angles of the sun.

From the law of cosines and sines,

$$\cos \gamma_s = \sin \varphi_z \sin \delta_s + \cos \varphi_z \cos \delta_s \cos t_z$$

$$t_z = RA(arc) - \lambda_z$$

$$\sin Az_s = \frac{\sin t_z \cos \delta_s}{\sin \gamma_s}$$

By simple interpolation between the known points, the values of φ_z and λ_z are not likely to be in error more than 2 seconds of arc and, without known points, more than 2 minutes of arc.

The coordinates of the two points are transformed to refer to a datum normal to the solar vector, whose *Y* axis in this plane coincides with the sun's azimuth.

$$XA^1 = XA \cos Az_s - YA \sin Az_s$$

$$XB^1 = XB \cos Az_s - YB \sin Az_s$$

$$YA^1 = (XA \sin Az_s + YA \cos Az_s) \cos \gamma_s + ZA \sin \gamma_s$$

$$YB^1 = (XB \sin Az_s + YB \cos Az_s) \cos \gamma_s + ZA \sin \gamma_s$$

$$ZA^1 = ZA \cos \gamma_s - (XA \sin Az_s + YA \cos Az_s) \sin \gamma_s$$

$$ZB^1 = ZB \cos \gamma_s - (XB \sin Az_s + YB \cos Az_s) \sin \gamma_s$$

Then from the law of cosines in plane trigonometry,

$$AB^2 = LA^2 + LB^2 - 2\, LA \cdot LB \cdot \cos aLb \quad . \quad . \quad . \quad . \quad . \quad (1)$$

where

$$AB^2 = (XA-XB)^2 + (YA-YB)^2 + (ZA-ZB)^2$$

$$LA^2 = (ZL^1 - ZA^1)^2 \sec^2 aLs \qquad LB^2 = (ZL^1 - ZB^1)^2 \sec^2 bLs$$

Also $LA^2 = (ZL - ZA)^2 \sec^2 aLn \qquad LB^2 = (ZL - ZB)^2 \sec^2 bLn$

$$\cos aLb = \frac{xa \cdot xb + ya \cdot yb + f^2}{La \cdot Lb}$$

$$\cos aLs = \frac{xa \cdot xs + ya \cdot ys + f^2}{La \cdot Ls}$$

$$\cos bLs = \frac{xb \cdot xs + yb \cdot ys + f^2}{Lb \cdot Ls}$$

$$La = (xa^2 + ya^2 + f^2)^{1/2}$$

$$Lb = (xb^2 + yb^2 + f^2)^{1/2}$$

$$Ls = (xs^2 + ys^2 + f^2)^{1/2}$$

s denotes sun image.

Substitution in equation (1), expanding, and collecting coefficients of common powers of ZL^1, yield a quadratic of the form:

$$A \cdot ZL^{1^2} + B \cdot ZL^1 + C = 0$$

where

$$A = [\sec^2 aLs + \sec^2 bLs - 2 \sec aLs \sec bLs \cos aLb]$$

$$B = 2[(ZA^1 + ZB^1)\sec aLs \sec bLs \cos aLb - (ZA^1 \sec^2 aLs + ZB^1 \sec^2 bLs)]$$

$$C = [ZA^{1^2} \sec^2 aLs + ZB^{1^2} \sec^2 bLs - 2ZA^1 ZB^1 \sec aLs \sec bLs \cos aLb - AB^2]$$

Solving for ZL^1,

$$ZL^1 = \frac{-B \pm (B^2 - 4AC)^{1/2}}{2A}$$

Then, as shown previously,

$$LA = (ZL^1 - ZA^1) \sec aLs$$

$$LB = (ZL^1 - ZB^1) \sec bLs$$

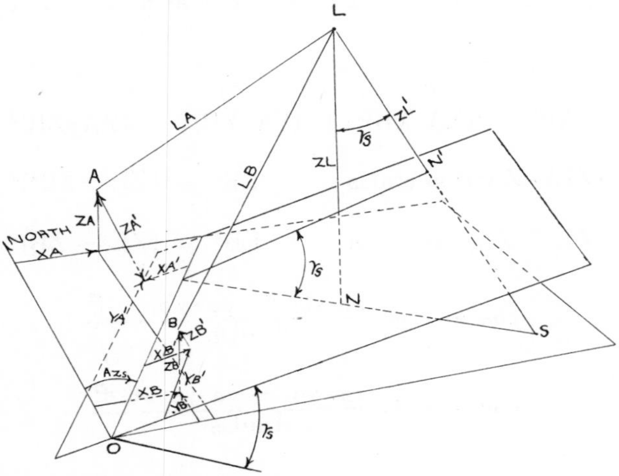

Fig. 45 Transformation of space coordinates through angles Az_s and γ_s.

Other quantities are required to determine the plane coordinates of the lens in the transformed reference plane. The radials from N^1 to the point-objects and the arbitrary datum distance between A and B are required. The relations may be seen in Figure 45.

$$RA^{1^2} = LA^2 - (ZL^1 - ZA^1)^2$$

$$RB^{1^2} = LB^2 - (ZL^1 - ZB^1)^2$$

$$AB^{1^2} = AB^2 - (ZA^1 - ZB^1)^2$$

With these linear values, interior angles $N^1A^1B^1$ and $N^1B^1A^1$ are computed:

$$\cos N^1A^1B^1 = \frac{RA^{1^2} + AB^{1^2} - RB^{1^2}}{2\, RA^1 \cdot AB^1}$$

$$\cos N^1B^1A^1 = \frac{RB^{1^2} + AB^{1^2} - RA^{1^2}}{2\, RB^1 \cdot AB^1}$$

These relations in the transformed datum are shown in Figure 46.

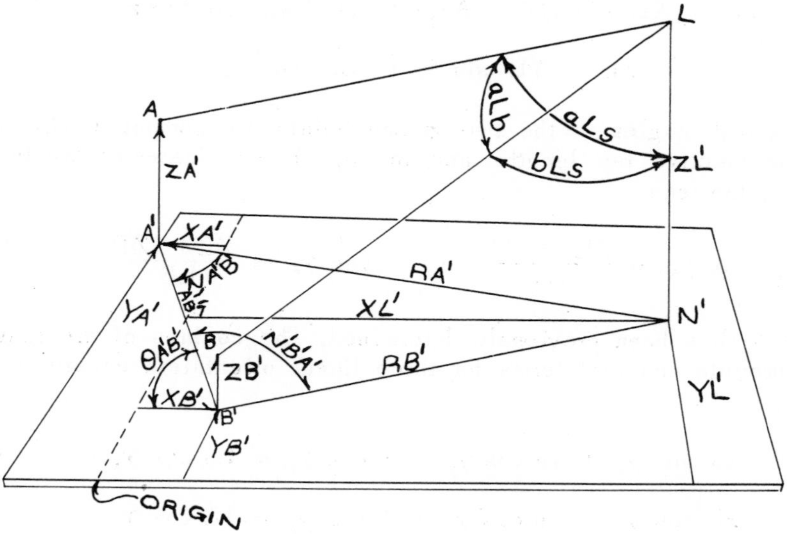

Fig. 46 Transformed datum.

The azimuth of the radials may be determined by combining the interior angles at A and B with the arbitrary azimuth of AB^1:

$$\tan \theta_{AB}{}^1 = \frac{XA^1 - XB^1}{YA^1 - YB^1}$$

Then

$$\varphi_A^{1} = \theta_{AB}^{1} + N^1A^1B^1 + 180°$$

$$\varphi_B^{1} = \theta_{AB}^{1} - N^1B^1A^1$$

Then the functions of the azimuth of the radials and the lengths of the plane coordinates of *L* in the transformed datum are computed:

$$XL^1 = RA^1 \sin \varphi_A^{1} + XA^1 = RB^1 \sin \varphi_B^{1} + XB^1$$

$$YL^1 = RA^1 \cos \varphi_A^{1} + YA^1 = RB^1 \cos \varphi_B^{1} + YB^1$$

Just as the space coordinates of *A* and *B* were transformed to a datum normal to the sun's vector and oriented on the azimuthal direction of the sun, the arbitrary space coordinates of *L* (XL^1, YL^1, ZL^1) in this plane may be transformed back to sea-level datum oriented on north.

$$YL_N^{1} = YL^1 \cos \gamma_s - ZL^1 \sin \gamma_s$$

$$XL = XL^1 \cos (360° - Az_s) - YL_N^{1} \sin (360° - Az_s)$$

$$YL = XL^1 \sin (360° - Az_s) + YL_N^{1} \sin (360° - Az_s)$$

$$ZL = YL^1 \sin \gamma_s + ZL^1 \cos \gamma_s$$

The zenith angles of the two ground points are computed with the space perspective ray lengths and the space coordinates of the two points and the lens.

$$\cos \gamma_A = \frac{ZL - ZA}{LA} \qquad \cos \gamma_B = \frac{ZL - ZB}{LB}$$

and $\cos \gamma_s$ has been previously determined. The cosines of the zenith angles provide constant terms for three linear orientation equations of the form:

$$xa \cos \gamma_x + ya \cos \gamma_y + f \cos \gamma_z = La \cos \gamma_A$$

$$xb \cos \gamma_x + yb \cos \gamma_y + f \cos \gamma_z = Lb \cos \gamma_B$$

$$xs \cos \gamma_x + ys \cos \gamma_y + f \cos \gamma_z = Ls \cos \gamma_S$$

These equations have the same meaning as those described for determining the angular orientation of a near vertical with conjugate images and the orientation of an overlapping oblique. Similarly, after simultaneous solution for $\cos \gamma_x$, $\cos \gamma_y$, and $\cos \gamma_z$,

$$\tan s = \frac{\cos \gamma_x}{\cos \gamma_y}$$

$$\cos t = \cos \gamma_z$$

The geometric meaning of the orientation is illustrated in Figure 47.

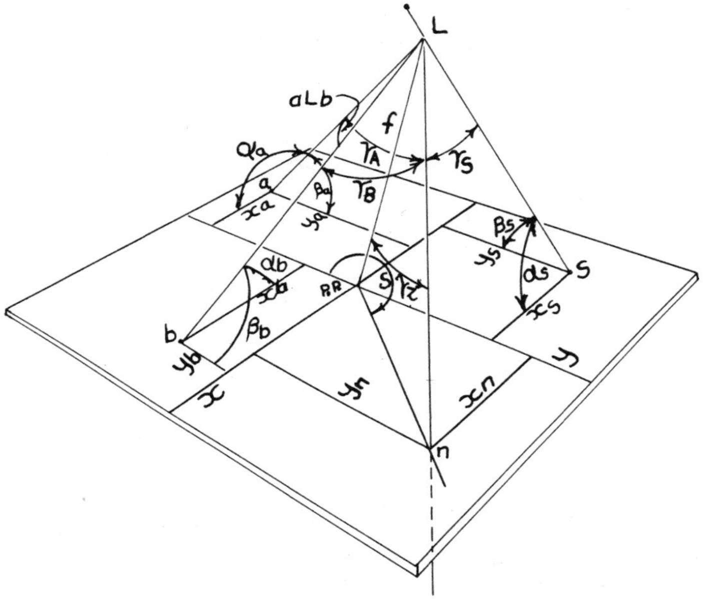

Fig. 47 Geometry of angular orientation equations.

The azimuth of the sun has been computed. With the tilt and swing known, the horizontal angle θ_s between the principal plane of the exposure and the zenith plane of the sun may be computed:

$$\tan \theta_s = \frac{xs \cos s - ys \sin s}{xs \sin s \cos t + ys \cos s \cos t - f \sin t}$$

The azimuth of the principal plane is the difference or sum of Az_s and θ_s. Therefore, by the law of tangents,

$$\tan Az = \frac{\tan Az_s - \tan \theta_s}{1 + \tan Az_s \tan \theta_s}$$

The relation between Az, Az_s, and θ_s is illustrated in Figure 48. This solution requires two known points and therefore does not conform to the no-ground-control specification.

This solution is considered, however, because ground points in combination with absolute independent sun orientation on each exposure increase the distance that control may be extrapolated. It is assumed that two points appear on the first stereo pair and that the photographs have 60 percent endlap.

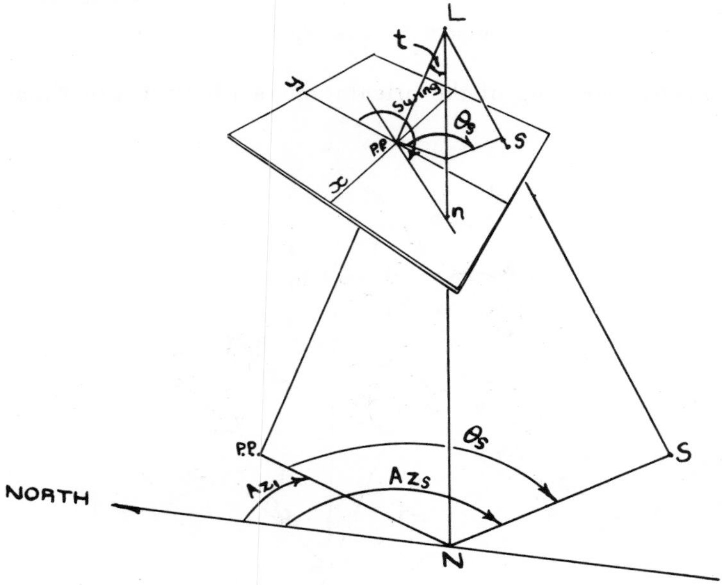

Fig. 48 Angular relation between Az, Az_s, and θ_s.

Since points A and B are common to both exposures and since the sun is recorded on each exposure, the space coordinates and complete angular orientation of the second exposure may be determined with the same procedure and ground data used to determine the space coordinates and angular orientation of the initial exposure. Then two ground points C and D are established in the trilap area of exposures 1, 2, and 3 with space-intersection equations, written with the space coordinates and absolute orientation data of the first and second exposures.

The plan of control extension is illustrated schematically in Figure 49.

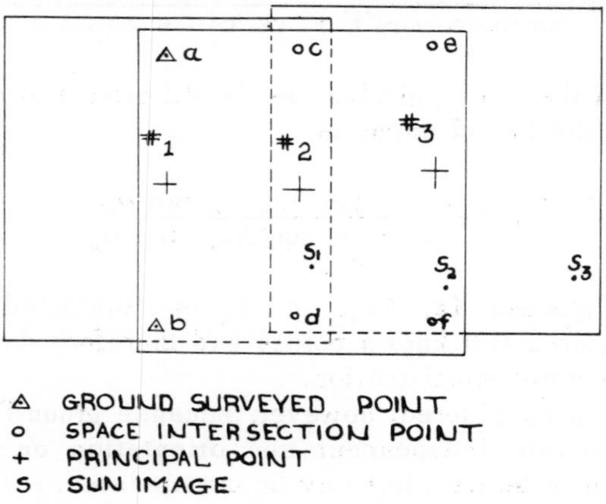

Fig. 49 Plan of control extension.

This procedure is repeated down the flight with exterior orientation alternating with space-intersection equations that are identical to those described in the preceding chapter.

4. Star Zenith Camera.

The real advantage of a sun or star zenith camera lies in the tremendous simplification of the reciprocal orientation equations when referred to a common azimuth in connection with extending control without ground control. This point is amplified later.

a. Position.

It is not possible to establish position or orientation by an observation on a single heavenly body. For this reason, sun exposures cannot be employed for position or orientation without the aid of two points at the flight ends. Star zenith exposures can provide orientation data but cannot provide adequate position data because of the stability requirements characterizing a position observation. Unlike the sun exposures, there is sufficient data for a position computation, but an unknown reference plane. A few fundamental considerations will show that position so determined is too inaccurate to be of value.

All surveying instruments whose function is position determination, whether that position be geodetic or astronomic, make a common minimum assumption: the z axis of the observing instrument defines the observer's gravitational vector.

On the ground, level vials are employed to orient the vertical axis; while in the air, gyros are employed to orient the vertical axis. An astronomic position can be no more accurate than the orientation of the observing instrument's vertical axis since astronomic position consists of solving for the direction cosines of the observing instrument's vertical axis.

Star exposures made with a gyro-oriented camera have for their prime purpose the provision of plate and astronomic coordinates whereby the direction angles of the gyro axis may be calculated.

The most precise claims for definition of the vertical with airborne gyros is in the vicinity of 5 minutes of arc. It would be impossible for a graphical resection of the principal point to be in error 5 nautical miles. Aside from positioning a flight terminal approximately in an unknown area, position with a gyro-oriented camera must be postponed for practical application until the gyro achieves a phenomenal stability of a fraction of an arc-second, since 1 arc-second means a coordinate error of approximately 100 feet.

There may be instances where only the approximate geographic location of an area is required. A single exposure would then provide the required position data to ± 5 miles. This would be adequate for areas on the Antarctic Continent.

The direction angles of the gyro (and of the plate perpendicular) are the geographic coordinates of the camera at the instant of exposure. The cosines of the zenith angles of three star images corrected for refraction are computed with interior orientation data. Let the images be denoted *a*, *b*, and *c*:

$$\cos \gamma_a = \frac{f}{(xa^2 + ya^2 + f^2)^{1/2}}$$

$$\cos \gamma_b = \frac{f}{(xb^2 + yb^2 + f^2)^{1/2}}$$

$$\cos \gamma_c = \frac{f}{(xc^2 + yc^2 + f^2)^{1/2}}$$

The lens axis is assumed to be collinear with the gyro axis. The zenith angles are constant terms for linear equations which, solved simultaneously, provide functions of the camera's geographic position:

$$\cos \alpha_{sa} \cos \alpha_z + \cos \beta_{sa} \cos \beta_z + \cos \gamma_{sa} \cos \gamma_z = \cos \gamma_a$$

$$\cos \alpha_{sb} \cos \alpha_z + \cos \beta_{sb} \cos \beta_z + \cos \gamma_{sb} \cos \gamma_z = \cos \gamma_b$$

$$\cos \alpha_{sc} \cos \alpha_z + \cos \beta_{sc} \cos \beta_z + \cos \gamma_{sc} \cos \gamma_z = \cos \gamma_c$$

where the unknowns are:

$$\cos \alpha_z, \cos \beta_z, \text{ and } \cos \gamma_z,$$

and the coefficients are formed as follows:

$$\cos \alpha_{sa} = \cos \delta_a \sin \lambda_a \qquad \cos \beta_{sa} = \cos \delta_a \cos \lambda_a \qquad \cos \gamma_{sa} = \sin \delta_a$$

$$\cos \alpha_{sb} = \cos \delta_b \sin \lambda_b \qquad \cos \beta_{sb} = \cos \delta_b \cos \lambda_b \qquad \cos \gamma_{sb} = \sin \delta_b$$

$$\cos \alpha_{sc} = \cos \delta_c \sin \lambda_c \qquad \cos \beta_{sc} = \cos \delta_c \cos \lambda_c \qquad \cos \gamma_{sc} = \sin \delta_c$$

Then

$$\cos \gamma_z = \sin \varphi_z$$

$$\tan \lambda_z = \frac{\cos \alpha_z}{\cos \beta_z}$$

There are numerous less elegant solutions to this problem that are omitted since position determination with an airborne zenith camera is of dubious value. These equations are outlined in Chapter III, under Total Orientation (Celestial Object Space).

The star zenith camera, while not suitable for the determination of absolute position, may provide the elements of angular orientation.

The gyro would not be required for this purpose. If the angular orientation can be determined at the instant of each nadir exposure, the airborne zenithal camera replaces the function of the gyro inasmuch as when the elements of angular orientation are considered to be known, the effects of tilt and swing on imaged objects can be canceled out by instrumentation or computation. Such an orientation procedure is justified for precise aerial triangulation. In such a case, a system of points geometrically distributed down a proposed flight line would be selected and illuminated with a light corresponding to the spectral sensitivity of an emulsion especially selected for the purpose of night aerial triangulation. Appropriate filters would reduce the transmission of other points of illumination.

Determination of the angular orientation of the camera is practical where the determination of absolute position is not. This is due to the fact that in the former a gyro is not required and the fact that a 5-minute error in tilt and swing is acceptable, whereas a 5-minute error in position is intolerable.

The zenith and nadir cameras mounted with x, y, and z axes collinear are tripped synchronously. The fiducial marks of both cameras are registered electronically, whereby the plate perpendiculars of both cameras are visually recoverable. The time of the exposures is recorded with the accuracy of time used in a navigator's fix.

Assume that the astronomic position of the exposure may be determined with varying degrees of accuracy from the navigator's fix, track chart, or existing maps. The error in the subsequent tilt and swing is approximately equal to the error in the position assumption. The accuracy of air navigation suggests this may be from 2 to 5 minutes' error in tilt and swing. This is negligible as far as it affects the accuracy of the quantitative data that may be extracted from an aerial exposure whose orientation data are known within ± 5 minutes.

In any case, the plate perpendicular of the zenith camera is located and three stars are identified. The apparent places of the stars identified are reduced and the plate coordinates of the corresponding images are corrected for refraction in the conventional manner. The cosines of zenith angles referred to the assumed position are computed with the direction cosines of the assumed position (φ_z, λ_z) and the corresponding stars:

$$\cos\alpha_{sa}\cos\alpha_z + \cos\beta_{sa}\cos\beta_z + \cos\gamma_{sa}\cos\gamma_z = \cos\gamma_a$$

$$\cos\alpha_{sb}\cos\alpha_z + \cos\beta_{sb}\cos\beta_z + \cos\gamma_{sb}\cos\gamma_z = \cos\gamma_b$$

$$\cos\alpha_{sc}\cos\alpha_z + \cos\beta_{sc}\cos\beta_z + \cos\gamma_{sc}\cos\gamma_z = \cos\gamma_c$$

where

$$\cos\alpha_{sa} = \sin GHA_a \cos\delta_a \qquad \cos\gamma_{sa} = \sin\delta_a$$

$$\cos\alpha_{sb} = \sin GHA_b \cos\delta_b \qquad \cos\gamma_{sb} = \sin\delta_b$$

$$\cos \alpha_{sc} = \sin GHA_c \cos \delta_c \qquad \cos \gamma_{sc} = \sin \delta_c$$

$$\cos \beta_{sa} = \cos GHA_a \cos \delta_a \qquad \cos \alpha_z = \sin \lambda_z \cos \varphi_z$$

$$\cos \beta_{sb} = \cos GHA_b \cos \delta_b \qquad \cos \beta_z = \cos \lambda_z \cos \varphi_z$$

$$\cos \beta_{sc} = \cos GHA_c \cos \delta_c \qquad \cos \gamma_z = \sin \varphi_z$$

and

$$GHA_a = [(GST\ 0^h + GCT + corr.) - RA_a]\ arc$$

$$GHA_b = [(GST\ 0^h + GCT + corr.) - RA_b]\ arc$$

$$GHA_c = [(GST\ 0^h + GCT + corr.) - RA_c]\ arc$$

These zenith angles are illustrated in Figure 50.

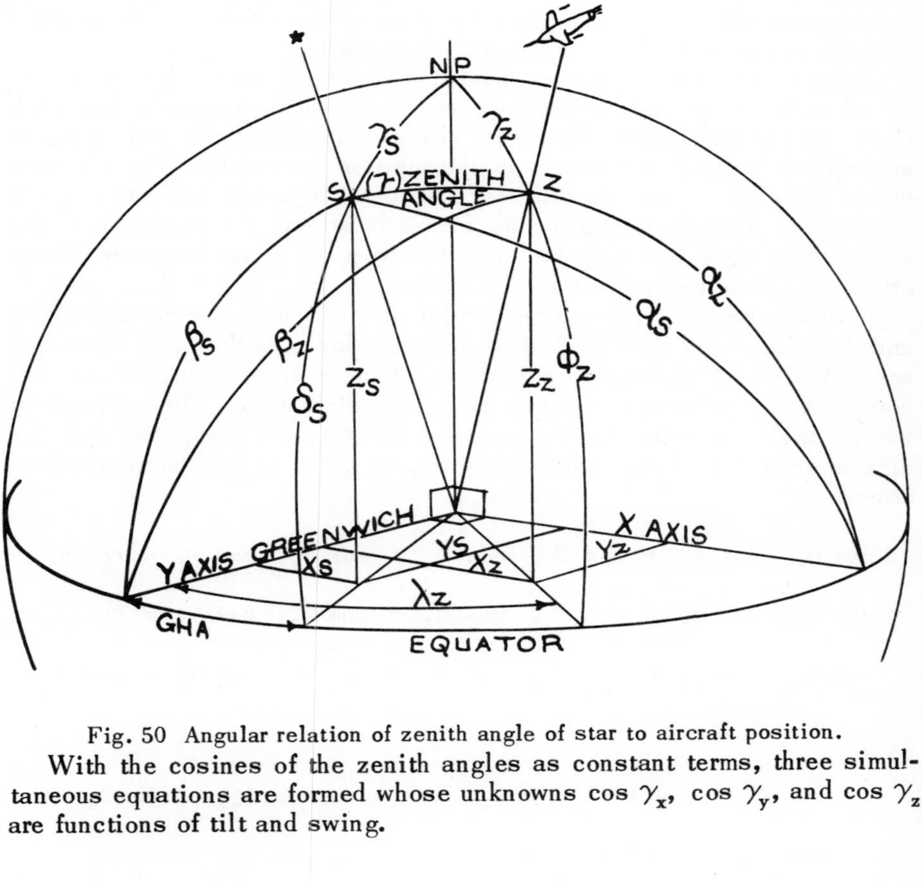

Fig. 50 Angular relation of zenith angle of star to aircraft position.

With the cosines of the zenith angles as constant terms, three simultaneous equations are formed whose unknowns $\cos \gamma_x$, $\cos \gamma_y$, and $\cos \gamma_z$ are functions of tilt and swing.

$$xa \cos \gamma_x + ya \cos \gamma_y + f \cos \gamma_z = La \cos \gamma_a$$

$$xb \cos \gamma_x + yb \cos \gamma_y + f \cos \gamma_z = Lb \cos \gamma_b$$

$$xc \cos \gamma_x + yc \cos \gamma_y + f \cos \gamma_z = Lc \cos \gamma_c$$

where the coefficients are the plate coordinates of the star images referred to the plate perpendicular, and

$$La = (xa^2 + ya^2 + f^2)^{1/2}$$

$$Lb = (xb^2 + yb^2 + f^2)^{1/2}$$

$$Lc = (xc^2 + yc^2 + f^2)^{1/2}$$

The new application of these frequently introduced tilt and swing equations is illustrated in Figure 51.

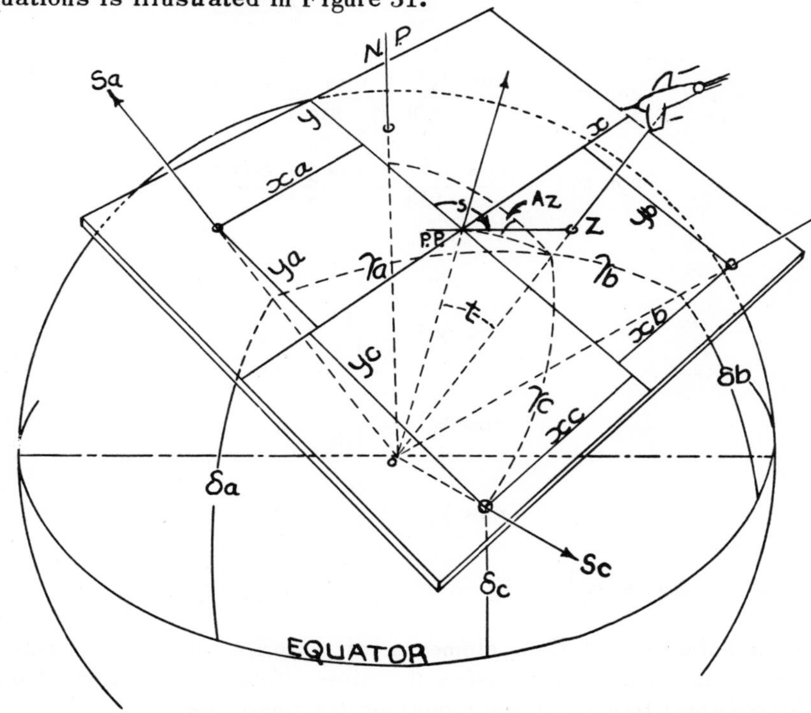

Fig. 51 Relation of astronomic coordinates of plate perpendicular and aircraft.

Then, as before,

$$\tan s = \frac{\cos \gamma_x}{\cos \gamma_y}$$

$$\cos t = \cos \gamma_z$$

Since the zenith angles refer to the star images, the values x, y, and L refer to the star-exposure camera. The azimuth of the principal line may be determined in several ways.

$$\cos \theta_a^1 = \frac{\sin \delta_a - \sin \varphi_z \cos \gamma_a}{\cos \varphi_z \sin \gamma_a}$$

$$\cos \theta_b^1 = \frac{\sin \delta_b - \sin \varphi_z \cos \gamma_b}{\cos \varphi_z \sin \gamma_b}$$

$$\cos \theta_c^1 = \frac{\sin \delta_c - \sin \varphi_z \cos \gamma_c}{\cos \varphi_z \sin \gamma_c}$$

$$\cos \theta_a = \frac{\cos \gamma_a^1 - \cos \gamma_a \cos t}{\sin \gamma_a \sin t}$$

$$\cos \theta_b = \frac{\cos \gamma_b^1 - \cos \gamma_b \cos t}{\sin \gamma_b \sin t}$$

$$\cos \theta_c = \frac{\cos \gamma_c^1 - \cos \gamma_c \cos t}{\sin \gamma_c \sin t}$$

where

$$\cos \gamma_a^1 = \frac{f}{La}$$

$$\cos \gamma_b^1 = \frac{f}{Lb}$$

$$\cos \gamma_c^1 = \frac{f}{Lc}$$

$$Az = \theta_a^1 - \theta_a = \theta_b^1 - \theta_b = \theta_c^1 - \theta_c$$

The angular orientation elements of exterior orientation may be determined still another way using the sines of the declination of three stars as constant terms in three simultaneous equations:

$$xa \cos \alpha_p + ya \cos \beta_p + f \cos \gamma_p = La \sin \delta_a$$

$$xb \cos \alpha_p + yb \cos \beta_p + f \cos \gamma_p = Lb \sin \delta_b$$

$$xc \cos \alpha_p + yc \cos \beta_p + f \cos \gamma_p = Lc \sin \delta_c$$

These equations are illustrated in Figure 52.

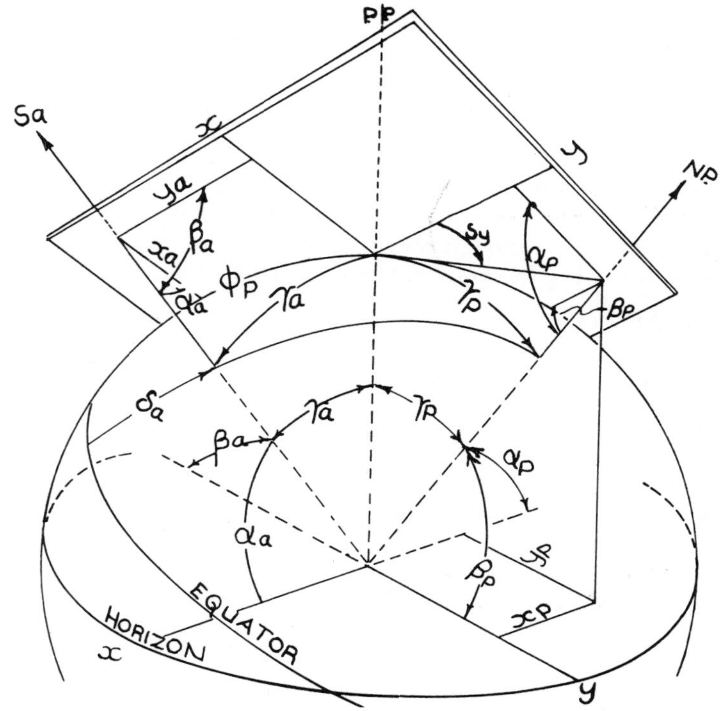

Fig. 52 Astronomic coordinates of the north celestial pole with respect to the principal point.

Solving for cos α_p, cos β_p, and cos γ_p,

$$\sin \varphi_p = \cos \gamma_p$$

$$\tan s_y = \frac{\cos \alpha_p}{\cos \beta_p} = \frac{\sin s_y}{\cos s_y} \cdot \frac{\cos \varphi_p}{\cos \varphi_p}$$

Then the hour angles of the stars referred to the principal point are computed.

$$\sin t_a = \frac{(xa \cos s_y - ya \sin s_y)}{La \cos \delta_a}$$

$$\sin t_b = \frac{(xb \cos s_y - yb \sin s_y)}{Lb \cos \delta_b}$$

$$\sin t_c = \frac{(xc \cos s_y - yc \sin s_y)}{Lc \cos \delta_c}$$

Then

$$\lambda_p = RA_a - t_a = RA_b - t_b = RA_c - t_c$$

and then with functions of the assumed coordinates of the aircraft,

$$\cos t = \sin \varphi_z \sin \varphi_p + \cos \varphi_z \cos \varphi_p \cos (\lambda_z - \lambda_p)$$

$$\cos Az = \frac{\sin \varphi_p - \sin \varphi_z \cos t}{\cos \varphi_z \sin t}$$

The usual two-point spherical solution may be employed in any of the situations where three points were used. The three-point solution is more elegant and, since there will never be a lack of star data, one justification for using the two-point solution will not exist.

B. *AIRBORNE DIMENSION.*

The weakest component in the development of an airborne system of pre-existing object-space control, is the component providing a dimension. Without an airborne dimension, only configuration and orientation are possible.

Differences in elevation of the exposure station have been measured with a statoscope [27] with a mean error of ± 1.4 meters or approximately 5 feet. A statoscope is a precise differential altimeter.

The vertical distance between ground and aircraft have been measured with radar altimetry, radio altimetry, and airborne profile recorders. The best results so far have been obtained with the airborne profile recorder [28, 29]. Accuracies of ± 10 feet are claimed with these devices when the measured wave is incident on a flat water surface.

Since, at the present, there is no accurate object-space dimension, the equations will be outlined on the assumption that future development is most likely to provide the necessary airborne dimensional accuracy in the realm of automatic elevation-measuring devices.

Shoran provides, electronically, the distance to the aircraft from two known points whose separation has been measured. The plane coordinates of the aircraft may be determined with the intersecting line lengths combined with the coordinates and distance between the ground stations. No emphasis has been placed on shoran since the system is not wholly airborne.

C. *SYSTEM FOR DEFINING OBJECT SPACE WITHOUT GROUND CONTROL.*

1. General.

Establishing the space coordinates of object points without extrapolation from presurveyed object points at one of the flight terminals, or interpolation between presurveyed ground points in the area to be dimensioned, is the purpose of this section. None of the items of equipment described constitutes an airborne system inasmuch as none singly is capable of providing data whereby ground control may be established. The final objective is the space coordinates *(X, Y, Z)* of a system of points oriented on a geographic azimuth referred to (1) an absolute geographic position with respect to location, and to (2) sea-level datum with respect to elevation. It has been previously stipulated that a dimension, the angular orientation of two overlapping pairs, an azimuth, and a position are required to determine these data. The star zenith camera is the only instrument that will provide absolute position, and a position so obtained is less accurate than that obtained from the navigator's fix. We conclude, therefore, that the track chart, being more accurate, will be employed for the aircraft's position. This is not as serious as it first appears. The error of absolute position is serious only when established near an area in which accurate positions exist or when successive absolute position is the means of establishing a system of terrestrial points. Neither of the critical situations applies to the problem at hand. Of much more importance is the relative accuracy of the system of points with respect to each other. Position, henceforth, will not be discussed inasmuch as only a very low order of accuracy may be obtained and inasmuch as the low order of accuracy is not critical.

Dimensions are required. This will be assumed to be some form of elevation difference recorded, whereby the absolute elevation of the exposure station may be considered known with respect to an assumed datum. This leaves the horizon cameras and the zenith cameras to be combined in a complete system.

For night exposures, the elevation recorder and the star zenith camera will provide complete data for defining the space coordinates and orientation of objects photographed with a nadir camera. The night system consists of:

(1) Automatic altitude recorder.
(2) Star zenith camera locked to a nadir camera.
(3) Chronometer and perhaps a chronometer-recording camera.

For day exposures, the automatic altitude recorder in combination with horizon or oblique cameras provides a ZL dimension and angular orientation for successive exposure stations. These data can be employed to establish the space coordinates of points. The system, however, is incomplete insofar as it does not have provisions for geographic azimuth orientation. Though the Santoni solar camera provides neither position nor angular orientation without presurveyed points at the flight ends, it will provide true azimuth when synchronized with horizon or oblique camera data. Thus the complete day exposure system will consist of:

(1) Automatic altitude recorder.
(2) Solar camera and one or two horizon or oblique cameras locked to a nadir camera.
(3) Chronometer and chronometer-recording camera.

The day exposure system is illustrated in Figure 53.

2. Daylight Photographic System.

Assume that the tilt and swing of two overlapping exposures have been determined with measurements made on the images of the horizons.

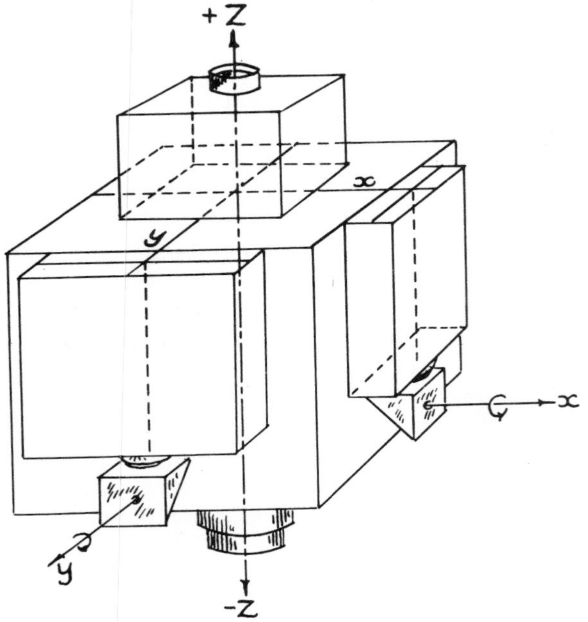

Fig. 53 Zenith-horizon-nadir camera system for daylight operations.

Assume also that astronomic positions of the camera at the two exposure stations have been interpolated from the navigator's track chart and that the altitudes of the two exposure stations have been accurately recorded.

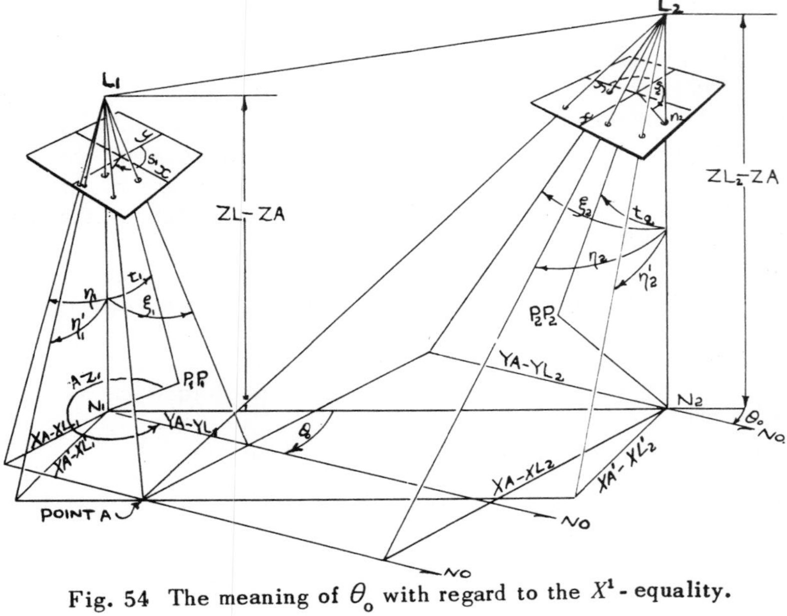

Fig. 54 The meaning of θ_o with regard to the X^1- equality.

It can be seen from Figure 54 that if the exposures are horizontalized (rectified) with their respective tilt and swing transformations and oriented on north from the azimuths of the sun, the following equations may be written:

$$\tan \eta_{a_1} (ZL_1 - ZA) = XA - XL_1$$

$$\tan \eta_{a_2} (ZL_2 - ZA) = XA - XL_2$$

But since neither XL_1, XL_2, XA, or ZA is known, and since $XA - XL_1 \neq XA - XL_2$, the equations are unsolvable as they stand. But if azimuth (θ_0) of the air base were known and the exposures were oriented on the air base in place of north, the following more useful equations could be written:

$$\tan \eta_{a_1}{}^1 (ZL_1 - ZA) = (XA - XL_1)^1$$

$$\tan \eta_{a_2}{}^1 (ZL_2 - ZA) = (XA - XL_2)^1$$

and $$(XA - XL_1)^1 = (XA - XL_2)^1$$

This is the desired equality, since when

$$(XA - XL_1)^1 = (XA - XL_2)^1,$$

$$ZA = \frac{ZL_1 \tan \eta_{a_1}{}^1 - ZL_2 \tan \eta_{a_2}{}^1}{\tan \eta_{a_1}{}^1 - \tan \eta_{a_2}{}^1}$$

Therefore the azimuth (θ_0) of the air base is required. That is, since

$$\tan \eta_{a_1}{}^1 = \tan \eta_{a_1} \cos \theta_0 - \tan \xi_{a_1} \sin \theta_0$$

and $$\tan \eta_{a_2}{}^1 = \tan \eta_{a_2} \cos \theta_0 - \tan \xi_{a_2} \sin \theta_0$$

θ_0 is required for the determination of $(ZL_1 - ZA)$ from which the X and Y of the same point (A) may be determined as a direct consequence of $ZL_1 - ZA$, inasmuch as

$$\tan \eta_{a_1} (ZL_1 - ZA) = XA - XL_1$$

$$\tan \eta_{a_2} (ZL_2 - ZA) = XA - XL_2$$

$$\tan \xi_{a_1} (ZL_1 - ZA) = YA - YL_1$$

$$\tan \xi_{a_2} (ZL_2 - ZA) = YA - YL_2$$

These relations are evident from Figure 54. The subscripts 1 and 2 denote initial and succeeding exposures. The above equations are written for a second point *B*, as well as for *A*. From previous considerations related to space-intersection equations,

$$\tan \eta_1 = \frac{x_1 \cos \alpha_{x_1} + y_1 \cos \alpha_{y_1} + f \cos \alpha_{z_1}}{x_1 \cos \gamma_{x_1} + y_1 \cos \gamma_{y_1} + f \cos \gamma_{z_1}}$$

$$\tan \eta_2 = \frac{x_2 \cos \alpha_{x_2} + y_2 \cos \alpha_{y_2} + f \cos \alpha_{z_2}}{x_2 \cos \gamma_{x_2} + y_2 \cos \gamma_{y_2} + f \cos \gamma_{z_2}}$$

$$\tan \xi_1 = \frac{x_1 \cos \beta_{x_1} + y_1 \cos \beta_{y_1} + f \cos \beta_{z_1}}{x_1 \cos \gamma_{x_1} + y_1 \cos \gamma_{y_1} + f \cos \gamma_{z_1}}$$

$$\tan \xi_2 = \frac{x_2 \cos \beta_{x_2} + y_2 \cos \beta_{y_2} + f \cos \beta_{z_2}}{x_2 \cos \gamma_{x_2} + y_2 \cos \gamma_{y_2} + f \cos \gamma_{z_2}}$$

for any point, where the direction cosines have been previously defined. Recalling that in reciprocal orientation equations,

$$\tan \eta_1^{11} = \tan \eta_2^{11}$$

where s_1^1, s_2^1, t_1^1, t_2^1, Az_1^1, and Az_2^1 refer to a fictitious datum that is parallel to the air base. A special case of the η-equality is employed to determine θ_o. The special case is developed from the fact that standard coordinates of conjugate images refer to a common geographic azimuth and parallel *Z* axes which are normal to datum. With these orientation properties,

$$s_1^1 = s_2^1 = \theta_o$$

$$t_1^1 = t_2^1 = t_o$$

$$Az_1^1 = Az_2^1 = 0$$

The η-equality is illustrated in Figure 55.

Therefore if $\tan \eta_1^{11} = \tan \eta_2^{11}$, and

$$\tan \eta_1^{11} = \frac{\tan \eta_1 \cos \theta_o - \tan \xi_1 \sin \theta_o}{\tan \eta_1 \sin \theta_o \sin t_o + \tan \xi_1 \cos \theta_o \sin t_o + \cos t_o}$$

$$\tan \eta_2^{11} = \frac{\tan \eta_2 \cos \theta_o - \tan \xi_2 \sin \theta_o}{\tan \eta_2 \sin \theta_o \sin t_o + \tan \xi_2 \cos \theta_o \sin t_o + \cos t_o}$$

Then

$$\frac{\tan \eta_1 \cos \theta_0 - \tan \xi_1 \sin \theta_0}{\tan \eta_1 \sin \theta_0 \sin t_0 + \tan \xi_1 \cos \theta_0 \sin t_0 + \cos t_0}$$

$$= \frac{\tan \eta_2 \cos \theta_0 - \tan \xi_2 \sin \theta_0}{\tan \eta_2 \sin \theta_0 \sin t_0 + \tan \xi_2 \cos \theta_0 \sin t_0 + \cos t_0}$$

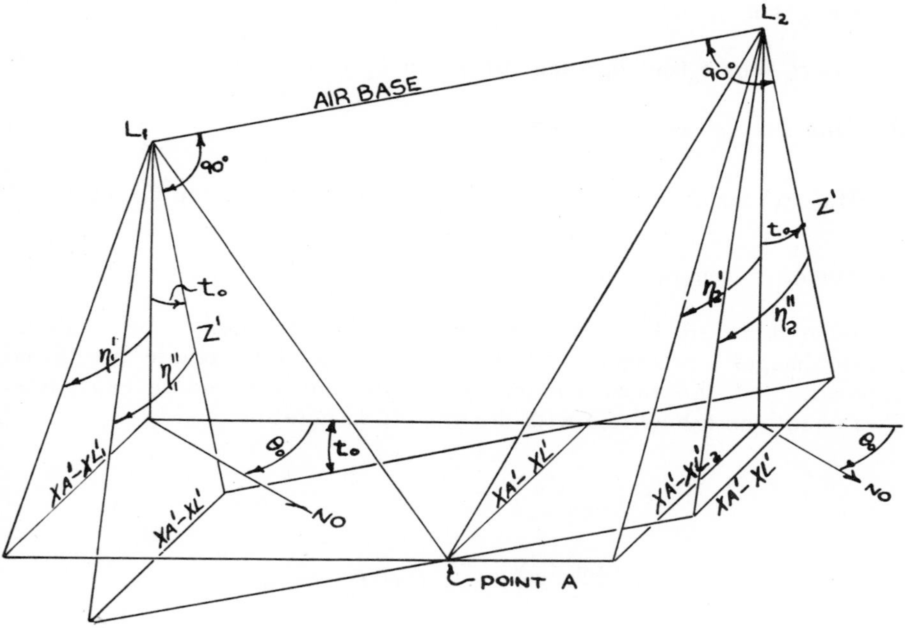

Fig. 55 The η-equality referred to an arbitrary datum parallel to the air base, L_1L_2.

Cross-multiplying,

$$+ \tan \eta_1 \tan \eta_2 \cos \theta_0 \sin \theta_0 \sin t_0 + \tan \eta_1 \tan \xi_2 \cos^2\theta_0 \sin t_0$$

$$+ \tan \eta_1 \cos \theta_0 \cos t_0 - \tan \xi_1 \tan \eta_2 \sin^2\theta_0 \sin t_0$$

$$- \tan \xi_1 \tan \xi_2 \sin \theta_0 \cos \theta_0 \sin t_0 - \tan \xi_1 \sin \theta_0 \cos t_0$$

$$= + \tan \eta_2 \tan \eta_1 \cos \theta_0 \sin \theta_0 \sin t_0 + \tan \eta_2 \tan \xi_1 \cos^2\theta_0 \sin t_0$$

$$+ \tan \eta_2 \cos \theta_0 \cos t_0 - \tan \xi_2 \tan \eta_1 \sin^2\theta_0 \sin t_0$$

$$- \tan \xi_2 \tan \xi_1 \sin \theta_0 \cos \theta_0 \sin t_0 - \tan \xi_2 \sin \theta_0 \cos t_0$$

Collecting, and factoring common terms,

$$\cos^2\theta_o \ \sin t_o(\tan\eta_1 \ \tan\xi_2 \ - \ \tan\eta_2 \ \tan\xi_1)$$

$$+ \ \sin^2\theta_o \ \sin t_o(\tan\eta_1 \ \tan\xi_2 \ - \ \tan\eta_2 \ \tan\xi_1)$$

$$+ \ \cos\theta_o \ \cos t_o(\tan\eta_1 - \tan\eta_2) + \sin\theta_o \ \cos t_o(\tan\xi_2 - \tan\xi_1) \ = \ 0$$

which reduces to

$$\sin t_o(\tan\eta_1 \ \tan\xi_2 \ - \ \tan\eta_2 \ \tan\xi_1)$$

$$+ \ \cos\theta_o \ \cos t_o(\tan\eta_1 - \tan\eta_2) + \sin\theta_o \ \cos t_o(\tan\xi_2 - \tan\xi_1) \ = \ 0$$

Dividing through by $\cos\theta_o \ \cos t_o$,

$$(\tan\eta_1 \ \tan\xi_2 - \tan\eta_2 \ \tan\xi_1)\frac{\tan t_o}{\cos\theta_o} + (\tan\xi_2 - \tan\xi_1)\tan\theta_o$$

$$= \ \tan\eta_2 \ - \ \tan\eta_1$$

Since there are two unknowns, the standard coordinates of two conjugate images are required. Let the odd subscripts denote the initial exposure and the even subscripts denote the succeeding exposures. Two equations are written with the simplified notation:

$$m_1\left(\frac{\tan t_o}{\cos\theta_o}\right) + n_1(\tan\theta_o) \ = \ q_1$$

$$m_2\left(\frac{\tan t_o}{\cos\theta_o}\right) + n_2(\tan\theta_o) \ = \ q_2$$

where

$$m_1 \ = \ \tan\eta_{a_1} \ \tan\xi_{a_2} \ - \ \tan\eta_{a_2} \ \tan\xi_{a_1}$$

$$m_2 \ = \ \tan\eta_{b_1} \ \tan\xi_{b_2} \ - \ \tan\eta_{b_2} \ \tan\xi_{b_1}$$

$$\eta_1 \ = \ \tan\xi_{a_2} \ - \ \tan\xi_{a_1}$$

$$\eta_2 \ = \ \tan\xi_{b_2} \ - \ \tan\xi_{b_1}$$

$$q_1 \ = \ \tan\eta_{a_2} \ - \ \tan\eta_{a_1}$$

$$q_2 \ = \ \tan\eta_{b_2} \ - \ \tan\eta_{b_1}$$

Solving for $\frac{\tan t_o}{\cos\theta_o}$ and $\tan\theta_o$,

$$\tan \eta_{a_1}{}^1 = \tan \eta_{a_1} \cos \theta_o - \tan \xi_{a_1} \sin \theta_o$$

$$\tan \eta_{a_2}{}^1 = \tan \eta_{a_2} \cos \theta_o - \tan \xi_{a_2} \sin \theta_o$$

$$\tan \eta_{b_1}{}^1 = \tan \eta_{b_1} \cos \theta_o - \tan \xi_{b_1} \sin \theta_o$$

$$\tan \eta_{b_2}{}^1 = \tan \eta_{b_2} \cos \theta_o - \tan \xi_{b_2} \sin \theta_o$$

and as previously stated,

$$ZA = \frac{ZL_1 \tan \eta_{a_1}{}^1 - ZL_2 \tan \eta_{a_2}{}^1}{\tan \eta_{a_1}{}^1 - \tan \eta_{a_2}{}^1}$$

$$ZB = \frac{ZL_1 \tan \eta_{b_1}{}^1 - ZL_2 \tan \eta_{b_2}{}^1}{\tan \eta_{b_1}{}^1 - \tan \eta_{b_2}{}^1}$$

$$XA-XL_1 = \tan \eta_{a_1} (ZL_1-ZA) \qquad XB-XL_1 = \tan \eta_{b_1} (ZL_1-ZB)$$

$$XA-XL_2 = \tan \eta_{a_2} (ZL_2-ZA) \qquad XB-XL_2 = \tan \eta_{b_2} (ZL_2-ZB)$$

$$YA-YL_1 = \tan \xi_{a_1} (ZL_1-ZA) \qquad YB-YL_1 = \tan \xi_{b_1} (ZL_1-ZB)$$

$$YA-YL_2 = \tan \xi_{a_2} (ZL_2-ZA) \qquad YB-YL_2 = \tan \xi_{b_2} (ZL_2-ZB)$$

Thus the space coordinates of any desired number of points may be defined and this system of points collectively referred to and oriented on a standard coordinate system without known object points.

The night exposure system is identical to the day system except that in the day system angular orientation is obtained from horizon cameras, and azimuth from a sun camera, whereas in the night system both azimuth and angular orientation are obtained from a single star zenith camera. All other details are the same.

Chapter VII

NOTATION AND DEFINITIONS

A. *GENERAL CRITERIA*.

The science of photogrammetry deals with the relation between points in object space and the conjugate points in an image plane. A set of definitions and symbols is essential to an adequate description and understanding of any subject. In this respect defined rules, concepts, and symbolism serve a useful purpose to both the writer and the reader. They serve as boundaries to the writer and provide a language and a guide to the reader.

Photogrammetry, like the subject of optics, has a dual language. If the rectilinear propagation of light is assumed to be a fact, geometric optics must be assumed to be a fact; if the diffraction phenomenon of light is assumed to be a fact, physical optics embracing the wave theory of light must be assumed to be a fact. Experimental data make it evident that the subject of light is more faithfully defined with the concepts embraced in physical optics and, moreover, that the rectilinear propagation of light is not rigorously true. Despite this apparent contradiction, the most precise lens formulae today are derived from the fundamental equations of geometric optics. Both kinds of optics are essential to a comprehensive treatment of light, and each kind of optics serves a useful scientific function. Therefore the dual language of optics, instead of being controversial, is accepted as necessary.

Photogrammetry has an analogous role. If point-objects and point-images are assumed to define straight lines having the lens as a common intersection point, the mathematical concept of photogrammetry is accepted as true. If the mathematical equations expressing a relation between point-objects and conjugate point-images in a plane are applied to real objects and conjugate photographic images, the physical nature of photogrammetry must be considered in connection with the lens and photographic emulsions. The latter form the basis of physical photogrammetry. This book deals with the idealized mathematical concepts of photogrammetry. Physical photogrammetry is mathematical photogrammetry subjected and adjusted according to reality. Physical photogrammetry cannot exist without a mathematical basis, and mathematical photogrammetry has no value unless extended to physical reality. Both concepts are essential to a comprehensive treatment of photogrammetry.

The inadequacy of a wholly mathematical concept of photogrammetry becomes evident when an attempt is made to apply exterior orientation equations to real photography. Most of the preliminary efforts are toward making the physical aspects of the image satisfy the assumption made in the mathematical concept, which is that the image, lens, and object define a straight line. The image physically undergoes a shift owing to lens distortion, film distortion, and refraction and fails to be a point owing to diffraction, lens aberrations, target geometry, size and contrast, and to film resolution. These physical properties of photogrammetry are not covered by the mathematical equation; nor is it practical to derive such an equation. On the other hand, the ultimate in photogrammetric camera and plotting instrument design is a mechanical optical system that fulfills a mathematical ideal. It is clear that the physical and mathematical concepts of photogrammetry are essential and interrelated to such a degree that one cannot exist without the other.

An attempt is made here to provide functional notations and definitions for both the mathematical and physical concepts of photogrammetry. Any lack of clarity that may arise in an attempt to provide a complete set of symbols and definitions for the subject of photogrammetry can be reduced by examining the nomenclature of older basic sciences of which photogrammetry is comprised. Though photogrammetry is basically a science of image measurements and calculations to establish the relation to conjugate point-objects, its physical structure consists of such general sciences as physics, chemistry, and mathematics and such composite subjects as photography, astronomy, surveying, and optics. Each of these sciences and subjects preceded photogrammetry historically and therefore has an established notation and terminology that has extended into the subject of photogrammetry.

In many cases, similarity of several prior definitions and symbols has resulted in duplication and ambiguity in the adopted photogrammetric nomenclature. In still other cases the precise photogrammetric meaning has been obscured by a prior meaning.

An example of duplication is the notation for tilt (t). Elsewhere in the application of analytical photogrammetry to field astronomy the notation for hour angle is also t. Since the notation t has a prior existence in field astronomy, it becomes necessary to find another notation for tilt, such as γ_z, which is the angle between the normals to two reference planes. In the case of tilt the reference planes are the image plane and the sea-level datum plane; the normals are the optical axis and the plumb line. Yet in photogrammetric position determination the planes are the image plane and the celestial equator; the normals are the optical axis and the polar axis. In the latter case γ_z corresponds to $(90^\circ - \varphi)$. It becomes more apparent that a mutually exclusive notation is nearly impossible. Since this is true, a general notation such as γ_z is more desirable, with qualifying statements regarding the application and coordinate system under consideration.

The confusion over the precise meaning of principal point is an example of ambiguity arising out of not considering the prior optical meaning of the term. The principal point in optical lens terminology is the intersection of the lens principal plane with the lens optical axis. An exposure with a camera having a lens properly mounted will provide an image of the optical principal point that corresponds perfectly with the photogrammetric principal point. The photogrammetric concept of principal point is a logical photographic extension of the optical principal point.

Many controversial definitions related to the principal point have arisen out of deviation due to manufacturing imperfections. If the image plane is normal to the optical axis and the lens is not decentered, all other definitions of the principal point resolve at once to a single point--the photographic extension of the optical principal point. It seems logical, therefore, to agree on the optical definition with a photographic prefix, such as *photo principal point*, just as the nadir point is prefixed with *photo* on the photograph and *ground* on the ground. When the photo nadir point, owing to manufacturing errors, falls elsewhere on the photograph, no attempt is made to find a new name for photo nadir point. Similarly, no attempt should be made to find a new name or definition for principal point simply because manufacturing errors cause the principal point as defined not to be recoverable in practice. These deviations from the definitions as they pertain to camera systems free from manufacturing errors should be regarded as definitions of errors in the location of the principal point and not new definitions set up to replace already accepted definitions.

Subtle definitions that require both background and experience to appreciate beyond that possessed by the student are avoided. Such a definition is "Photogrammetry is the science of obtaining reliable measurements from photographs." To appreciate this definition one must interject a wealth of meaning into the word reliable. Taken literally it might mean a high degree of reproducibility in linear measurements, which is equivalent to saying that close agreement with repeated measurements on a photograph is satisfying the definition of photogrammetry. Or it may mean the science of ascertaining all the factors affecting the position and resolution of an image whereby reliable photographic measurements are assured. Neither of these literal suppositions says anything about establishing the relation between point-objects and point-images whereby the configuration of areas or the shape of objects may be determined, nor anything about the true role of the metrical camera as a photographic goniometer. The stated definition is too subtle and brief to the point of poverty for the student, inasmuch as only one with prior background and experience can embody the phrase "reliable measurements from photographs" with enough connotations and data to satisfy the fundamental purpose of photogrammetry.

That definitions should as far as possible establish boundaries and reduce ambiguity and duplication, and that the notation should serve the purpose of standardized photogrammetric shorthand cannot be challenged.

In this book standard mathematical notation and terminology are employed wherever possible. The definitions and notations in this chapter include terms used in subjects closely related to photogrammetry, such as surveying, astronomy, and optics.

Secondary definitions and notations appear as subheadings under major definitions and notations to provide the essential nomenclature of the related subjects and to prevent confusion where they are duplicated in two or more subjects. An effort is made for a standardization that will provide continuity between the common terms of different equations without a loss of flexibility.

Two of the most frequently misunderstood terms are *depth of focus* and *depth of field.* The phrase *depth of focus* is often employed as meaning both *depth of focus* and *depth of field.* Sometimes the terms are inverted or it is insisted that they have one and the same meaning. Much of this ambiguity arises from the interdependence of one on the other: that is, for every *depth of object space* (depth of field) there is an exact *depth of image space* (depth of focus). This interdependence is established in the formula for conjugate foci.

$$\frac{1}{u} + \frac{1}{v} = \frac{1}{f}$$

v cannot be altered without altering u and u cannot be altered without altering v. Despite this interdependence *depth of image space* and *depth of object space* have two distinctly different meanings.

Depth of image space is the permissible shift of the image plane that will not impair the photographic definition for a given object distance. Depth of object space is the permissible movement of an object toward and away from the camera that will not impair the photographic definition for a given image distance. The terms *depth of focus* and *depth of field* are inadequate and therefore are not defined. The terms *depth of image space* and *depth of object space* are used and defined as being less ambiguous.

The mathematical concept makes possible a simple classification of various image movements. All equations assume the image, lens, and object to define a straight line. Any movement of the image that does not alter the straight line relation of object, lens, and image is regarded as a *displacement.* Movements of the image introduced by relief and tilt therefore are relief displacements and tilt displacements. This is consistent with the mathematical concept of the photograph as an idealized perspective projection.

Any movement of the image that does alter the straight-line relation is regarded as a *distortion.* Distortions are further cataloged as symmetrical and asymmetrical or random. Movements of the image introduced by film expansion and contraction, lens aberrations, and atmospheric refraction are distortions.

Since the subject matter is computational photogrammetry, definitions related to the equivalent instrumental solutions are given in the most general terms. For example, the term *stereo plotting instrument* is defined, while specific types such as the multiplex and stereo comparagraph within the stereo plotting class are not defined.

B. *DEFINITIONS AND NOTATIONS.*

ABERRATION--A condition in an optical system in which image points are imperfect or are improperly located. There are seven optical aberrations: astigmatism, lateral chromatic aberration, longitudinal chromatic aberration, spherical aberration, coma, curvature of field, and distortion. The failure of light from a point on an object, after passing through the lens, to converge to a point on the image.

Distortion--That aberration of an image resulting in the incorrect geometrical representation of the object; extra-axial image points are either too near to, or too far away from, the center.

ACCURACY--Degree of conformity with a *standard.* Accuracy relates to the quality of a result and is distinguished from precision, which relates to the quality of the operation by which the result is obtained.

AIR BASE--A line joining two air camera stations or the length of the line joining two air camera stations.

AIR BASE DIRECTION--The azimuth and inclination of the air base.

AIRY'S DISK--A diffraction pattern point-image of a point-object.

ALTIMETER--An instrument which indicates the vertical distance above a specified datum.

ALTITUDE--The vertical distance above the datum, usually mean sea level, to an object or point in space. Also the angular height of an object above a level line.

ANGLE--That relationship of lines on surfaces which is measured by the amount of rotation necessary to make one coincide with or parallel to another. An angle may be expressed as a difference in directions of lines: (1) in a plane, giving a *plane angle,* (2) in a curved surface, giving a *spherical angle,* (3) in two planes, measuring the inclination of one plane to the other, giving a dihedral angle. In each case the magnitude of the angle is reckoned in units derived from a complete circumference of a circle. (1) The degree ($^{\circ}$) is 1/360th part of a circumference. The degree is divided into 60 minutes ($60'$) and the minute into 60 seconds ($60''$). (2) The hour (h) is 1/24th part of a circumference. The hour is divided into 60 minutes (60^{m}) and the minute into 60 seconds (60^{s}).

Angle of coverage--The apex angle of the cone of rays passing through the front nodal point of a lens. *Normal-angle lens*--A lens having an angle of coverage up to 70°; *wide-angle lens*--A lens having an angle of coverage greater than 70°.

Angle of incidence--The angle between a ray of light approaching the boundary of an optical medium and the normal to that boundary at the point of contact.

Angle of reflection--The angle between a reflected light ray and the normal to the reflecting surface at the point of contact.

Angle of refraction--The angle between a refracted light ray and the normal to the refracting surface at the point of contact.

Intersection angle--The angle defined by the intersection of two observed directions to a distant object which is not occupied by the observer at any time. An intersection angle is one that is not observed but rather deduced by subtracting from 180° the sum of the angles observed at the two other points which form a triangle with the intersection point.

Plane angle--The angle between two nonparallel lines, generally associated with horizontal angles.

Spherical angle--An angle between great circles on a sphere. A spherical angle is measured either by (1) the dihedral angle of the planes of great circles or by (2) the plane angle between tangents to great circles at their intersection.

Swing angle--Rotation of the principal line about the principal point in the plane of the film. The swing rotation is measured clockwise from the positive y axis.

Vertical angle--Angle between any point and a reference datum.

Zenith angle-- The spherical side of the astronomic triangle defined by the observer's zenith and any star. The zenith angle is a vertical angle generated from the vertical at the observer.

Zone angle--Angle defined by an image lying in any zone and the principal point, at the rear nodal point. Usually designated γ with the appropriate subscript.

APERTURE--An opening. The optical projection of the aperture stop upon the objective.

APPROXIMATE--Approaching closely but not attaining a specified accuracy. Failure to take enough observations, or observations made with an inferior instrument will give an approximate result. Omission of corrections or the neglect of terms having significant values will produce an approximate result, even where the observations themselves are satisfactory.

ARC--Circumferential interval, generated by an angle at the radii intersection points, of a curve that is mathematically defined or capable of mathematical definition.

AXIAL ALINEMENT--The alinement of the lens axis of two optical instruments; the alinement of an optical axis with a mechanical axis, such as the lens axis of the camera being normal to the camera image plane.

AXIAL DEVIATION--A lens axis not parallel with a mechanical axis. This defect may occur in a lens cell, a camera cone, or a telescope barrel.

AXIAL ORIENTATION--The direction of the axis of an instrument, such as the lens axis of a camera, defined by angles measured from a system of reference planes. Tilt and azimuth define the axial orientation of a camera lens axis in a space-coordinate system.

AXIAL PENCIL--That pencil of light rays which is symmetric about the principal axis.

AXIS--

Axis of rotation--The axis about which an instrument rotates. A zenith camera rotates about a vertical axis and its own lens axis; a theodolite telescope rotates about horizontal and vertical axes; an astrolabe rotates about a vertical axis with the optical axis lying in the horizon plane. One axis is always fixed with respect to a standard or arbitrary reference.

Camera axis--The line perpendicular to the image plane and passing through the rear nodal point. The lens axis (optical axis) coincides with the camera axis in a camera free from manufacturing imperfections.

Horizontal axis--The axis of rotation in a vertical plane of a mechanical or photographic angle-measuring instrument.

Instrument axis--The mechanical axis about which an instrument such as a surveying camera or transit telescope rotates. Angle-surveying instruments usually have two axes: the spindle for horizontal rotation about the vertical, and the horizontal axis for vertical rotation about the horizontal.

Optical axis--The line defined by the front and rear nodal points of a thick lens, or the line defined by the centers of curvature of the incident and emergent surfaces of any lens system.

Vertical axis--The Z axis in conventional geodetic object space and the axis of the spindle on a level, adjusted surveying instrument.

AZIMUTH--The horizontal direction measured clockwise from the meridian plane.

Astronomic azimuth--At the point of observation, the angle measured from the vertical plane through the celestial pole to the vertical plane through the observed object.

Geodetic azimuth--The angle between a geodetic meridian and a geodetic line.

Photogrammetric azimuth--A horizontal angle measured clockwise at the camera ground nadir from a vertical reference plane through the camera lens to the principal plane.

AZIMUTH MARK--A reference object whereby a north line may be recovered at an observation station.

BAROMETER--An instrument for measuring atmospheric pressure. There are two general types: those in which atmospheric pressure is balanced by the weight of a column of liquid (usually mercury); and those in which atmospheric pressure is balanced by some elastic device. The latter are termed aneroid (without liquid) barometers.

BASE LINE--A surveyed line established with more than usual care, to which surveys are referred for *coordination* and *correlation.* The measured side of an initial triangle of a triangulation scheme.

BENCH MARK--A relatively permanent material object, natural or artificial, bearing a marked point whose elevation above or below an adopted datum is known.

BLUNDER--A mistake. A blunder is not an error, though a small blunder may remain undetected in a series of observations and have the effect of an error in determining a result. Examples of blunders are reading a horizontal circle incorrectly by an even degree or reading the micrometer scale of a measuring machine incorrectly by an even millimeter.

BRIDGING--The extension and adjustment of photogrammetric surveys between bands of ground control.

BUNDLE--In optics, a collection of light rays, all pertaining to a given object point or image point.

CALCULATOR--A mechanical or electronic device capable of addition, subtraction, multiplication, and division.

Antilog calculator--Rapid computer based on an electronic model of a specific problem.

Desk calculator--An instrument capable of addition, subtraction, multiplication, and division singly or in series. Some are operated manually while most are operated with electrical power. The types usually used are capable of handling 10-digit numbers.

Electronic calculator--Antilog computer capable of terrific speeds with iterative solutions.

CALIBRATION--See CAMERA CALIBRATION.

CALIBRATOR--An optical mechanical device for production camera calibration consisting of one or two banks of collimators arranged so that the collimator axes intersect at a common point in object space. The front nodal point of the camera being calibrated is usually placed near this point with the image plane perpendicular to the axis of the central collimator.

CAMERA--A chamber or box in which the images of exterior objects are projected on a sensitized surface.

Aerial camera--A camera designed for use in aircraft.

Amateur camera--A camera, usually small and highly portable, designed to obtain pictorial rather than metrical photography. Metrical properties of such cameras are subordinated to general utility. The variable image distance feature for the purpose of photographing subjects at any desired object distance increases the general utility of an amateur camera at the expense of its metrical properties.

Camera lucida--A monocular instrument using a half-silvered mirror or the optical equivalent thereof to permit superimposition of a rectified virtual image of a photograph over a map manuscript.

Camera x axis--Opposite pairs of fiducial marks define the x and y axes. Which pair define the x and which pair define the y is entirely arbitrary. Generally the pair of fiducial marks defining a line normal to the flight line is designated the x axis with aerial cameras, whereas the pair parallel to the horizon is designated the x axis with ground cameras.

Camera y axis--Generally the pair of fiducial marks defining a line approximately parallel to the flight is designated the y axis with aerial cameras, whereas the pair defining a vertical plane is designated the y axis with ground cameras.

Camera z axis--The z axis is the optical axis of the camera lens system.

Collimating camera--A precise camera with a system of intersections in the image plane in which the camera lens and the intersections serve the purpose of a solid bank of collimators. Such a camera is employed to calibrate other cameras.

Ground camera--A camera designed specifically for ground operation. Either hand-held or tripod-mounted, but never gimbals-mounted as aerial cameras may be.

High-oblique camera--An airborne camera, generally, with a cone angle and a tilt angle capable of providing an image of the visible horizon. The oblique cameras of the trimetrogon camera system are of this class.

Horizon camera--Any aerial camera intended to provide successive images of the horizon. The conventional type is mounted in pairs with their lens axes perpendicular to each other and parallel to the nadir camera's focal plane. One horizon camera optical axis is usually parallel to one fiducial axis of the nadir camera, while the other is parallel to the other fiducial axis of the nadir camera.

Metrical camera--Any camera designed to provide image coordinates sufficiently precise for photogrammetric calculations. Metrical cameras are usually fixed focus with the lens, inner cone, and image frame constructed as one rigid symmetrical unit. The lens is highly corrected and the image frame equipped with fiducial marks for recovery of the principal point.

Multilens camera--Cameras locked together with different relative orientations to provide more comprehensive coverage of terrain, with the interlocking angles between the various cameras known.

Nadir camera--An airborne camera intended to provide vertical exposures of terrain.

Nonmetrical camera--A camera intended for pictorial, record, or interpretation purposes or for purposes other than those of measurement. Such cameras usually have a variable image distance feature, are not calibrated, and do not have fiducial marks or, except by accident, a small angle of decentration.

Normal-angle camera--A camera having a cone angle of 70° or less.

Oblique camera--Any camera that by virtue of its purpose or fixed mount is employed to photograph terrain that lies predominantly between the nadir and the horizon. Either may be recorded on one edge of the image frame. Whether the nadir or the horizon line is photographed depends on the cone angle, and which is recorded depends on whether the exposure is a high oblique or a low oblique.

Pinhole camera--A camera made of a light-tight box containing a covered pinhole in one of the sides.

Stereo camera--A combination of two cameras mounted with parallel optical axes on a short rigid base, used in terrestrial photogrammetry for taking photographs in stereoscopic pairs.

Surveying camera--A camera designed to provide photographs for map construction or the establishment of photogrammetric control.

Terrestrial camera--A camera designed for exposure from ground stations, usually spindle-mounted and almost always tripod-mounted. Most terrestrial cameras are intended for low-order horizontal and vertical control.

Wide-angle camera--Any camera, usually a mapping camera, having a cone angle greater than 70°.

CAMERA CALIBRATION--The determination of the calibrated focal length, the location of the principal point with respect to the fiducial axes, the resolution of the lens, the degree of flatness of the image plane, and the lens distortion effective in the focal plane of the camera and referred to the calibrated focal length.

Analytical calibration (air calibration)--Determination of camera interior-orientation data from an aerial exposure with the space and plate coordinates of seven imaged objects as the given data.

Goniometer camera calibration--A method of calibrating cameras which consists of measuring the angles subtended by a system of points marked on a glass plate locked in the image plane with a goniometer or theodolite sighting through the camera lens from a position in object space near the incident lens surface.

Photographic camera calibration--Any method of camera calibration which is dependent on a photographic record of a system of objects whose subtended angles at the camera station are known.

Terrestrial target calibration--A method of field camera calibration consisting of exposures of a line of terrestrial targets of known subtended angles, lying in the horizon plane of the camera lens.

Vanishing-point calibration--A method of determining the focal length and principal point by location of three vanishing points on a single exposure of a rectilinear building.

CANTILEVER EXTENSION--The prolongation of a strip of photographs by photogrammetric methods from a controlled area to an area of no control.

CELL--A device for holding a lens or mirror.

CENTIMETER--One-hundredth part of a meter; 0.3937 inch.

CIRCLE OF CONFUSION--The circular image of a distant point-object as formed in the focal plane by a lens. A distant point-object (e.g., a star) is imaged in a focal plane of a lens as a circle of finite size which may be caused by (1) the focal plane not being placed at the point of sharpest focus, (2) the effect of certain aberrations, (3) diffraction at the lens, (4) the grain of a photographic emulsion, (5) poor workmanship in the manufacture of the lens, etc.

COAXIAL--Having coincident axes, such as those in two collimators facing each other.

COEFFICIENT--Any numeral or literal symbol placed before another symbol or combination of symbols, as a multiplier.

COLLIMATION--The process of alining the optical axis of two or more optical instruments such as a collimator and a camera.

Autocollimation--Establishing a plane perpendicular to the optical axis of a collimator by coincidence of a projected and reflected image of a center cross in the focal plane of the collimator.

COLLIMATION POINT--The image of an object that with the front nodal point of the camera lens defines a line that is perpendicular to the camera image plane in object space. The image of the center cross of a collimator whose axis is perpendicular to the camera image plane is considered the photographic collimation point. Some authorities consider this image to be identical with the principal point.

COLLIMATOR--An optical device used for alining optical axes, consisting of a convergent lens with a marked place in the plane of its principal focus, so that rays from the mark through the lens emerge along parallel lines.

COLLINEAR--Lying in the same straight line. When the optical axis of a camera lens is collinear with the optical axis of a collimator, the reticle of the collimator is imaged at the collimation point of the camera.

COMPARATOR (PLANE-COORDINATE)--An instrument consisting of a viewing ocular with reference cross-hairs, a stage with two motions, one perpendicular to the other, and a graduated scale indicating the distance between two points parallel to the two motions. The instrument is employed to measure the x and y coordinates of images on photographs, film, or plates.

COMPUTE--To determine by calculation, to reckon. Same as numbering, estimating, or enumerating.

CONCURRENT--Meeting in, or directed to, the same point.

CONE--The geometrical surface produced by the revolution of a line that makes a fixed angle with the axis of revolution.

CONE ANGLE--The angle enclosed by the image frame of a camera at the rear nodal point and sometimes referred to as the field of view.

CONFIGURATION--The shape or form from a single viewpoint. The outline of an object traced on a plane section.

CONFORMATION--The shape of an object.

CONJUGATE DISTANCE--The corresponding distances of object and image from the nodal points of a lens. The conjugate distances u and v and the focal length are related by the formula:

$$\frac{1}{u} + \frac{1}{v} = \frac{1}{f}$$

or by Newton's formula,

$$u'v' = f^2$$
$$u' = u - f$$
$$v' = v - f$$

CONJUGATE-IMAGE POINT--The images on two or more overlapping photographs of a single object point.

CONJUGATE-IMAGE RAYS--Rays connecting each of a set of conjugate-image points with its particular perspective center.

CONSTANT--A magnitude that is supposed not to change its value in an equation, or is fixed while other values change at will.

CONTOUR--A line joining points of equal elevation above a specified datum surface.

CONTROL--In general, coordinated and correlated position data forming a framework to which the space coordinates and angular orientation of an exposure station are referenced.

CONTROL EXTENSION--Determining the coordinates of ground points by photogrammetric means by extrapolation from known points.

CONTROL POINT--A point on the ground whose position (horizontal and vertical) is used as a base for a dependent photographic survey.

CONVERGENCE ANGLE--An angle, at the object viewed, formed by lines from each end of the eye base.

COORDINATES--Linear or angular quantities, or both, which designate the position of a point in relation to a given reference frame. There are two general divisions of coordinates used in surveying: polar coordinates and rectangular coordinates. These may each be subdivided into three classes: plane coordinates, spherical coordinates, and space coordinates.

Astronomic coordinates--A system of spherical coordinates, defining the position of a star on the celestial sphere, consisting of right ascension (*RA* or α) and declination (δ). Right ascension is measured eastward from the sidereal zero hour (O^h) circle, in the plane of the celestial equator, to the hour circle passing through the star. Declination is the angle measured in the plane of the hour circle through the star from the celestial equator to the star. Sometimes right ascension is modified to refer to the Greenwich meridian and is designated Greenwich hour angle (*GHA*). Azimuth and zenith angle are the astronomic coordinates of a star referred to a specific point of observation.

Camera coordinates--Cartesian coordinates (x, y, z) referred to three mutually perpendicular lines which are the two fiducial axes and the optical axis. The origin of the system is at the foot of a normal to the image plane from the rear nodal point. The normal presumably coincides with the optical axis and the foot of the normal coincides with the principal point and fiducial axes' intersection. Opposite pairs of fiducial marks define the x and y axes, respectively, while the normal to the image plane is the z axis terminating at the rear nodal point.

Cartesian coordinates--Linear coordinates of a point that are the perpendicular distances to three mutually perpendicular reference planes. For instance, a point has three linear coordinates, x, y, z: the x value is the perpendicular distance from the yz plane; the y value is the perpendicular distance from the xz plane; and the z value is the perpendicular distance from the xy plane.

Geodetic coordinates--Quantities which define the position on the spheroid of reference with respect to the planes of the geodetic equator and of a selected geodetic meridian. The quantities are designated geodetic latitude and geodetic longitude.

Geographic coordinates--An inclusive term used to designate both geodetic coordinates and astronomic coordinates.

Photographic coordinates--A system of coordinates either rectangular or polar that describes the position of a point on a photograph. The image plane is the datum plane of the system and the x and y axes of the image plane are the same as or parallel to the fiducial axes. The vertical axis of the system is the lens optical axis and the reference for linear measurement along the vertical is the perpendicular distance from the rear nodal plane to the image plane. The vertical separation, due to lens distortion, of the image plane and rear nodal plane varies with zone angle.

Plane coordinates--Coordinates locating a point in a specified plane (such as *xy*, *yz*, or *xz*), consisting of the two coordinates defining the plane.

Polar coordinates--The location of a point in a plane by the distance from an origin and the angle the origin and point define with a reference line passing through the origin; the location of a point in space by a distance along a line from an origin and the angles the line makes at the origin with any two of three mutually perpendicular axes intersecting at the origin; or the location of a point in space with a distance and any two or three direction angles.

Space coordinates--Three numbers which locate a point in space. These numbers give the location of a point in a plane (*X*, *Y*) referred to an arbitrary origin and the vertical distance *(Z)* above or below the *XY* plane.

Spherical coordinates--Two quantities, angular or linear or both, on a sphere, defining the position of a point with reference to two great circles which form a pair of axes, or with reference to an origin and a great circle through the point. The term *spherical coordinates* includes coordinates on any surface approximating a sphere. Geographic, geodetic, and astronomic coordinates are considered spherical coordinates.

Standard coordinates--The angles subtended by the *x* and *y* values of a point at the origin in the *xz* and *yz* planes, respectively.

COORDINATION--The placing of survey data on the same coordinate system or datum. Coordination does not imply the adjustment of observation to remove discrepancies. Two field surveys over the same area may be coordinated by computation on the same datum, but there may remain between them discrepancies that can be removed only by correlation.

COPLANAR--All points in a surface lying in the same plane, or all points defining a flat surface.

CORRECTION--A quantity which is applied to an observation or function thereof to diminish or eliminate the effects of errors and to obtain an improved value of the observation or function. It is also applied to reduce an observation to some arbitrary standard.

CORRELATION--The removal of discrepancies that may exist among survey data so that all parts are interrelated without apparent error. The terms *coordination* and *correlation* are usually applied to the harmonizing of surveys of adjacent areas or of different surveys over the same area. Two or more such surveys are coordinated when they are computed on the same datum; they are correlated when they are adjusted together.

CROSS-HAIR--A mark on the axis of a telescope and in the focal plane of a telescope lens; usually a horizontal line intersecting a vertical line at a 90° angle in the form of a cross. These crosses have been constructed of spider web or platinum wire stretched across an opening. Recently the crosses are usually scribed on glass.

DANGER CIRCLE--The circle defined by three control points. A position falling on the circumference of this circle cannot be established by resection.

DANGER CYLINDER--The cylinder whose base is defined by three control points imaged on a photograph. The position of an exposure station occupying a point in the wall of this cylinder is indeterminate with either the iterative perspective ray method or the scale-point method and provides a weak solution with other methods.

DATA--Given quantities or facts regarded as true for the purpose of a solution.

DATUM--Any numerical or geometrical quantity or set of such quantities which may serve as a reference or base for other quantities.

Arbitrary datum--Any convenient numerical or geometrical quantity or set of quantities which may serve as a reference. Frequently it is convenient in reciprocal orientation computations to employ a reference plane that is not parallel to the observer's tangent plane. Such a reference plane is designated an arbitrary reference plane.

DEPTH OF FIELD--See DEPTH OF OBJECT SPACE.

DEPTH OF FOCUS--See DEPTH OF IMAGE SPACE.

DEPTH OF IMAGE SPACE--The permissible shift of the image plane normal to the lens axis either side of the plane of best definition. A permissible shift is one that will produce circles of confusion less than or equal to the maximum permissible diameter. Depth of image space is sometimes called the *depth of focus.*

DEPTH OF OBJECT SPACE--The permissible object distances greater than and less than the precise object distance for a given image distance. The permissible depth is a depth that will not result in circles of confusion with a diameter greater than the maximum permissible diameter. Depth of object space is usually referred to as the *depth of field.*

DETERMINANT--An orderly array of the given quantities of a given number of equations having the same number of common unknowns. Determinant means that these quantities establish the boundaries of the unknowns. Solving for the unknowns generally consists of expanding the determinant of each unknown according to a defined arrangement of the known quantities.

DEVIATION--Departure from a standard value, line, plane, or reference.

DIFFERENTIAL ALTITUDE--The vertical difference between two exposure stations. The vertical differences between airborne exposure stations are measured with a statoscope.

DIHEDRAL--The angle enclosed by two nonparallel planes defined by two lines lying in the planes and perpendicular to the intersection line of the two planes. Tilt is the dihedral angle between the image plane and the sea-level datum plane. Any angle defined by lines not perpendicular to the intersection line of two planes is not a dihedral angle and is always smaller than the dihedral angle.

DIP OF THE HORIZON--The angle between the apparent horizon and the horizon of an observer above or below the standard sea-level datum. The term is usually applied to airborne cameras and is therefore the angle between a horizon plane through the camera and the apparent horizon which falls away with increased altitude.

DIRECT OBSERVATION--A measurement made with an instrument on a point in which the point is examined visually during the measurement.

DIRECT TENSION--A method of holding film flat in nonmetrical cameras or cameras with small-dimension formats. It is essentially a film flatness dependent on the tension exerted by the take-up spool.

DIRECTED LINE SEGMENT--The projection of a line to any plane defined by two axes of a Cartesian coordinate system.

DIRECTION ANGLES--The angles between a line in space and each of the three mutually perpendicular axes to which the line is referred.

DIRECTION COSINES--The differences in X, Y, Z coordinates between two points on a line, each divided by the distance between the two points, are equal to the cosines of the angles between the line and each axis of the coordinate system.

DISCREPANCY--A difference between results of duplicate or comparable measures of a quantity. The difference in computed values of a quantity obtained by different processes using data from the same survey. Discrepancy is closely associated with, but not identical to, closure error.

DISPLACEMENT--Any shift of the image that does not impair the straight-line relation between image, nodal points, and object. Shifts of the image due to perspective, tilt, or relief are regarded as displacements since they in no way affect the straight-line relation.

Relief displacement--The difference in position of an image along a radial from the photo nadir point from that position the image would occupy if all the objects had zero elevation. Displacement of the image due to relief is away from the photo nadir point for object points below the reference datum. Relief is not a distortion inasmuch as it in no way impairs the mathematical concept of the image, lens, and object lying in the same straight line. In fact, relief displacement is defined only for the sake of convention.

Tilt displacement--The difference in the position of an image on a tilted photograph from that on the equivalent vertical. Shift of an image due to tilt is called a displacement, not a distortion, since the position of an image on a tilted photograph in no way impairs the mathematical concept of image, lens, and object defining a straight line.

DISTORTION--Any shift of the image that impairs the straight-line relation between image, nodal points, and object. Shifts of the image due to lens aberrations or film shrinkage are considered to be distortions as they impair the straight-line relationship.

Angular distortion--The angular deviation of a ray upon passage through a lens system, due largely to the inherent aberrations of the lens.

Asymmetrical distortion curves--Distortion curves exhibiting different numerical magnitudes at equal and opposite distances from the lens axes. Asymmetrical distortion curves may be caused by decentration or decentered lens elements.

Cartesian distortion--The shift of an image due to lens aberrations along the *x*, *y*, and *z* axes: *x* distortion = dx, *y* distortion = dy, and *z* distortion = dz.

Fictitious asymmetrical distortion--An absence of symmetry in computed values of camera lens distortion arising from any of the following causes: (1) errors in measured data, (2) inequality of the radial distances to opposite pairs of points, (3) unequal number of opposite points, and (4) distortion in the center point due to excessive distance from the true principal point.

Film distortion--Movement of the images due to contraction and/or expansion of the film subsequent to the instant of exposure. This movement is considered a distortion inasmuch as it impairs the straight-line mathematical definition of image, nodal points, and object.

Negative distortion--According to many photogrammetrists negative distortion is a movement of the image toward the principal point. Atmospheric refraction produces a shift of the image toward the nadir point which for near verticals would be regarded as negative distortion.

Point-by-point distortion--Lens distortion is usually evaluated along two intersecting diagonals. Where high precision is required distortion is determined at each intersection of an orthogonal system of lines scribed on a glass plate clamped in the image plane. The term *point-by-point distortion* arises from the fact that lens distortion is evaluated over the entire image-forming lens surface.

Positive distortion--Shift of an image from its true position away from the principal point.

Radial distortion--The component of lens distortion along a radial from the principal point. It is assumed that if the lens is not decentered and if the principal point coincides with the foot of a normal from the rear nodal point, radial distortion is the only measure of distortion and radial distortion has equal magnitude for equal radii.

Random distortion--Image distortion without systematic pattern such as that of lens and atmospheric refraction. The residual distortion of film after the negative has been adjusted for the obvious scale change between the *x* and *y* image frame edge is considered random distortion defying correction without an orthogonal, close-interval reference system located in the focal plane during the exposures.

Resultant distortion--The distortion found in operational photography. This distortion differs from the lens distortion found in the laboratory inasmuch as operational photography has combined lens distortion, film distortion, distortions arising from any departure from focal-plane flatness, and the negative distortion of atmospheric refraction. Resultant distortion is the only true yardstick for the accuracy of a photographic direction or position.

Symmetrical distortion--The assumption that radial distortions of a camera lens are symmetrical in the image plane when there is no decentration and the image plane is normal to the lens axis. Equal radii with the principal point have equal radial distortions through 360°.

Tangential distortion--The shift of an image in a direction normal to a radial from the principal point. Tangential distortion is believed to be negligible in a camera lens system free from manufacturing errors. Therefore tangential distortion is considered to be the partial effect of decentered lens elements, or the image plane not being perpendicular to the optical axis, or radial distortion.

x distortion--Any shift of an image in an x direction having a specific x and y value that impairs the mathematical concept of image, object, and lens nodal points defining a straight line. The movement of an image in x due to film distortion, lens aberrations, atmospheric refraction, or all three.

y distortion--The movement of an image in a y direction due to one or more distortions.

z distortion--For any distortion in the image plane there is a z value that will provide a true object-space angle when combined with the image-plane values having x and y distortion. The difference between the specific z value and the calibrated z is the z distortion of a point.

ELEVATION--The vertical distance of a point above or below a reference surface or datum (usually sea-level datum).

EMERGENT SURFACE--The surface of a lens forming the optical boundary of image space.

EMULSION--A suspension of a light-sensitive silver salt, especially silver chloride or silver bromide, in a colloidal medium, usually gelatin, used for coating photographic films, plates, or papers.

EMULSION BASE--The support of emulsions, usually glass or some type of cellulose.

ENDLAP--The amount of photographic duplication between successive exposures in flight.

EQUATIONS--

Condition equation--Equation which expresses exactly certain relationships that must exist among related quantities, which are not independent of one another, exist *a priori*, and are separate from relationships demanded by observation. That there are 180° in a plane triangle is a condition that could be imposed on an equation.

General equation--Equation that embraces the elements of both interior and exterior orientation as unknowns without imposing special geometric properties on the given data.

Iterative equation--Equation generally of a calculus derivation in which the unknowns are corrections to approximate values employed in forming the equations. The corrections converge in successive solutions as the approximate values approach the true values. The corrections or differentials vanish when the successively revised approximations coincide with the true values. The adjective *iterative* is a natural consequence of the necessity for repeated solutions to obtain the desired values.

Normal equation--The form that observation equations assume when they are squared, summed, and differentiated, and coefficients of common unknowns are collected for a Least Squares solution. The mathematical form for a Least Squares solution when the number of observation equations exceeds the number of unknowns.

Observation equation--Equation connecting interrelated unknowns by means of an observed function. Also equations connecting the function observed and the unknown quantity whose value is sought.

Personal equation--A term applied to personal errors that may, by calibration, be assigned a value for correction purposes. Such an error is systematic, arising from the mental or motor reaction of an observer to the sensory perception of a phenomenon and may be eliminated from a result either by an observing program which neutralizes positive values with negative values, or by determining the sign and size of the error by some mechanical means. Personal equations have particular application to time measurements.

Plane calibration equation--Linear equation consisting of two unknowns for determining two components of interior geometry in a plane: the perpendicular distance to a line of images from the rear nodal point (z_x or z_y) and the distance along the line of images from the foot of the normal (Δx or Δy) to any one of the images chosen as an origin.

Plane resection equation--Equation for determining an unknown position with the coordinates of three points and the plane angles subtended by the three points at the unknown point. Plane resection equations simplify to plane calibration equations when the three points define a straight line.

Simultaneous equations--Equations that have common unknowns and are related mathematically so that they may be combined to determine the value of the unknowns. The mathematical combining of similar equations is called simultaneous solution, the act of which makes them simultaneous equations.

Space calibration equation--Equation in which the unknowns are the three numbers required to define the interior geometry of a camera. Space calibration equations always involve angles in two planes that are perpendicular to each other and are always associated with a plane defined by three or more points not in a line and a point not in the plane.

Special-case equation--General equation that becomes simplified or depressed because some of the unknowns normally solved for are observed directly or because of advantageous geometric properties.

ERROR--The difference between an observed or calculated value of a quantity and the ideal or true value of that quantity. Since the true value of a quantity, with few exceptions, cannot be known with exactness, the term *error* is applied to a difference between an observed or calculated value of a quantity and some value determined by established procedure and used in lieu of the ideal or true value. Exceptions: (1) a mathematical value independent of observation, such as 180° in a plane triangle and (2) a value established by authority, such as the length of the meter (unit) defined by the international prototype meter at the International Bureau of Weights and Measures. Errors are of various kinds depending on where and how they originate.

Accidental error--An error, sometimes designated as an irregular error, produced by irregular causes whose effects upon individual observations are governed by no fixed law connecting them with circumstances and which therefore can never be subjected to *a priori* computation. Least Squares solutions eliminate accidental errors.

Average error--The mean of all the errors taken without regard to sign.

Closure error--Failure of successive measurements to define an intended closed figure.

Constant error--A systematic error which is the same in both magnitude and sign through a given series of observations. The index error of a precision instrument is an example.

Instrumental error--A systematic error arising from imperfection of the instrument used, such as graduations of the circle. Instrumental errors are susceptible of laboratory determination; they may be eliminated from a result by a suitable program of field procedure.

Mean square error--The quantity whose square is equal to the sum of the squares of the individual errors divided by the number of errors.

Personal error--A systematic error caused by an observer's personal habits in making observations or due to his tendency to react mentally and physically in the same way under similar conditions.

Probable error--A quantity of such size that the probability of the occurrence of an error larger than that quantity is the same as the probability of the occurrence of an error of less magnitude.

Random errors--Random errors are those resulting from the inability of an observer to precisely identify an image, or those that are neither distortions nor displacements. There are tilt and relief displacements and film, lens, and refraction distortions; none of these are considered random errors in the sense of significant figures.

Residual error--The difference between a quantity in a series of observations corrected for known systematic errors and the value of the quantity obtained from the combination or adjustment of the series. Residual errors correspond to the corrections obtained in a Least Squares adjustment.

Systematic error--An error whose algebraic sign and to some extent magnitude bear a fixed relation to some condition or set of conditions.

Theoretical error--A systematic error arising from natural conditions outside the observer (temperature, atmospheric refraction, etc.).

EXPLICIT--A term applied to equations that provide unique exact solutions when the given data are exact--or solutions not dependent on approximate data or successive approximations.

EXPOSURE--The total quantity of light received per unit area which may be expressed as the product of the illumination and exposure time, such as meter-candle-seconds. Also used to mean the act of exposing a section of film, and exposure time.

EXTRA-AXIAL ANGLE--Any pencil of rays defining an angle greater than several minutes with the lens axis.

EXTRA-AXIAL POINT--Any point in object space or in the image plane not on the lens axis.

FICTITIOUS PHOTOGRAPH--A system of conjugate images and corresponding objects whose coordinates and angular relations are based on mathematical computations with no physical existence. Fictitious photographs are computed to test the theoretical efficiency of photogrammetric equations.

FIDUCIAL AXES--Opposite fiducial marks define a reference line. Two pairs of opposite fiducial marks define two reference lines that intersect at 90°. These two lines are referred to as the x and y axes or the fiducial axes.

FIDUCIAL MARK--One of two, three, or four marks located in contact with the photographic emulsion in a camera's image plane to provide a reference line or lines for the plate measurement of images.

FIELD OF VIEW--The view defined by the angle subtended by the object detail imaged within the image frame at the front nodal point. *Field of view* is equal to *cone angle.*

FILM BASE--A thin, flexible, transparent sheet of cellulose nitrate, cellulose acetate, or similar material, which is coated with a light-sensitive emulsion and used for taking photographs.

FILM MAGAZINE--A holder to contain the film, take-up spool, and film-advance mechanism while exposures are being made.

FILM REEL--Cylinder on which film is wound.

FILTER--Any transparent material which absorbs a certain portion of the spectrum, such as for use in the optical path of a camera lens to prevent certain portions of the spectrum from reaching the sensitized negative.

FLATNESS--A relative measure of the departure of the platen or focal-plane plate from a mathematically ideal plane.

FLIGHT LINE--A line drawn on a map to represent the track of the aircraft.

FLOATING MARK--Two marks, seen as one, occupying a position, in a three-dimensional space formed by the stereoscopic fusion of a pair of photographs, and used as a reference mark in examining or measuring the stereoscopic model.

FOCAL LENGTH (f)--The distance measured along the lens axis from the rear nodal point satisfying the relation

$$f = \frac{u \cdot v}{u + v}$$

where u and v are conjugate object and image distances.

Back focal length--The distance measured along the lens axis from the back vertex of the lens to the plane of best average definition. This value is sometimes used in setting a lens in a camera.

Calibrated focal length--A focal length so chosen as to make plus distortion equal to the minus distortion in a specified zone. Also a focal length mathematically adjusted to make residual lens distortion over the image plane a minimum.

Equivalent focal length--The distance of the image plane from the rear nodal point yielding the best average definition. The equivalent focal length usually deviates slightly from the focal distance giving the maximum equal positive and negative distortions. This is due largely to the fact that two different criteria are being used.

Front focal length--Distance along the lens axis from the front foci to the front nodal point. The front foci comprise a focal point in object space for an image at infinity on the lens axis.

Particular focal length--The precise focal length satisfying the normal distance from the rear nodal point to a plane defined by three photographic images. It is assumed here that any three images of any particular exposure have residual distortions arising from film shrinkage and variations in film flatness that may be different from a preceding exposure, a succeeding exposure, or a calibration exposure. Hence for each exposure and each three images defining a triangle there is one and only one unique focal distance.

FOCAL PLANE--Same as image plane; the plane (perpendicular to the axis of the lens) in which images of points in the object space of the lens are focused.

FOCUS--A point where light is converged by a lens or mirror.

To bring light together at a point.

Fixed focus--Nonadjustable focus at a fixed image distance. Metrical cameras are usually rigidly locked at an image distance corresponding to objects at or beyond the hyperfocal distance, since accuracy of calibration data is not possible with a variable image distance. Such cameras are referred to as fixed-focus cameras.

Infinity focus--The image distance of best definition for an object distance sufficiently great to produce a parallel bundle of rays. This image distance is by definition the focal length of the camera lens.

Variable focus--The mechanical feature of an amateur camera that permits changing the axial image distance to bring objects of different object distances into sharp focus.

FORMAT--Image register of image frame.

GEOMETRIC OPTICS--That branch of optics based on the assumption that light travels in straight lines and conforms rigorously to the rectilinear propagation theory.

GEOMETRY OF TARGET--The pattern of objects photographed. Natural features usually have irregular patterns without clearly defined geometry, and therefore are not as well resolved as man-made features, which usually have regular patterns and clearly defined geometry. Resolution is a function of target or object geometry.

GIMBALS MOUNT--A support consisting of two rings: an outer ring supported on a horizontal axis and rotatable about that axis, and an inner ring supported on the outer ring with a horizontal axis normal to the outer ring axis and attached to the outer ring. A third horizontal axis supports an object on the inner ring. The outer ring, the inner ring, and the object supported are each capable of rotation and retention of horizontal position on a line normal to the axis supporting each. Ships' chronometers are usually gimbals-mounted to keep the instruments horizontal. This reduces positional errors of the chronometer.

GLASS CIRCLES--Circular glass scales for reading horizontal and vertical angles on a precision theodolite.

GLASS PLATES--Precision metrical photography is generally exposed on glass-backed emulsion. Cameras using glass plates need no provisions for holding the film flat. Star exposures for astronomic position are made on glass plates in support of the high precision requirements.

GONIOMETER--An instrument designed to measure angles--generally associated with measuring angles subtended by images through the camera lens.

GRADUATION--The placing of marks on an instrument or device to represent standard values thereon. Also the marks so placed. Graduation is more often applied to the placing of intermediate marks on an instrument (tape, thermometer, or circle).

GRATICULE--A system of finely scribed lines on glass, generally employed as a reference of optical measurements.

GROUND PARALLEL--Any line on the ground perpendicular to the photograph principal plane.

GROUND PHOTOGRAPHY--Exposures made at ground stations of terrestrial object space. For instance, exposures of stars from ground stations are not considered to be ground photography, but rather celestial photography.

GROUND PLANE--A plane tangent to the sea-level datum at the ground nadir point.

GROUND SPEED--The velocity of an aircraft relative to fixed ground points.

GYRO ORIENTATION--Angular orientation of the exposure camera from the image of a vertical beam of light on the exposure. The vertical orientation of the beam is achieved with a gyro not rigidly locked to the camera. The point of light on the exposure negative is the image position of the photographic nadir. Tilt and swing are computed directly with the coordinates of the beam image referred to the principal point.

GYROSCOPIC STABILIZATION--Near-vertical orientation of the camera optical axis by mechanical coupling of a gyro to the camera in such manner that the gyro axis and camera axis are collinear. Some authorities claim that deviations from the vertical as small as 5 minutes of arc can be maintained.

HEIGHT OF CAMERA--The vertical distance of the front nodal point of a ground exposure camera from a point on the ground. This point is generally known as a survey station established by nonphotographic means on the terminal of a base line occupied by the camera.

HIGH OBLIQUE--An exposure intentionally tilted with the angle between the visible horizon and the optical axis of the exposure camera less than one-half the camera cone angle.

HORIZON--A plane through the lens parallel to a plane tangent to the earth's sea-level datum at the ground nadir point.

HORIZON LINE--The image of the visible or apparent horizon on a high-oblique exposure.

HORIZON PLANE--The plane of the horizon passing through the lens. See HORIZON.

HORIZONTAL CIRCLE--A graduated circle whose axis is the vertical spindle of an angle-measuring instrument and whose purpose is to indicate the relative horizontal direction of a sighting telescope or camera lens axis.

HYPERFOCAL DISTANCE--The distance in object space beyond which all objects are in sharp focus, which applies only when the image distance of the camera is equal to the back focal length.

ILLUMINATION--The quantity of light falling on or passing through a given space or object.

IMAGE--A representation of an object by means of light rays, produced by an optical system. A cone of light originating at each object point is converged at the image point.

Latent image--An invisible image produced by a physical or chemical effect of light upon matter (usually silver halide or other halides) which can be rendered visible by the subsequent chemical process of photographic development.

Real image--An image formed by the actual intersection of rays of light, as opposed to a virtual image, where the intersection is only apparent.

Virtual image--An image formed by the apparent intersection of light rays. Diverging light rays form a virtual image. A virtual image cannot be recorded photographically.

IMAGE DISTANCE--The distance from the rear nodal point to the image plane. The image distance decreases as object distance increases until the object distance is equal to or greater than the hyperfocal distance. When the object distance is equal to or greater than the hyperfocal distance, the image distance is equal to the focal length and never gets any smaller.

Variable image distance--The mechanical feature of an amateur camera that permits changing the axial image distance to bring objects of different object distances into sharp focus.

IMAGE FRAME--That which limits the object detail photographed, and defined usually by a rectangular shape outside of which there is no object detail recorded. The image frame size is usually chosen to eliminate image points being recorded in the zones of maximum distortion. Generally the fiducial marks are attached to the middle of opposite sides of the image frame.

IMAGE MEDIUM--The substance or optical vehicle containing the image.

IMAGE MOTION--Abnormal elongation of images caused by movement of the object or camera or both. Star trails are examples of object movement, or strictly speaking camera movement, but not in the conventional sense. However, image motion associated with star trails, like that associated with moving terrestrial objects, results in a blurring that reduces the metrical properties of an image.

IMAGE PLANE--Same as the focal plane, or the plane in which an image is formed.

IMAGE SPACE--The space which is associated with an image, or space from which an image is viewed. If the image is virtual, it may be located in the medium from which it is observed.

IMAGE SURFACE--The surface which is generally spherical or slightly curved defined by an infinite number of images. The image plane so frequently referred to is in reality a compromise for convenience and reproducibility.

INCIDENT SURFACE--The surface of a lens or a reflecting plane forming an optical boundary to object space.

INDETERMINANT--Equations that are unsolvable because the number of equations are less than the unknowns, or the given data exhibit weak geometry such as the lens being in the wall of the danger cylinder, or the separated equations not being geometrically related.

INTERLOCKING ANGLE--The angle defined by the intersection of the optical axes of two cameras that are mechanically locked to provide overlapping exposures at a constant angle.

INTERPRETATION--The science of identifying objects and phenomena on a photographic record without immediate access to the specific objects and/or phenomena.

INTERSECTION, SPACE--Determination of the space coordinates of a point by conjugate rays from two space camera stations.

INTERVALOMETER--A mechanical or electronic device that causes exposures to be made at predetermined, equally spaced times. The time lapse between airborne exposures in flight is determined by (1) the altitude of the aircraft, (2) the required endlap, (3) the width of the image frame along the flight line, (4) the focal length of the taking camera, and (5) the velocity of the aircraft.

INTERVISIBILITY--In connection with triangulation those points capable of reciprocal observations. The word comes into use when planning a field survey from stereo pairs or a contoured map. It becomes necessary to draw profiles between two points selected in the office to determine whether or not the points are intervisible. Sometimes points visible from the terminals of a base line upon being occupied are found not to provide adequate visibility to the points beyond.

INVERSE SQUARES, LAW OF--Law of intensity of light which states that the illumination produced by a given source of light at a given point is inversely proportional to the square of the distance from the source.

IRIS DIAPHRAGM--An adjustable diaphragm constructed of rotatable leaves whereby the diameter of the opening may be varied.

LATITUDE--

Astronomic--The angle between the plumb line and the plane of the celestial equator; also defined as the angle between the plane of the horizon and the axis of rotation of the earth.

Geodetic--The angle which the normal to the spheroid at a point makes with the plane of the geodetic equator.

Spherical--The angle at the center of a sphere between the plane of the equator and the line to the point on the surface of the sphere.

LEAST SQUARES, METHOD OF--A mathematical method of determining the most probable values of a series of quantities from a set of observations greater in number than the minimum required to determine those quantities.

LENS--The optical medium contained between two refracting surfaces. More loosely, a piece of glass or other optical material comprising two surfaces, whose purpose is to converge or diverge light.

LENS SPEED--The capacity of a lens to collect and converge light to an image point. This capacity is dependent on the magnitude of the cone angle subtended by the lens at the image, which is similar to relative aperture. Generally lens speed is expressed as a ratio of the focal length to the lens diameter and applies only to an image on the axis. Lens speed is essentially a measure of the amount of illumination received by an image.

LEVEL VIAL, CIRCULAR--A spirit level vial having the inside surface of its upper part ground to spherical shape, the outline of the bubble formed being circular and the graduations being concentric circles. The form of spirit level is used where a high degree of precision is not required. Sometimes referred to as a universal level, or a bull's-eye level.

LINE OF CONSTANT SCALE--A line parallel to sea-level datum on a tilted aerial photograph. Such a line is perpendicular to the principal line, which is the direction of lines undergoing the most rapid scale change.

LONGITUDE--

Astronomic--The angle measured in the plane of the celestial equator between the plane of the observer's celestial meridian and the plane of an initial meridian, arbitrarily chosen.

Geodetic--The angle measured in the plane of the geodetic equator between the plane of the geodetic meridian and the plane of an initial meridian, arbitrarily chosen.

LOW OBLIQUE--An exposure intentionally tilted with the angle between the visible horizon and the optical axis of the exposure camera greater than one-half the camera cone angle.

MAGNIFICATION--Increase in real or apparent size of an image with respect to its object.

Angular magnification--Increase in the apparent size of an object by an optical system.

Linear magnification--The ratio of size of an image to the corresponding object measured perpendicular to the optical axis.

MANOMETER--A gage for measuring the pressure of a gas consisting of a U-shaped tube closed at one end and containing mercury.

MAP--A representation on a plane surface, at an established scale, of the physical features (natural, artificial, or both) of a part or the whole of the earth's surface, by means of signs and symbols, and with the means of orientation and projection indicated. Also a similar representation of the heavenly bodies.

MEAN--The average value of a series.

Arithmetical mean--The value obtained by dividing the sum of a series of values by the number of values in the series.

MEASURING MACHINE--A term used for plane-coordinate comparator.

MEDIAN--The middle value of a series.

MENSURATION--The science of observing, recording, and determining distances between points and angles subtended by points.

MERIDIAN--A north-south line by which longitude is reckoned and from which azimuths are reckoned.

Astronomic meridian--A line on the surface of the earth having the same astronomic longitude at every point.

Celestial meridian--The hour circle containing the zenith or the vertical circle containing the pole.

Geodetic meridian--A line on a spheroid which has the same geodetic longitude at every point.

Observer's meridian--A plane defined by the geodetic or celestial poles and a point at which a specific observation is made.

MERIDIANS, CONVERGENCE OF--Meridians are great circles defining planes that intersect at the earth's axis and are perpendicular to the equator. As adjacent meridians approach the pole, the separation between them on the earth's surface gradually narrows to zero at the pole. This narrowing is called convergence of the meridians.

METER--A unit of length equivalent in the United States to 39.37 inches exactly. A centimeter, a millimeter, and a micron are one-hundredth, one-thousandth, and one-millionth of a meter, respectively.

MILE--

Nautical mile--The value in linear measure of 1 minute of arc at the equator. A close approximation is 6,080 feet.

Statute mile--A length of mile used in distance measurements on land, and equal to 5,280 feet (1,609.35 meters).

MOSAIC, AERIAL--A group of photographs exposed from an aircraft and selectively cut or joined together to produce a continuous area.

NADIR POINT--All points cut by a vertical line passing through the lens. The photographic image of this line is the *photo nadir.* The datum intersection with this line is the *ground nadir.*

NAPIER'S RULES--Simple rules for the relation of the elements of a right spherical triangle. Rule I: The sine of the middle part is equal to the product of the cosines of the opposite parts. Rule II: The sine of the middle part is equal to the product of the tangents of the adjacent parts.

NEGATIVE--A sensitized plate or film which has been exposed in a camera and which has the lights and shades in inverse order to those of the original subject. The plate or film does not become a negative until it is exposed, after which it may be an undeveloped or a developed negative.

NODAL PLANE--A plane perpendicular to the optical axis at a nodal point.

NODAL POINT--Either of two points on the optical axis of a lens (or a system of lenses) so located that when all object distances are measured from one point and all image distances are measured from the other they satisfy the simple lens relation

$$\frac{1}{u} + \frac{1}{v} = \frac{1}{f}$$

(conjugate foci). Also a ray emergent from the second point is parallel to the ray incident at the first. A concentric lens system has a nodal separation of zero; hence, a single nodal point.

Emergent nodal point--The rear nodal point or the nodal point nearest image space.

Front nodal point--The point where rays from objects at infinity with different angles of incidence appear to intersect.

Incident nodal point--The front nodal point or the nodal point nearest object space.

Rear nodal point--The point where image rays making different angles with the lens axis appear to intersect on the lens axis.

NORMAL--A line that intersects another line or a plane, or a plane that intersects another plane, at 90°.

OBJECT MEDIUM--The medium filling the space containing the object.

OBJECT PLANE--The plane in object space satisfying the conjugate foci formula for a specific image distance:

$$u = \frac{f \cdot v}{v - f}$$

OBJECT POINT--Any point of which an optical system forms an image.

OBJECT RAYS--The bundle of rays defined by a point-object and the incident lens surface.

OBJECT SPACE--Space containing all objects photographically recorded within the boundaries of the image frame.

OPTICAL AXIS--The line containing the nodal points of a centered optical system.

OPTICAL INFINITY--Any distance equal to or greater than the hyperfocal distance.

ORIENTATION--The angular relation of a line, or plane, or three-space-coordinate system with respect to an arbitrary system of reference planes.

Absolute reciprocal orientation--The angular relation between two overlapping photographs referred to a geodetic datum.

Angular orientation--The angular relation between the camera coordinate system and an object-space-coordinate system expressed with three elements: tilt, swing, and azimuth.

Basal orientation--The determination of the space coordinates of the terminals of an air base; the determination of the space coordinates of one and the length and direction angles of the other; the space coordinates of one and the difference in space coordinates between the two.

Exterior orientation--A set of quantities that completely define the angular relation of the camera coordinate system with a standard reference system in object space and the position of the camera with respect to the origin of the standard coordinate system. The elements of angular orientation are tilt, swing, and azimuth; the elements of position are X, Y, and Z.

Interior orientation--The dimensional and geometric relation of a camera lens to its image plane: the focal length or normal distance to the image plane from the rear nodal point; the coordinates of the foot of the normal or the principal point with respect to the fiducial axes; the degree of flatness of the image plane; the diameter of the relative aperture; the resultant lens distortion and resolution in the image plane; the precise x and y dimensions of the image frame; the intersection angle of the fiducial axes; and the cone angle of the camera.

Orthogonal orientation--The process of making the coordinate reference lines of a camera parallel to a corresponding system of lines in object space. This is frequently done in connection with camera calibration to simplify the determination of camera data. The image plane of the camera is made perpendicular to an established optical line of sight in nearly all but the most general methods of camera calibration. Complete orthogonal orientation would consist of making the x and z axes of the camera lie in a horizon plane, and the y axis vertical.

Reciprocal orientation--The tilts, swings, and azimuths of two overlapping photographs with respect to each other.

Relative reciprocal orientation--The tilts, swings, and azimuths of two overlapping photographs exposed at different camera stations with respect to an arbitrary datum parallel to a line connecting the two exposure stations.

Total orientation--A term applied to general equations capable of determining the following unknowns: the three elements of interior orientation, consisting of focal length (f) and the coordinates of the principal point (Δx, Δy); and the six elements of exterior orientation, consisting of the rectangular coordinates of the nadir (XL, YL), the altitude (ZL), tilt (t), swing (s), and azimuth (Az).

Vertical orientation--Making the optical axis coincide with or define a small angle with the vertical by use of level bubbles for zenith exposures on the ground and gyro for nadir exposures in the air.

ORIENTATION ELEMENT--Three angles are required to define completely the angular relation of one coordinate with respect to another. Any single angle of the three is classed as an element of orientation. For instance, the tilt, swing, and azimuth completely define the angular relation of the camera coordinate system with respect to an object-space-coordinate system. Tilt, swing, and azimuth are the three required elements. Elements may be trigonometrically combined to produce components. See *Components of tilt* under TILT.

ORIGIN--The point on a line or in a plane or in a space treated as zero and to which all other points refer. The origin in a plane-coordinate system is the intersection of two mutually perpendicular axes and in a space-coordinate system the intersection of three mutually perpendicular axes. Normally the principal point is the origin for image-plane coordinates.

Arbitrary origin--Any origin chosen locally for convenience. Sometimes for a particular problem some point other than the principal point is used. Such a point is usually referred to as an arbitrary origin.

OVERLAPPING PAIR--Photographs taken at adjacent camera stations and having some image detail in common.

PASS POINT--A point whose horizontal and/or vertical position is determined from photographs by photogrammetric methods and which is intended for use after the manner of a ground control point in the orientation of other photographs.

PENCIL OF LIGHT--A portion of a bundle of rays originating at, or directed to, a single point. See BUNDLE.

PERSPECTIVE CENTER--The point of origin or termination of bundles of perspective rays. The two such points usually associated with a survey photograph are the interior perspective center and the exterior perspective center. In a distortionless-lens camera system one perspective center encloses the same angles as the other, and in a perfectly adjusted lens camera system the interior and exterior centers correspond to the rear and front nodal points, respectively.

PERSPECTIVE PLANE--Any plane containing the perspective center. Inasmuch as the intersection of two planes defines a straight line, the intersection of a perspective plane with a ground plane defines a straight line on the photograph. And any straight line in object space will be imaged as a straight line in image space.

PERSPECTIVE RAY--A line joining a perspective center and a point-object.

PHOTOGRAMMETRIC CONTROL--Control established by spatial intersection of rays from the conjugate images of two or more overlapping photographs.

PHOTOGRAMMETRIC SYSTEM--Any combination of photogrammetric instruments and procedures assembled for the definition of data in accordance with the particular criteria.

PHOTOGRAMMETRY--The science of determining the relation between a system of objects and the conjugate images recorded on a plane.

Analytical photogrammetry--Interior orientation, exterior orientation, space resection, space intersection, and reciprocal orientation determined by computation with camera and/or space coordinates as given data.

PHOTOGRAPH--A general term for a positive or negative picture made with a camera on sensitized material, or prints from such a camera original.

Aerial photograph--A photograph of an object surface taken by a camera mounted in an aircraft.

PHOTOGRAPHIC EXTRAPOLATION--The science of extending from the examination of an image in a plane the physical and descriptive properties and purpose of an object in space.

PHOTOGRAPHIC INTERPRETATION--The determination of the nature and description of objects that are imaged on a photograph.

PHOTOGRAPHIC PYRAMID--A pyramid whose base in a triangle formed by three images and whose apex is the interior perspective center.

PHOTOMETRY--The science related to the methods and instrumentation employed in the measurement of the intensity of light.

PHOTOTHEODOLITE--A spindle-mounted metrical camera capable of rotation about the vertical whereby horizontal exposures may be made at any desired azimuth. More elaborate models are capable of horizontal and vertical rotations and are equipped with horizontal and vertical circles whereby the azimuth and tilt of the camera axis may be read directly.

PHYSICAL OPTICS--The branch of optics that deals with the quality and nongeometrical nature of light.

PICTURE PLANE--A term employed for the focal plane or image plane when used in connection with discussions on the laws of perspective apart from metrical considerations. The photograph corresponds to the picture plane in photography.

PLANAR--Flat, usually with the wave length of light as the unit of measurement in the degree of flatness.

PLATEN--A flat metallic surface located behind the exposure negative for holding the emulsion flat. In the more complex cameras the film is drawn flat against the platen by vacuum or air pressure, while in ground cameras the film is held flat by the platen bearing against the image frame.

PLUMB LINE--The direction in which the force of gravity acts. Same as vertical line.

POINT OF TANGENCY--The point on a plane touching the earth's surface where a perpendicular to the plane coincides with the earth's surface.

POSITION, OBSERVER'S--Any position established by terrestrial or celestial observations made at the point. An intersection point, for example, is not an observer's position.

PRECISION--Degree of refinement in the performance of an operation or in the statement of a result. *Precision* relates to the quality of execution, and is distinguished from *accuracy* which relates to the quality of the result. The term precision not only applies to the fidelity with which the required operations are performed, but by custom has been applied to methods and instruments employed in obtaining results of a high order of accuracy. Precision is exemplified by the number of decimal places to which a computation is carried and a result stated. In a general way, the accuracy of a result should determine the precision of its expression. Precision is of no significance unless accuracy is also obtained.

PRESSURE PLATE--Same as platen. A flat plate, usually of metal but frequently of glass or other substance which, by means of mechanical force, presses the film into contact with the focal-plane plate of the camera.

PRINCIPAL DISTANCE--The perpendicular distance from the internal perspective center to the plane of a particular finished negative or print. This distance is equal to the calibrated focal length corrected for both the enlargement or reduction ratio and the film or paper shrinkage or expansion, and maintains the same perspective angles at the internal perspective center to points on the finished negative or print as existed in the taking camera at the moment of exposure. This is a geometrical property of each particular finished negative or print.

PRINCIPAL LINE--The line on a photograph defined by the principal point and the photo nadir point.

PRINCIPAL PLANE (OPTICS)--The plane where rays from a point in the back or front focal plane appear to intersect the corresponding parallel bundle emerging from the opposite side of the lens from the point. The principal planes defined by bundles from a point in the front and back focal planes are the front and back principal planes, respectively. Also the planes perpendicular to the optical axis at the front and back principal points.

PRINCIPAL PLANE (PHOTOGRAMMETRY)--The plane defined by the lens, the ground nadir point, and the principal point produced to the ground, or the plane defined by the rear nodal point and the principal line.

PRINCIPAL POINT--The point defined by the intersection of the lens axis with the camera image plane. The principal point is the foot of a perpendicular to the image plane from the rear nodal point in a camera lens system free from manufacturing errors.

Calibrated principal point--A principal point mathematically adjusted to make lens distortion equal in magnitude for equal radii.

Emergent principal point--The point where the optical axis cuts the principal plane defined by the intersection of the image rays of a bundle that are parallel to each other and the axis in object space.

Front principal point--Point where the optical axis pierces the front principal plane. A bundle of rays incident on the front surface of a lens from the front foci emerge as a parallel bundle. The intersections of emergent and incident rays define the front principal plane.

Incident principal point--The front principal point or the principal point nearest object space.

Particular principal point--A precise principal point different for each exposure because of slight differences in flatness among negatives. In a camera free from manufacturing errors the principal point is at the foot of a normal from the rear nodal point. Residual departures of each exposure negative from a perfectly flat surface introduces a shift in the position of the foot of the normal and hence the position of the principal point.

PRINT--A photographic copy made by projection or contact printing from a photographic negative or from a transparent drawing as in blueprinting.

PROJECTION--

Map projection--An orderly system of lines on a plane representing a corresponding system of imaginary lines on an adopted terrestrial or celestial datum surface. Also the mathematical concept of such a system. For maps of the earth a projection consists of a network (graticule) of lines representing parallels of latitude and meridians of longitude, or of a grid based on such parallels and meridians.

Optical projection--The process of forming a second system of images on a plane in simulated object space by passing light from the initial system of images through a suitable lens system.

Orthographic projection--A map projection produced by straight parallel lines through points on the sphere and perpendicular to the plane of the projection. The orthographic map projection corresponds to a perspective projection with the point of projection at an infinite distance from the sphere.

Perspective projection--A projection produced by straight lines radiating from a selected point and passing through points on the sphere to the plane of projection. Sometimes called a geometric projection. The plane of projection is usually tangent to the sphere. If the selected point is the center of a sphere, there results a gnomonic projection.

RADIAN--The angle subtended by an arc of a circle equal to the radius of the circle. For very small angles a value in radians

$$\Delta = \sin \Delta = \tan \Delta.$$

RAY--A line representing a path of light.

RAY TRACING--A trigonometric calculation of the path of a light ray through an optical system.

RECONNAISSANCE, PHOTO--General examination of an area on the ground from the air by study of photographs for purposes of planning a survey or a photo mission, the photographs of which will be employed in a photogrammetric survey. In any case, reconnaissance presupposes that a more systematic survey of the area than that of the actual reconnaissance itself will follow.

RECTIFICATION--The process of projecting a tilted or oblique photograph onto a horizontal plane. This projection may be by mathematics, graphics, or by photography in a special camera called a rectifier or rectifying camera which produces rectified prints from a tilted original.

RECTILINEAR PROPAGATION OF LIGHT--The transmission of light in straight lines. That light travels in straight lines is evidenced by the fact that apart from distortions a system of images of a lens and a conjugate system of objects define a bundle of straight lines intersecting at the lens. The deviation of light rays from straight lines is easily established by the phenomenon of diffraction and interference. These deviations are too small to affect the accuracy of photogrammetric equations based on the rectilinear assumption.

RECYCLING TIME--The interval between successive exposures. The recycling capabilities of a camera are sometimes referred to as the number of exposures per unit of time. The recycling velocity of a camera is significant in photographing phenomena in motion.

REFLECTION--The change in the direction of light incident on a plane surface so that the light leaves the surface at the same angle at which it strikes the surface.

REFRACTION--The bending of light rays upon passing from an optical medium of one density to an optical medium of another density. If the light rays are passing from an optical medium of one density to one of greater density, the rays bend toward the normal. If the reverse occurs, the light rays bend away from the normal. The angle of refraction increases with the angle of incidence and the difference in density. For this reason atmospheric refraction is a function of barometric pressure and temperature, both of which are recorded for a precise determination of refraction corrections. Refraction is expressed according to Snell's law.

$$n_2 \sin R = n_1 \sin I$$

where R = angle of refraction,
I = angle of incidence,
n_1 = refractive index of medium of incident ray, and
n_2 = refractive index of medium of refracted ray.

Refraction effects a negative displacement on images in cameras having a plano-parallel plate in the focal plane. Images on nadir exposures from airborne camera stations are displaced toward the photo nadir point. The barometric pressure and temperatures of both the ground points and camera station must be known to compute a precise refraction correction to an image. Needless to say, Snell's law is the most fundamental equation in the development of lens formulae. The refraction correction for images of ground objects on nadir exposures is much smaller than the refraction correction for images of stars on zenith exposures, since the light from stars enters the camera lens from the outer atmosphere.

Atmospheric refraction--The bending of a path of light incident on the atmosphere from outer space. The amount of bending or refraction is dependent on the ratio of the optical density of a vacuum to that of a particular atmosphere and the angle of incidence or zenith angle.

RELATIVE AZIMUTH--The dihedral angle defined by the principal planes of two overlapping photographs exposed at the same camera station or at different camera stations.

RESECTION--The graphical or analytical determination of a position as the intersection of at least three lines from the position to three known points and enclosing known angles at the intersection point.

Space resection--Determination of the space coordinates of a point with the space coordinates of three objects and the corresponding camera coordinates of three images as the given data.

RESOLUTION--A measure of the smallest array of point-objects distinguishable as independent point-images, frequently expressed in lines per millimeter, where "line" refers to the distance between the centers of two distinguishable point-images.

Limit of resolution--The smallest image that may be formed from theoretical considerations. The theoretical limit is not able to account for all factors in nature affecting resolution and seldom therefore agrees with the resultant resolution obtained with operational photography.

Photographic resolution--The smallest distinguishable image formed by an emulsion by contact printing and independent of a camera lens resolution.

Resultant resolution--The resolution found on operational photography. Resultant resolution is less than that found for the lens or particular emulsion in the laboratory for two reasons: In the first place, the resolution of the system is always less than that of any of the components; and in the second place, objects in nature do not have the clear atmosphere object space, the target geometry, or contrast. Each of these factors would reduce the resolution of the components from that found in the laboratory. The resultant resolution under operating conditions is the only measure of a camera's useful accuracy.

RESOLUTION TARGET--A system of geometric patterns arranged in decreasing object size to provide when photographed a measure of the resolution of the camera system by a count of the smallest distinguishable target pattern. Conventionally the target was a pattern of black lines and white spaces. This target has been challenged by many as being unlike targets in nature. For this reason other targets are being introduced, the most prevalent of which is the annulus target.

RESOLVING POWER--The ability of a camera system to form separate identifiable images of close object points.

REVERSE POSITION--180° from an initial measurement in rotations about a vertical axis and 2γ from an initial measurement in rotations about a horizontal axis where γ is an initial zenithal angle.

ROTATION--Any element of angular orientation. Tilt is a rotation of the principal point in a vertical plane about the lens referred to the vertical. Swing is a rotation of the principal line in the image plane about the principal point referred to the camera y axis. Azimuth is a rotation of the principal plane in a horizontal plane at the ground nadir referred to the ground Y or geographic meridian.

SCALE--The ratio of a distance on a photograph to a corresponding distance on the ground. Scale is constant when the optical axis of the camera is vertical and the object surface is a level plane. The ratio of the focal length to the camera altitude (f/ZL) is usually employed as an approximate scale.

SCALE CHANGE--The variation in image size on a photograph due to tilt of the photograph and/or the difference in the elevations of objects.

SEA LEVEL, MEAN--The average height of the sea for all stages of the tide. Mean sea level is obtained by averaging observed hourly heights of the sea on the open coast or in adjacent waters having free access to the sea, the average being taken over a considerable period of time.

SHORAN--An electronic measuring system for indicating distance from an airborne station to each of two ground stations. The term is a contraction of the phrase "short range navigation."

Shoran control--Control of aerial photography by registration of the distance of the exposure station from two ground stations. Shoran line crossing is a method of determining distance between two points by flying across the joining line.

SHUTTER--The mechanism of a camera which, when set in motion, permits light to reach the sensitized surface of the film or plate for a predetermined length of time.

Between-the-lens shutter--A shutter located between the lens elements of a camera and usually consisting of thin metal leaves which open and close or revolve to make the exposure.

Focal-plane shutter--A shutter located near the focal plane and consisting of a curtain with a slot which is pulled across the focal plane to make the exposure.

Louver shutter--A shutter consisting of a number of thin metal strips or louvers which operate like a venetian blind to make the exposure. Usually located just in front of or just behind the lens.

SHUTTER EFFICIENCY--The ratio of light transmitted by the shutter, to the amount that would have been transmitted had the shutter been wide open for the entire exposure. Used with regard to iris shutters.

SHUTTER SPEED--Elapsed time from the start of opening of the shutter until the completion of the closing of the shutter.

SIDELAP--Ratio of conjugate image area to the whole image area on photographs of adjacent flights.

SIGNIFICANT FIGURES--The number of places from left to right of a given quantity that are known to be correct. For instance, with a length 75.2 measured with a tape graduated to single feet, only the first two numbers are significant. Significant figures are considered in the correctness of a solved-for or observed value and economy in computation. Computations should never be performed with more decimal places than there are significant figures in the given data; and the errors in an answer can never be less than the greatest error in the given data, providing the answer is the consequence of a unique solution.

SOLUTION--

Analytical solution--A photogrammetric determination based on computation with camera and space coordinates or object-space angles as given data.

Back solution--Substitution of an initially determined unknown back in the preceding equations to determine the remaining unknowns.

Forward solution--A term applied to the operations leading to the determination of the first of a series of unknowns. Simultaneous equations are solved numerically by successive elimination of unknowns with corresponding reduction in the number of equations. This process continues until there is one equation with one unknown. When this point is reached, the one unknown is equal to the quantity on the opposite side of the equal sign divided by the coefficient of the unknown.

Graphical solution--Photogrammetric determinations based largely on geometric constructions, nomographs, or templates. The scale-point method of tilt determination is an example of a graphical solution based on geometrical construction of lines on the photograph.

Mechanical solution--Determination of the elements of exterior orientation and relative orientation by instrumental simulation of the camera orientation at the instant of exposure with the aid of reference points. Many plotting instruments are designed to provide mechanical solutions to the elements of relative orientation.

SPECTRAL SENSITIVITY--The wave lengths of light that a lens transmits, that the rods and cones of the eye respond to, and that may record an image on an emulsion.

SPECTRUM--The band of colored light, or any part of it embracing more than a single wave length, produced when the light from a given source is distributed by wave length along a continuous band.

Visible spectrum--That part of the spectrum to which the eye is sensitive.

SPEED, FILM--The response or sensitivity of the material to light, often expressed numerically according to one of several systems, e.g., H. and D., D.I.N., Scheiner, and A.S.A. exposure indexes.

SPHEROID, OBLATE--A sphere whose polar diameter is less than its equatorial diameter. The planes defined by the equator and parallels of equal latitude are circles, while planes defined by any meridian through 360° is an ellipse. The earth is regarded as an oblate spheroid.

STANDARD--An exact value, or concept thereof, established by authority, custom, or common consent to serve as a model or rule in the measurement of a quantity, or in the establishment of a practice or procedure.

STANDARD OF LENGTH--A physical representation of a linear unit that is approved by competent authority. A standard of length is not independent of temperature, pressure, and other physical conditions to which it is subjected, but is an exact embodiment of the unit which it represents only under definite, prescribed conditions.

STANDARDIZATION--The comparison of an instrument or device with a standard to determine the value of the instrument or device in terms of an adopted unit. A tape is standardized when the distance between its fiducial marks in terms of a unit of length is determined by comparing it, under prescribed conditions, with a standard which represents that unit.

STATION--

Air station--A camera station resulting from exposures made while the camera is airborne.

Astronomic station--A point on the earth whose position has been determined by observations on heavenly bodies.

Camera station--A point in space, in the air, or on the ground occupied by the camera lens at the instant of exposure. Sometimes referred to as the exposure station.

Exposure station--Same as camera station.

Geodetic station--A point defined with geodetic coordinates which are based on a mathematical configuration of the earth.

Intersection station--A survey station or control point located from two other stations without being occupied itself. Such a point is the apex of a triangle, the side opposite of which is known and the other two angles of which are measured.

Space station--A point in an aircraft flight established by an airborne camera exposure.

Survey station--Any point whose position has been determined by direct angle or linear measurement or both angle and linear measurement.

Triangulation station--A point on the earth whose position has been determined from the measurement of angles from at least two other points.

STATOSCOPE--A sensitive barometer used in aerial photography for measuring small differences in altitude between successive air stations.

STEREO PLOTTING INSTRUMENT--Any instrument permitting an operator to define the shape of an object by observation of the stereoscopic model formed by a single stereoscopic pair of photographs.

STEREOSCOPE--An optical instrument for aiding the observer to view two properly oriented overlapping photographs or diagrams to obtain the mental impression of a three-dimensional model.

STRENGTH OF FIGURE--The relation of the lens position to control points and the ratio of altitude to area defined by control points. Both affect the accuracy of any kind of survey reduction. A spatial pyramid is said to have strength of figure when the camera is on the axis of the danger cylinder and when the height of the cylinder is not more than twice the diameter of the cylinder.

SURVEYING--The science of measuring angles and distances with which azimuth, position, and elevation may be determined.

SURVEYING SPINDLE--The vertical axis of a theodolite, transit, or terrestrial metrical camera. Usually the vertical axis is centered in a horizontal circle and is perpendicular to the plane of the horizontal circle.

TANGENT PLANE--A plane normal to the earth's radius at the observation station or exposure station, and therefore the point at which the plane and earth coincide.

THEODOLITE--A precision surveying instrument consisting of an alidade with telescope, mounted on an accurately graduated circle, equipped with necessary levels and reading devices. Sometimes the alidade carries a graduated vertical circle. There are two general classes of theodolites: direction theodolites and repeating theodolites.

TILT--The vertical angle defined by the intersection at the lens of the optical axis of a camera lens with a normal to the chosen datum plane. Tilt is also the dihedral angle defined by the intersection of the negative plane with the chosen reference plane.

Component of tilt--Any angle between two planes less than the maximum angle which is the tilt angle. A component of tilt decreases as the angle between the tilt and component increases. The component of tilt is zero 90° from the maximum angle. Tilt may be deduced from two components and the included angle. Frequently tilt and swing are expressed in x and y components which then are the tilts of the x and y axes of the camera.

Induced tilt--The tilt remaining in a photograph after mathematical or instrumental rectification. The former may be due to incorrect location of the principal point or various errors so that the tilt is some determined value plus some residual undetermined value. In the latter case induced tilt is due to the precision limitations of instrumental rectification when the angular elements of tilt are imposed visually.

Relative tilt--The dihedral angle defined by two overlapping photographs. The relative tilt is the inclination of the second photograph to the first if the first photograph is treated as an arbitrary reference.

TOLERANCE--The permissible deviation from a standard. Generally associated with the permissible deviation from exactness in the fitting together of the component parts of physical apparatus.

TRANSFORMATION--Any rotation of coordinates of one system to another.

TRANSIT--The apparent passage of a star or other celestial body across a defined line of the celestial sphere, as a meridian, prime vertical, or almucantor. The apparent passage of a star or other celestial body across a line in the reticle of a telescope or some line of sight. A surveying instrument less precise than a theodolite. Generally has the same meaning as upper and lower culmination.

TRANSLATION--A movement of the origin as to decrease or increase one or all space coordinates by a constant; movement without rotation.

TRIANGULATION--

Aerotriangulation--Any type of triangulation for control extension.

Geodetic triangulation--Measuring the angles of a system of triangles with the methods and instrumentation specified in geodesy.

Graphical triangulation--A method of establishing secondary control points by radial lines drawn on the photographs or by slotted templates to images common to two or three photographs. The photographs are usually oriented along the lines established by conjugate principal points. The method is based on the fact that relative directions are true on a vertical photograph and that small tilts do not appreciably affect the accuracy of the relative directions. The secondary points are located at the intersection of two or three rays. Slots in templates often are employed in place of drawn radials.

TRIANGULATION NET--A system of points on the ground that are the vertices of a chain of triangles whose angles are observed instrumentally and whose sides are derived by computation from selected triangle sides called base lines, the lengths of which are obtained from direct measurements on the ground.

TRIGONOMETRIC FUNCTION--The numerical quotient of two sides of a right triangle depending on the function specified.

TRILAP--An image common to three successive aerial photos. When photographs in flight image more than 50 percent of conjugate object space in successive pairs, there is an area having images of a narrow strip of object space that is common to three photographs. This is known as trilap and plays a critical part in photogrammetric control extension.

TRIMETROGON--A term applied to tricameras consisting of a nadir camera and a left and right oblique which photograph the horizon and a portion of the terrain imaged on the left and right edge of the near vertical. The metrogon lenses were used in the early tricamera installations and hence the term trimetrogon.

UNIQUE--A term applied to equations in which the given data are neither less than nor in excess of that required for a determination. Unique means that with the given data there is one answer and only one answer.

UNIT OF DIMENSIONAL MEASURE--A nominal distance in space fixed by definition, and independent of temperature, pressure, and other physical conditions.

UNKNOWN--One of the quantities to be determined by the simultaneous solution of two or more equations, or the quantity to be determined by the substitution of given data in a formula or an equation.

VANISHING POINT--The image trace of that part of any line or system of lines in object space at infinity and not parallel to the image plane. Geometrically, the point where a line parallel to the system of lines in object space and passing through the lens pierces the image plane. Any line or system of lines in object space parallel to the image plane cannot, therefore, have a vanishing point.

VERTICAL, NEAR--A term applied to photography with deviations from the vertical between 0° and 10°; photography that was intended to be vertical.

VERTICAL CIRCLE--The graduated arc on a surveying instrument that indicates the vertical angle defined by a sighting telescope.

VERTICAL COMPONENT--The vertical distance from a point to a reference plane when the reference plane is at sea-level datum; also vertical distortion. Any line not parallel to the vertical axis has a vertical component.

VERTICAL LINE--Any line normal to a plane defined by two horizontal level bubbles that are mounted perpendicular to each other.

VIEWFINDER--An auxiliary camera, having the same cone angle as the exposure camera, for the purpose of determining quickly the area covered by the exposure camera. The exposure camera and viewfinder are usually mounted rigidly together with their optical axes parallel.

VIGNETTING--Loss of illumination in the extra-axial regions due to the lens-barrel depth or projection.

WAVE LENGTH OF LIGHT--The distance between two similar points on successive light waves.

WAVE THEORY OF LIGHT--Light behaves as waves defining a continuous locus of points in an optical medium; the locus of points represents the limit which the wave front has reached at a given instant. The continuous locus of points is in the same phase and defines a surface.

X AXIS--The object-space reference line perpendicular to the meridional reference line.

Y AXIS--The meridional object-space reference line. The meridional reference is the line from which azimuth angles are generated.

Z AXIS--The line normal to the *XY* reference plane at the intersection of the *X* and *Y* axes.

Z DISTANCE--The vertical difference between a point-object or image and the arbitrary reference plane for the object or image. Conventionally the *XY* plane is a tangent plane and the *Z* distance is the vertical difference between a point and the *XY* plane or the elevation of the point. (The notation *Z* refers to object space and *z* to image space.)

APPENDIX:

LITERATURE CITED

[1] McNeil, G.T. *Focal length determination by vanishing point method on low-oblique photography.* Report III. Washington: U.S. Naval Photographic Interpretation Center, 1949.

[2] Rock, D.L. *Preliminary analysis of camera calibration without angle measurement.* Report 106. Washington: U.S. Naval Photographic Interpretation Center, 1950.

[3] Merritt, E.L. *Explicit interior-exterior orientation of the camera in space.* Report 121. Washington: U.S. Naval Photographic Interpretation Center, 1950.

[4] Merritt, E.L. *Introduction to camera calibration.* Report 127. Washington: U.S. Naval Photographic Interpretation Center, 1950.

[5] Merritt, E.L. "Methods of field camera calibration." *Photogrammetric engineering* XVII:610-635 (September 1951) and XVIII:665-678 (September 1952).

[6] Merritt, E.L. *Explicit exterior orientation of the camera in space.* Report 105. Washington: U.S. Naval Photographic Interpretation Center, 1951.

[7] Merritt, E.L. *Explicit four-point resection in space.* Report 118. Washington: U.S. Naval Photographic Interpretation Center, 1949.

[8] Gruber, O.V. *Photogrammetry: collected essays and lectures.* London: Chapman and Hall, Ltd., 1932.

[9] Merritt, E.L. "Explicit three-point resection in space." *Photogrammetric engineering* XV:649-665 (December 1949).

[10] Merritt, E.L. "Space resection." *Photogrammetric engineering* XIII: 415-441 (September 1947).

[11] Merritt, E.L. *Iterative determination of the interior-exterior orientation of the camera in space.* Report 126. Washington: U.S. Naval Photographic Interpretation Center, 1951.

[12] Church, Earl. *Revised geometry of the aerial photograph.* Bulletin No.15. Syracuse, New York: Syracuse University, 1945.

[13] Church, Earl. *Theory of photogrammetry.* Bulletin No.19. Syracuse, New York: Syracuse University, 1948.

[14] Anderson, R.O. *Applied photogrammetry.* Ann Arbor, Michigin: Edwards Brothers, 1946.

[15] Underwood, P.H. "Space resection problems in photogrammetry." *Transactions, A.S.C.E.*112:921 (1947).

[16] Hotine, M. *Surveying from air photographs.* London, 1930.

[17] Hart, C.A. *Air photography applied to surveying.* London: Longmans, Green, and Co., 1943.

[18] McGaw, G.T. *The plate constants and their determination in aerial survey.* London: General Staff, War Office, 1922.

[19] Miller, O.M. "An approach to exterior orientation." *Photogrammetric engineering* XIV:155-179 (March 1948).

[20] Merritt, E.L. *Exterior orientation by iteration.* Report 117. Washington: U.S. Naval Photographic Interpretation Center, 1951.

[21] Merritt, E.L. *Relative and absolute orientation of overlapping exposures from the same station.* Report 108. Washington: U.S. Naval Photographic Interpretation Center, 1951.

[22] Merritt, E.L. *Relative orientation of two overlapping photographs.* Report 109. Washington: U.S. Naval Photographic Interpretation Center, 1951.

[23] Merritt, E.L. *Photogrammetric control extension by analytical means.* Report 110. Washington: U.S. Naval Photographic Interpretation Center, 1951.

[24] Keiskanen, W. *The horizon and statoscope method of photogrammetry.* Technical Paper No.127. Columbus, Ohio: Mapping and Charting Research Laboratory, December 1950.

[25] United States Air Force. "Reconnaissance mapping with trimetrogon photography." In *Manual of photogrammetry.* New York: Pitman Publishing Corporation, 1945. Pp.645-711.

[26] Santoni, Ing. H.C. Ermenegildo. *Solar aerial triangulation.* Lecture given at the United States Army Engineer Board, Fort Belvoir, Virginia.

[27] Wild, Henry. *Wild statoscope equipment.* Heerbrugg, Switzerland.

[28] McCaffrey, B.I. "Airborne profile recorder." *Photogrammetric engineering* XVI:673-681 (December 1950).

[29] Kelsh, Harry T. "Report on airborne profile recorder." *Photogrammetric engineering* XVIII:92-95 (March 1952).

INDEX

P

Q

R

S

T